BUSES
RESTORED
2009

BUSES
RESTORED
2009

Ian Allan
PUBLISHING

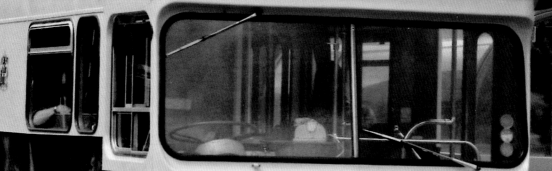

26   BROMFORD BRIDGE ESTATE VIA DREWS LANE

FROM CITY

PAY AS YOU ENTER
PLEASE TENDER EXACT FARE

NOV 880G

Contents

Cover: A Willowbrook-bodied AEC Regent V new in 1965, Devon General 518 (CTT 518C) is nowadays one of the growing number of vehicles owned by members of the Devon General Society. *Philip Lamb*

Half title: An all-Seddon Pennine IV, initially numbered EX56, SELNEC 1700 (YDB 453L) now forms part of the large collection of former SELNEC and Greater Manchester vehicles in the care of the SELNEC Preservation Society. *Philip Lamb*

Title page: New in 1969, Birmingham Corporation Transport 3880 (NOV 880G) is a Park Royal-bodied Daimler Fleetline. *West Midlands Bus Preservation Society*

Note: Please be aware that vehicles on display can vary from time to time as not all museums display their entire 'fleet'. Visitors wishing to see a particular vehicle should make enquiries prior to their visit.

First published 2009

ISBN 978 0 7110 3371 9

© Ian Allan Publishing Ltd 2009

Published by Ian Allan Publishing

an imprint of Ian Allan Publishing Ltd, Hersham, Surrey KT12 4RG.
Printed by Ian Allan Printing Ltd, Hersham, Surrey KT12 4RG.

Code: 0903/A1

Visit the Ian Allan Publishing web site at:
www.ianallanpublishing.com

Part 2
Other Collections of Preserved Buses & Coaches

Part 3
Privately-Preserved Vehicles

Part 4
Heritage Bus Services

Useful addresses
NARTM, PO Box 5141, Burton-upon-Trent
   DE15 0ZF.
The Transport Trust, 202 Lambeth Road,
   London SE1 7JW.
British Bus Preservation Group, 7 Dukeries Lane,
   Oakwood, Derby DE21 2HA.
The PSV Circle, 26 Ashville Grove, Halifax
   HX2 0PN.

Introduction and Background

It is a pleasure once again to be writing the introduction to another edition of *Buses Restored*. This is the 10th edition and details over 2,400 buses and coaches. As we have stressed before, this is by no means all of the historic buses and coaches that exist in the UK today, and the full total is probably over 5,000. The National Association of Road Transport Museums (NARTM) database now holds details of over 4,000 of these vehicles. The data in this book is an extract from the database, because although a number of owners are happy for NARTM to hold information about their vehicles, they understandably don't all want to have details published.

It will be noted that the book includes four main groups of collections. The first details those museums and collections that are regularly open to the public and are obviously pleased to welcome visitors to their premises; that, after all, is why they exist. The second group includes collections that may occasionally be open to the public — or which are available to be seen by special appointment — but also some that are never open, and we ask our readers to respect owners' privacy by not visiting or entering premises without permission. However, many of the vehicles from these collections make regular appearances at the numerous historic-vehicle rallies held each year all over the country, so it will be possible to see them from time to time. The third section to the book lists those buses and coaches owned by members of the British Bus Preservation Group. Once again, we do not show the locations of these vehicles, as many are kept at the owners' home addresses or on farms and other private premises. The fourth section of the book lists yet more vehicles, but there is a difference: these are historic vehicles owned by operators that use them regularly on heritage tours and services, and you will be able to pay to have a ride on them.

The last edition of *Buses Restored* included a plea for help, because after 10 years maintaining the database Tim Stubbs was looking to step down, and we were in need of a successor. Fortunately, at the Autumn 2008 meeting of NARTM at London Transport Museum's Acton Depot, Nick Webster came forward and offered to take over the database from Tim. In the weeks leading up to Christmas the database has been through its annual update and, once the copy for this book has been proof-read, the database will be formally handed over. I should like to take this opportunity to thank Tim for setting it up and for all his work over the years since we first mooted the idea at a NARTM meeting back in 1998. Thanks are due also to Nick, for agreeing to take on this interesting but challenging task.

At NARTM we try to represent all the owners of historic buses and coaches, from collections of over 100 vehicles in size through smaller collections to the single bus or coach owned by a family or individual. This is because all historic vehicle owners face the same issues, ranging from the difficulty of obtaining spares for elderly vehicles to the impact of proposed legislation on their continued operation. Finding secure accommodation for such large vehicles is another issue common to all of us. How often we have all thought how much simpler it would have been to collect something smaller! Even a classic car can usually be kept at home or in a nearby garage, but a double deck bus or 40ft-long coach is another matter.

NARTM meets formally just twice a year, visiting members' premises up and down Britain usually in March and October, and on each occasion between 30 and 40 people attend to exchange ideas and listen to internal and external speakers on a number of topics. In recent years we have met at Acton, Beamish, Birmingham, Ipswich, Bristol, Lathalmond and Blackpool. The NARTM committee also meets a couple of times a year, and in the meantime the organisation runs on E-mails and phone calls. We have around 80 current members, and more join every year. Our website www.nartm.org.uk is being revamped at present, so do have a look at the changes to be found there. We also publicise our collections in conjunction with *Bus & Coach Preservation* magazine, each spring producing a new leaflet, which is widely distributed.

To be topical for a moment, what about the 'credit crunch', and how will it affect NARTM, its members and the wider heritage movement? At the time of writing the news is full of high-street shops that are closing or going into administration, car manufacturers going on short-time working and general doom and gloom. For good or bad, it is fair to say that many of our readers, members and visitors to our collections are older rather than younger. That often means that they will have some disposable income, having bought the house, raised the family, restored the bus and paid for life's other essentials, and are hopefully still in a position to spend a little money on their hobby and leisure pursuits.

Visitor numbers to most heritage attractions seem to have held up quite well through 2008 (the busiest year for some time in a number of museums), only outdoor attractions reporting a significant reduction, which can generally be put down to the poor summer weather. It is likely that in 2009 more people will spend more holiday time at home in the UK and will therefore be more likely to visit our collections. Conversations with traders at a number of events late in 2008 confirm that the regular customers are still spending, and new books on transport themes continue to be published at a steady rate, which must be regarded as an indicator that the market remains buoyant.

Operating costs of historic buses and coaches rose significantly last summer; filling the bus up in July 2008 with diesel at 134.9p per litre was bit painful, but the usual price of diesel is now around £1 a litre — still expensive, but a bit more manageable. (Incidentally, why is diesel now around 12p a litre more expensive than petrol?) The main costs of owning an historic bus or coach lie in restoring it, but more especially in housing the thing. The economic downturn may mean that industrial and agricultural premises — the usual storage places for old vehicles outside museums — will fall in price along with domestic property prices, so it may be that purchasing or renting such accommodation becomes more of a possibility to some groups and individuals. Equally, the dramatic slowdown in the construction industry new may take pressure off some heritage sites and storage locations that had been earmarked for redevelopment, thus retaining the sites in heritage use.

Industry and the financial sectors are obviously feeling the pinch, so commercial sponsorship is probably less likely in the next few years than in the past, but apart from a few prestige projects, how much money has been available from such sources, even in the recent 'boom' years? It may actually be that as the Government tries to spend its way out of recession, more funding could be made available for heritage projects, despite the sums being taken from the Heritage Lottery Fund's allocation to help fund the London Olympics in 2012.

Despite the hopeful signs and possibilities noted above, it is unlikely that our small part of the economy will escape entirely. Running costs of property continue to increase, and any accumulated funds put by for a rainy day will not earn as much interest as in recent years. This source of income is important for many heritage organisations and trusts. Will people continue to donate money and make bequests at the same rate as in the past? 'Downsizing' might be a relatively easy option for some companies seeking to reduce their overheads, but where does one start to reduce the size of a collection of old vehicles and artefacts accumulated over many years? This is something we in Manchester decided to address just over a year ago, and we have identified half a dozen vehicles that we (reluctantly) felt we could dispose of. The due process as laid down in our Collections Management Plan was followed, and eventually the vehicles were advertised for sale. New owners (who have provided detailed plans of how the vehicles will be restored, housed and made available to the public) have been found for most of them, and they are in the process of leaving our collection. A similar exercise is being applied to smaller objects and documents, some items being offered for sale after careful consideration and adherence to the due processes — not easy, after 30 years of collecting. This does not mean we have stopped adding to our collection (although no vehicles joined in 2008 we are still keen to fill gaps), but for the time being we will use the space vacated to display some of the vehicles to better effect, with a little more space around some of them. We will not, however, be following the example of certain high-profile museums and leaving just two or three buses in acres of space to tell the story of passenger road transport over the past 150 years!

So, how can NARTM help its members as they face the uncertainties of the future? The answer is that we will continue to do what we do well, and keeping members in touch with each other is a good first step. One project's innovation are probably quite applicable to another, whether it be a new method of publicising the visitor attraction to a new sector of the visiting public, a new type of special event, a new accounting or collection recording system or a new method of fund-raising — all these can be available to all our members simply by talking to each other, sending in notes and articles to the *NARTM Newslink* (our quarterly magazine) or by contacting the NARTM website.

One idea tried in 2008 was holding a day for retired bus-company employees, inviting them to visit free of charge and helping them recall their days of working in the bus industry. Recording their memories on video, asking them to identify colleagues on old group photographs and generally making them feel welcome virtually guarantees lots of return visits — at minimal cost to the Museum — as well as providing great pictures to accompany press releases to the local papers!

With reference to a recent *Sunday Herald* article about the Scottish National Trust, now is not the time to retreat into our comfort zones or sell off all the family silver but to embrace change and invest in the future; this might be in a only small way, as finances permit, but we must maintain our confidence and vision that we can achieve things. The public in general are fascinated by their past, and our collections of old buses and coaches, plus all that goes with them, are an ideal medium to attract their interest. In many cases they used the bus every day to go to work or school or the shops or the pictures, and it was so familiar; what a great day out, therefore, for grandparents to take their grandchildren to visit one of our museums and relate their experiences — especially if the visit can be brought to life by a ride on one of the buses on which they used to travel.

We must continue to have that optimism that has successfully taken our movement through previous recessions and difficult times in the 1970s, 1980s and 1990s. If, 20 or 30 years ago, we had all said "Too difficult", how many of the 4,000 buses and coaches on the NARTM database would be around today?

Aside from more visitors (in the case of those open to the public), the most pressing requirement among almost all the collections listed in this book is for more volunteers. A job that can be shared or done as part of a team becomes so much less daunting. Even if you don't have extensive experience of mechanical work, vehicle bodybuilding or coach-painting, there are a whole host of other jobs to be done in any group or society. If you go and brew tea and wash up afterwards you will be most welcome! To quote the Manchester experience again, we have a few dedicated enthusiasts who are very interested in buses but whose sole (but very valuable) contribution is to come to our busiest events and to wash pots for a few hours — and very welcome they are too!

Finally, thankyou very much for picking this book up off the shelf, having a look and then buying it. Once you have had a good read through, do come and visit some of the museums and collections listed. Bring your friends and family — you may discover that they find old buses and coaches just as fascinating as we do!

Dennis Talbot
Chairman, NARTM

For more information about NARTM please write to
NARTM, PO Box 5141, Burton upon Trent, Staffordshire, DE15 0ZF
or visit our website at www.nartm.org.uk.

A meeting of Bristol Ls at the East Anglia Transport Museum finds L5Gs LL711 and LL718 (KNG 711/8) alongside L4G LL407 (KAH 407) from the Ipswich Transport Museum. LL718 is from the Eastern Transport Collection at Norwich, whilst LL711 is privately owned. All three carry the customary ECW bodywork. *Philip Lamb*

Model Buses from TRANSMAC

www.transmac.net

For details of the latest release programmes see our web site or contact us for a **FREE** information pack.

ORIGINAL OMNIBUS COMPANY

Spring 2009 Releases

AEC Regent II - Liverpool Corporation	£25.45
Wright Eclipse Gemini - London Central	£25.45
Crossley DD42 - Glasgow	£25.45
East Lancs Myllennium - London Sovereign	£25.45
Leyland Lynx - North London Railways	£25.45
Dart Pointer SLF - Cardiff, Christmas Livery	£25.45
BMMO C5 - (Birmingham/Worcester)	£25.45
Plaxton Paragon - Wallace Arnold	£25.45
Plaxton Panther - Yelloway	£25.45
Crossley DD42 - Portsmouth	£25.45
Bedford Val - West Riding	£25.45
Blackpool Balloon Tram - HMS Coastguard	£25.45
Wright Solar - Wilts & Dorset	£25.45
Plaxton Panther - East Yorkshire Coaches	£25.45
Scania Irizar PB - Bus Eireann	£25.45

CORGI 1:50 Scale

2009 Release - Buses in Britain

RT - London Transport - Plain Green	£48.95

BRITBUS

AN1-12   AN2-05

Leyland Atlantean, East Yorkshire	£32.30
Atlantean, Ribble - Sealink Windermere	£32.30
Bristol LHW/ECW, Devon General NBC	£27.40
Albion Lowlander, Western SMT	£32.30
Atlantean AN68, Ribble - (556 - Keswick)	£32.30
Leyland Atlantean AN68, Black Prince	£31.35
Atlantean, London Country North East	£31.35
Dennis Loline - 'Black Prince'	£32.30
Alexander R, Stagecoach in East Kent	£31.35
Leyland Olympian Leaside Buses	£32.30

CREATIVE MASTER NORTHCORD

Forthcoming Releases

Sunwin SWB6100V2 - Shanghai Sightseeing	£31.30
Dublin Bus Open Topper	£29.40
Alexander ALX400 - 'Stagecoach Devon'	£29.40
Dennis Trident/ALX400 - Lothian Buses	£29.40
Dennis Dart MPD - 'Go NorthEast'	£27.45
MB Citaro EEV - Oxford Bus Company	£31.35
Citaro rigid - 'NCP Services Heathrow'	£31.35
Mercedes Citaro rigid - 'Go NorthEast'	£31.35
MB Citaro G artic - 'Arriva London' Route 29	£33.20
Alexander Dennis Enviro400 - West Midlands	£32.30
Enviro400 - 'ADL Hybrid Demonstrator'	£32.30
Scania Omnicity - First Potteries	£31.35
Scania Omnicity - 'Arriva Durham County'	£31.35
Scania Omnicity - 'Ipswich Buses'	£31.35
Dennis Enviro200 - Yellow Buses	£31.35
Dennis Enviro200 - 'Arriva London'	£31.35
Transport for London Bus Stop, Shelter, Seat, & Ticket Machine (Blister Pack)	£5.00

EXCLUSIVE FIRST EDITIONS

Forthcoming Releases

AEC Routemaster and Trailer RMA - BEA	£24.50
AEC RM RM1563, London Transport	£23.00
AEC RT3, London Transport	£24.00
AEC RT3, London Country	£22.55
AEC Mandator artic flat, BRS North Wales	£19.60
Leyland Olympian, Northumbria	£23.20
Bristol Lodekka FLF; Eastern Scottish	£23.20
Wright Volvo Renown, First Aberdeen	£23.20
Trader dropside, Eldridge Pope & Co. Ltd.	£20.00
AEC RLH, London Transport (red)	£23.20
Bedford TK dropside, G M Buses	£20.00
Plaxton Pointer Dart, MTL London	£23.00
Alexander Y Type, West Coast Motors	£23.00
AEC RF (RF584); London Transport Green	£22.55
Daimler DMS 1 door, Bexleybus	£21.50
Leyland Titan 1 door, Stagecoach East London	£23.00
Leyland Olympian, Arriva Serving The Shires	£22.55

Models will be dispatched as soon as they are in stock.
Post free. International Air Mail at cost
TransmaC, PO Box 124, LEEDS, LS26 0WJ.
Tel/Fax 0113 282 5349 Email:bus@transmc.net

What is NARTM?

The National Association of Road Transport Museums (NARTM) is an informal organisation of museums and collections. Volunteers operate many of them, although others, such as the Glasgow and London Transport Museums, are managed by full-time staff. This mix of museum types gives the opportunity to share ideas and experiences and the volunteers involved each bring their own professional skills to their projects and best practices can then be shared by all the member collections.

NARTM has been in existence for almost 20 years and now has around 30 member organisations, with more joining each year. The buses and coaches that form part of the NARTM collections are generally regarded as forming the nucleus of the National Collection of Buses and Coaches. However, it must be stressed that many important examples are in private hands outside the scope of NARTM and its members.

What does NARTM do?

Many of the people involved in running transport museums are busy people and have little spare time after making significant contributions to their own projects, such as the Museum in Manchester. This is why NARTM only holds two meetings each year at the various member museums and in recent years we have visited Devon, Lincoln, Glasgow, Oxford and Portsmouth. In between meetings, the quarterly *Bulletin* keeps members in touch with each other and we are often in touch. Indeed, one of the main functions of NARTM is to put people in touch with each other and there are many instances of restoration projects progressing and spare parts being located through NARTM contacts. Discussion topics at recent meetings have included the encouragement and role of junior members, bus services, grant applications, museum registration, visitor facilities, risk assessment, documentation and links with other bodies.

NARTM's unique service to its members is also as an information exchange about running museums — after all, as so many of our members are volunteers, their skills and experiences are not within the heritage and leisure industry. It is often the case that another project in another area has already been faced with exactly the same issues as we have today, and by sharing ideas and pooling resources, progress can be made more quickly.

Over the years NARTM has also taken a lead role in campaigning on new legislation to lessen its impact on the historic bus preservation movement. Vehicle licensing, driver licensing, tachographs and the retention of original registration numbers have all received our attention, with some success in each case through our work in conjunction with other groups within the movement. NARTM is also a club authorised to endorse applications from historic vehicle owners to retain, or regain, the original registration of their vehicle.

The future

NARTM is currently working closely with the Transport Trust to define the bus preservation sector of the heritage transport industry. It is also addressing the major issues currently facing the movement — storage, documentation, human resources and skills, public access and the future of vehicles in preservation. A database is now maintained which lists all vehicles in NARTM and associated collections and this will eventually form part of a decision-making process to ensure that the most historically important vehicles have a secure long-term future.

For more information about NARTM please contact:
NARTM, PO Box 5141, Burton-upon-Trent,
Staffordshire, DE15 0ZF.
Website: **www.nartm.org.uk**
e-mail: **email@nartm.org.uk**

Useful addresses

The Transport Trust, 202 Lambeth Road, London SE1 7JW.

British Bus Preservation Group, 7 Dukeries Lane, Oakwood, Derby DE21 2HA.

The PSV Circle, 26 Ashville Grove, Halifax HX2 0PN.

BUSES

THE WORLD'S BIGGEST SELLING BUS MAGAZINE SINCE 1949!

The UK's highest circulation and most widely read magazine covering the bus and coach industries, *Buses* is written for and read by an audience that extends from senior industry professionals to passionately interested enthusiasts.

Buses carries the latest news written with authority on serious issues in a readable and entertaining format, and offers the most comprehensive photographic coverage of new developments. It succeeds in being fiercely independent and unafraid to criticise aspects of the industry that could be improved.

Unique to *Buses* is Fleet News, a comprehensive section detailing the latest changes to bus and coach fleets in the UK and Ireland.

How to Use this Book

This book lists both formal museums and the more informal types of collection, and gives details of opening times, contact addresses and the facilities available, together with a list of the buses, trolleybuses and coaches on display. Many of the sites are open to the public on a regular basis. Admission fees vary and some are even free to visitors, although donations towards the upkeep of the collections are always welcome. Please be aware that the vehicles on display can vary from time to time. Not all museums are able to display their entire 'fleet', and some practise the regular rotation of exhibits for added interest. In addition, some of the vehicles may be in the process of restoration in a workshop off-site, and there is always the possibility that a bus may be on loan to another museum! Visitors wishing to see a particular vehicle should make enquiries prior to the visit.

Some collections are not normally available for public access. However, the owners usually welcome visitors and will arrange for viewing by prior application. In addition, many such groups do have open or public days from time to time. Contact addresses are provided in this book, and those wishing to visit a particular site are asked to contact the address given. Please bear in mind that most are run by volunteers — please enclose a stamped self-addressed envelope when writing and respect the privacy of individuals. This book does not grant or imply any permission whatsoever to enter premises to look at old buses except by the agreement of the group involved. Note that, where buses are licensed for use on public passenger-carrying services, the use of individual vehicles will vary from time to time, as the demands of their preservation dictate.

Whilst some of the restored vehicles detailed here have been 'officially' preserved by their former operators, the majority have been restored and conserved by volunteers, often working in difficult conditions with limited resources of time, money and materials. That there are so many buses and coaches fully restored is a testimony to the

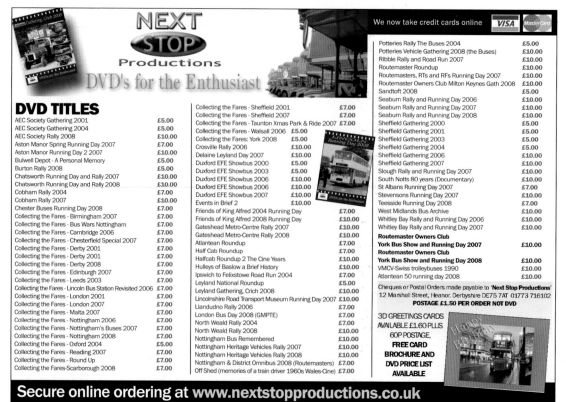

dedication of bus enthusiasts over the last 40 years or more, and it is intended that the vehicles will have a long and secure future.

The information used in this book is as provided by the organisations listed, for which the authors express their thanks. Any information on further collections not included in the current edition will be most welcome. If you own vehicles, or are associated wih such an organisation, please contact NARTM at the address given on page 7.

For each vehicle, details given include the present registration number, year first registered, brief chassis and body details (including seating) and original operator. Standard PSV Circle body codes are used, as outlined below.

Body type (before seating capacity):

A	articulated
B	single-deck bus
C	coach (single-deck)
CH	double-decker coach
Ch	charabanc
CO	convertible open-top double-decker
DP	dual-purpose (eg coach seats in bus shell)
F	full-front (where not normal for chassis)
H	Highbridge double-decker
L	Lowbridge double-decker (ie with sunken side gangway upstairs; all other types — with conventional gangways — are 'H', regardless of overall height)
O	open-top double-decker
OB	open-top single-decker
PO	partially-open-top double-decker
R	single-decker with raised rear saloon (eg over luggage compartment)
T	Toastrack

Seating capacity:

For double-deckers this is shown with the upper-deck capacity first, eg 43/31

Door position (after seating capacity):

C	centre entrance/exit
D	dual doors (usually front entrance and centre exit)
F	front or forward entrance/exit
R	open rear platform
RD	rear entrance/exit with doors
RO	open rear platform with open staircase
T	triple doors (eg on articulated vehicles)

Suffix:

t	fitted with toilet
l	fitted with wheelchair lift

The restoration state is given in accordance with the following code:

R	restored;
RP	restoration in progress;
A	awaiting restoration.

Alexander R266 (WG 9180), a Leyland TD7 with lowbridge Alexander bodywork, and SMT J66 (DSG 169), an all-Leyland TD5, offer a chance to compare contemporary double-deck bodywork from different builders. *Philip Lamb*

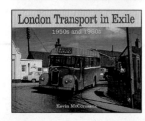
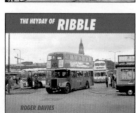

Part 1

Manchester Corporation 4632 (4632 VM), a 1963 Metro-Cammell-bodied Daimler CVG6, is a resident at the Manchester Museum of Transport.
Philip Lamb

Key to facilities

A	Audio/visual displays	H	Baby-changing facilities
B	Bus rides (regular)	L	Lecture theatre
B(e)	Bus rides (at events)	M	Band stand
C	Children's information pack	P	Car parking
D	Access for disabled	R	Refreshments
E	Picnic facilities	S	Enthusiasts' shop
F	School activity pack	T	Toilets
G	Gift shop			

Note: Please be aware that vehicles on display can vary from time to time as not all museums display their entire 'fleet'. Visitors wishing to see a particular vehicle should make enquiries prior to their visit.

Abbey Pumping Station
Leicester

Contact address: Corporation Road, Leicester LE4 5PX

Phone: 0116 299 5111

Fax: 0116 299 5125

Brief description: The Museum is a Victorian pumping-station dating from 1892 with four beam-engines. The vehicle collection is on view on special open days. On these occasions, one of the beam-engines is steamed.

Events planned: Opening times for special events: Saturdays 11.00-14.30, Sundays 13.00-17.00
4 April, 2 May, 6, 27/28 June, 4 July, 1 August, 5 September, 3 October 2009 — Railway Running Days;
19 April 2009 — April Celebrations Steam Day
2 May 2009 — Classics and Railway Day
27/28 June 2009 — Urban Steam Rally
13 September 2009 — Steam Spectacular Day
6 December 2009 — Christmas Toys and Steam Day
10 January 2010 — Meccano Day
7 February 2010 — Steam Toys in Action
Please see the enthusiast press for further details.

Opening days/times:
1 February-31 November, plus 9 December and 12 January 2008. Saturday, Monday to Friday 11.00-16.30; Sundays 13.00-13.60.
Museum closed December and January except for above dates

Directions by car: A6 (north of Leicester) joins Abbey Lane at Redhill Island. Corporation Road is off Abbey Lane.

Directions by public transport: From City Centre (Charles Street) take bus 54 to top of Corporation Road.

Charges: Free except on special open days.

Facilities: C D E G H P R (on open days) T

Registration	Date	Chassis	Body	New to	Fleet No	Status
note c	1932	Horse bus		Leicester City Transport		R
CBC 921	1939	AEC Renown O664	Northern Counties H32/32R	Leicester City Transport	329	R
MTL 750	1958	Leyland Tiger Cub PSUC1/2	Yeates DP43F	Delaine Coaches of Bourne	47	R
TBC 164	1958	Leyland Titan PD3/1	Willowbrook H41/33R	Leicester City Transport	164	R
B401 NJF	1984	Ford Transit 190D	Rootes B16F	Midland Fox	M1	R

Notes:

note c	replica built for Leicester City Transport.; on view at Snibston Discovery Park
CBC 921	on view at Snibston Discovery Park
B401 NJF	on view at Snibston Discovery Park

Note: Please be aware that vehicles on display can vary from time to time as not all museums display their entire 'fleet'. Visitors wishing to see a particular vehicle should make enquiries prior to their visit.

Amberley Working Museum

Contact address: Amberley, Arundel, West Sussex, BN18 9LT
Phone: 01798 831370
Fax: 01798 831831
E-mail: office@amberleymuseum.co.uk
Brief Description: The industrial museum has a wide range of attractions, including rail and bus operations. Some buses in the collection are museum-owned and others are owned by the Southdown Omnibus Trust or are in private hands.
Events planned:
13 September 2009 — Annual Bus Show, ride in buses dating from Edwardian days to recent times. Our Tilling-Stevens body is 100 years old
Opening days/times:
14 February to 1 November: Tuesday to Sunday (also bank holiday Mondays)
Directions by car: Situated close to Amberley railway station on the B2139. Approach from the north and west via the A29 and from the east via the A24 and A283.
Directions by public transport: Hourly rail service calls at Amberley station which is adjacent to the museum.
Charges: Adults £9.30, OAP £8.30.
Facilities: A B B(e) C D E F G H L P R T

Registration	Date	Chassis	Body	New to	Fleet No	Status
IB 552	1914	Tilling-Stevens TS3 Petrol-Electric	Newman O22/16R	Worthing Motor Services	52	R
CD 5125	1920	Leyland N	Short O27/24R	Southdown Motor Services	125	R
CD 4867	1923	Tilling-Stevens TS3A Petrol-Electric	(chassis only) Ch32	Southdown Motor Services	67	RP
BP 9822	1924	Shelvoke & Drewry Freighter	Hickman (replica) B18F	Tramocar of Worthing	1	R
MO 9324	1927	Tilling Stevens B9A	Brush B32R	Thames Valley Traction Co	152	R
UF 1517	1927	Dennis 30cwt	Short B19R	Southdown Motor Services	517	R
BR 7132	1929	Leyland Lion LT1	Leyland B34F	Sunderland Corporation	2	R
UF 4813	1929	Leyland Titan TD1	Brush O27/24R	Southdown Motor Services	813	R
UF 6473	1930	Leyland Titan TD1	Leyland H24/24R	Southdown Motor Services	873	R
UF 6805	1930	Tilling=Stevens B10A2	Short B31R	Southdown Motor Services	1205	RP
UF 7428	1931	Leyland Titan TD1	Short H26/24R	Southdown Motor Services	928	R
ECD 524	1937	Leyland Cub KPZ2	Park Royal B20F	Southdown Motor Services	24	RP
EUF 184	1938	Leyland Titan TD5	Leyland	Southdown Motor Services	0184	R
XMD 47A	1957	Leyland Titan PD2/12	Metro-Cammell O32/26R	Trent Motor Traction Co	1006	A

Notes:

IB 552	body new 1909
CD 5125	rebodied 1928; restored using Leyland P or Q 5- or 6-ton chassis
CD 4867	peplica charabanc body under construction
BP 9822	replica body built at Amberley
UF 1517	all-metal body
BR 7132	stored off-site
UF 4813	on loan from Southdown Motor Services Ltd
EUF 184	converted from bus 184; fitted with breakdown vehicle body ex Leyland TD1 872 (UF 6472)
XMD 47A	new as H32/26RD, registered KCH 106; on loan from Big Bus Company, London

Aston Manor Road Transport Museum

Contact address: The Old Tram Depot, 208-216 Witton Lane, Aston, Birmingham B6 6QE
Phone: 0121 322 2298
Fax: 0121 449 4606

Web site: www.amrtm.org

Affiliation: NARTM

Brief description: The 19th-century former tram depot houses a selection of buses, coaches, commercial vehicles and tramcar bodies in an authentic setting — the depot still has tram tracks and stone sets in situ. There are also many small exhibits, working model layouts and video presentations.

Events planned:
28 March 2009 — Spring Running Day.
25 May 2009 — Two Museums Running Day. Bus service linking Aston Manor and Wythall.
12 July 2009 — Open day/Outer Circle running day.
12/13 Sept 2009 — Heritage Open Days.
18 October 2009 — Special Running Day.
29 Nov 2009 — Collectors' fair with free bus rides.
Please see the enthusiast press for other events.

Opening days/times:
Saturdays, Sundays and Bank Hols 11.00 to 17.00 (November–February 11.00-16.00). Other times by arrangement.
Opening times may vary over Christmas/New Year period.

Directions by car: Easy access from M6 junction 6.

Directions by public transport: Rail to Witton Station and a short walk (170yd)
Bus No 7 from Birmingham City Centre or bus No 11, outer circle to Witton Square.

Charges:
Adults £1.50, Child and Concessions 75p, Family £4.00.
Admission charges may vary on special event days.

Facilities: A B(e) D H P R S T

Other information: Not all of the vehicles listed are on display at the museum. To view any vehicle not normally accessible, visitors should enquire at the museum as to arrangements for viewing.

Registration	Date	Chassis	Body	New to	Fleet No	Status
note z	1925	AEC S	Buckingham	Birmingham Corporation Tramways	215	A
OP 237	1926	(body only)	Short H32/26R	Birmingham Corporation Tramways	208	A
EA 4181	1929	Dennis E	Dixon B32F	West Bromwich Corporation	32	R
HA 4963	1930	SOS RR	(chassis only)	BMMO ('Midland Red')	963	A
JF 2378	1931	AEC Regal 662	Burlingham C32R	Provincial of Leicester	R1	R
OJ 9347	1933	Morris Commercial Dictator	Metro-Cammell B34F	Birmingham Corporation Tramways	47	RP
AOG 679	1935	Daimler COG5		Birmingham Corporation Tramways	83	RP
EHA 775	1938	SOS SON	(chassis only)	BMMO ('Midland Red')	2207	A
RC 7927	1940	BMMO SON	Willowbrook DP34F	Trent Motor Traction Co	417	R
FON 630	1942	Leyland Titan TD7	(chassis only)	Birmingham City Transport	1330	A
KHA 301	1948	BMMO C1	Duple C30C	BMMO ('Midland Red')	3301	R
KHY 383	1948	Bristol L6B	BBW DP35R	Bristol Tramways & Carriage Co	2382	R
GUJ 608	1950	Sentinel STC4	Sentinel B40F	Sentinel (demonstrator)		R
JOJ 222	1950	Leyland Titan PD2/1	Park Royal H29/25R	Birmingham City Transport	2222	A
JOJ 526	1950	Guy Arab IV	Metro-Cammell H30/24R	Birmingham City Transport	2526	A
JOJ 548	1950	Guy Arab IV	Metro-Cammell H30/24R	Birmingham City Transport	2548	RP
KHA 352	1950	BMMO CL2	Plaxton C26C	BMMO ('Midland Red')	3352	RP
SB 8155	1950	Guy Wolf	Ormac B20F	Alexander MacConnacher of Ballachulish		R
JOJ 847	1952	Daimler CVG6	Crossley H30/25RD	Birmingham City Transport	2847	A
LOG 301	1952	Guy Arab IV	Saunders Roe H30/25R	Birmingham City Transport	3001	RP
LJW 336	1953	Guy LUF	Saunders Roe B44F	Guy Motors (demonstrator)		R
LOG 302	1954	Daimler CLG5	Metro-Cammell H30/25R	Birmingham City Transport	3002	R
MOF 90	1954	Guy Arab IV	Metro-Cammell H30/25R	Birmingham City Transport	3090	RP
TOB 377	1956	AEC Reliance MU3RV	Burlingham C37C	Flights Coaches of Birmingham		R
XDH 72+	1956	Sunbeam F4A	Willowbrook H36/34RD	Walsall Corporation	872	RP
773 FHA	1958	BMMO D9	BMMO H40/32RD	BMMO ('Midland Red')	4773	A
1294 RE	1959	Guy Arab LUF	Burlingham C41F	Harper Bros of Heath Hayes	60	R
WLT 506	1960	AEC Routemaster R2RH	Park Royal H36/28R	London Transport	RM506	R
264 ERY	1963	Leyland Titan PD3A/1	Park Royal O41/33R	Leicester City Transport	264	R
3035 HA	1963	BMMO D9	BMMO O40/32RD	BMMO ('Midland Red')	5035	RP
334 CRW	1963	Daimler CVG6	Metro-Cammell H34/29R	Coventry City Transport	334	RP
6479 HA	1963	BMMO S17	Willowbrook B52F	BMMO ('Midland Red')	5479	R

Registration	Date	Chassis	Body	New to	Fleet No	Status
6370 HA	1964	BMMO D9	BMMO H40/32RD	BMMO ('Midland Red')	5370	R
KOX 663F	1967	AEC Swift MP2R	MCW B37D	Birmingham City Transport	3663	RP
LHA 870F	1967	BMMO S21	BMMO DP49F	BMMO ('Midland Red')	5870	R
XNX 136H	1970	Leyland Leopard PSU3A/4R	Alexander DP49F	Stratford-upon-Avon Blue Motors	36	R
XON 41J	1971	Daimler Fleetline CRG6LX	Park Royal H43/33F	West Midlands PTE	4041	R
JOV 714P	1976	Bristol VRTSL6LX	MCW H43/33F	West Midlands PTE	4714	R
NOE 602R	1976	Leyland National 11351A/1R	Leyland National B49F	Midland Red Omnibus Co	602	A
OOX 825R	1977	Leyland National 11351A/1R	Leyland National DP45F	West Midlands PTE	6825	RP
SOA 658S	1977	Leyland National 11351A/1R	Leyland National B49F	Midland Red Omnibus Co	658	RP
WDA 700T	1979	Leyland Fleetline FE30AGR	MCW H43/33F	West Midlands PTE	7000	A
BVP 784V	1979	Leyland Leopard PSU3E/4R	Plaxton C53F	Midland Red Omnibus Co	784	A
A110 WVP	1984	MCW Metrobus GR133/1	MCW H43/30F	West Midlands PTE	8110	RP
F685 YOG	1988	MCW Metrorider MF150/113	MCW B23F	West Midlands PTE	685	RP
G292 EOG	1990	Leyland Lynx LX112C15Z4R	Leyland B49F	West Midlands Travel	1292	RP
G142 HNP	1990	Leyland Lynx LX112C15Z4R	Leyland B49F	Midland Red (West)	1142	A
+ trolleybus						

Notes:

note z	registration unknown
OJ 9347	renumbered 77 in 1935
AOG 679	new as bus 679, with Northern Counties H26/22R body; rebodied 1947 as van
RC 7927	on loan from Trent Motor Traction
KHA 352	rebodied 1963
LOG 302	chrome-plated chassis exhibited at 1952 Commercial Motor Show
XDH 72	last Walsall trolleybus; owned by British Trolleybus Society
3035 HA	originally H40/32RD; converted to open-top by Marshall ('Obsolete Fleet'), London (OM6)
264 ERY	originally H41/33R
OOX 825R	Volvo engine fitted by WMPTE
A110 WVP	guided-wheel experimental vehicle

Black Country Living Museum Transport Group, Dudley

Contact address: Tipton Road, Dudley, West Midlands DY1 4SQ

Phone: 0121 557 9643

Web site: www.bclm.co.uk

Brief description: Tramway operation daily. Trolleybus operation on Sundays and Bank Holidays.

Opening days/times: Summer: daily 10.00-17.00. Winter: Wednesdays to Sundays 10.00-16.00. Some evening openings

Directions by car: M5 (jct 2) signposted on Motorway. follow signs on A4123 to 'Black Country Living Museum'.

Directions by public transport: Central Trains to Tipton station. Travel West Midlands 224, 263, 270, 311-313 to Museum.

Facilities: A, B, B(e)C, D, E, F, G, H, L, P, R, T

Contact (Transport Group): Black Country Museum Transport Group, 28 Farm Close, Etchinghill, Rugeley, Staffs WS15 2XT.

Registration	Date	Chassis	Body	New to	Fleet No	Status
UK 9978+	1931	Guy BTX	Guy H26/24R	Wolverhampton Corporation	78	A
HA 8047	1933	SOS REDD	Metro-Cammell H26/26R	BMMO ('Midland Red')	1047	A
DKY 735+	1946	Karrier W	East Lancs H37/29F	Bradford Corporation	735	RP
DUK 833+	1946	Sunbeam W	Roe H32/28R	Wolverhampton Corporation	433	R
FEA 156	1949	Daimler CVG5	Metro-Cammell B38R	West Bromwich Corporation	156	RP
TDH 912+	1955	Sunbeam F4A	Willowbrook H36/34RD	Walsall Corporation	862	R
2206 OI+	1958	Sunbeam F4A	Harkness H36/32R	Belfast Corporation	246	R
SCH 237+	1960	Sunbeam F4A	Roe H37/28R	Derby Corporation	237	R

Note: Please be aware that vehicles on display can vary from time to time as not all museums display their entire 'fleet'. Visitors wishing to see a particular vehicle should make enquiries prior to their visit.

Registration	Date	Chassis	Body	New to	Fleet No	Status
VRD 186+	1961	Sunbeam F4A	Burlingham H38/30F	Reading Corporation	186	RP
6342 HA	1963	BMMO D9	BMMO H40/32RD	BMMO ('Midland Red')	5342	R
GHA 327D	1965	Leyland Leopard PSU4/4R	Plaxton -	Midland Red Omnibus Co	5827	R
XDH 519G	1969	Daimler Fleetline CRG6LX	Northern Counties H41/27D	Walsall Corporation	119	RP
+ trolleybus						

Notes:

HA 8047	sole surviving SOS double-decker
DKY 735	rebodied 1959
DUK 833	rebodied 1959
2206 OI	on loan from East Anglia Transport Museum
VRD 186	operated by Teesside Municipal Transport 1968-71 and currently in Teesside livery
GHA 327D	converted to breakdown vehicle in 1979

British Commercial Vehicle Museum Leyland

Contact address: King Street, Leyland, Lancashire, PR25 2LE

Phone: 01772 451011

Fax: 01772 451015

Website: www.bcvm.co.uk

Brief description: The Museum is dedicated to preserving the physcal evidence of the history of the road transportation industry in the United Kingdon. This proud history is illustrated through a collection of fully restored vans, trucks and buses produced and sold by the British commercial vehicle industry over the past 100 years, including dramatic 'sound and light' sets which bring the vehicles to life.

Events planned:
5 April 2009 — Model Transport Exhibition
19 April 2009 — Classic and Vintage Ford Day
17 May 2009 — Spring Transport Show
14 June 2009 — American Road Show
12 July 2009 — Leyland Society Transport Event
26 July 2009 — Bus & Coach Show Day
9 August 2009 — ERF and Foden Road Show
16 August 2009 — The Atkinson and Seddon-Atkinson Show Day
20 September 2009 — The Autumn Transport Show
25 October 2009 — Model Transport Show
For further information and entry forms, phone the Museum on 01772 451011.
Please see web site/enthusiast press for extra events and updates.

Opening days/times:
April to September: Sunday, Tuesday, Wednesday, Thursday and Bank Holiday Mondays, 10.00 to 17.00
October: Sundays and Tuesday, 10.00 to 17.00
Closed: November to March

Directions by car: 1 mile from juction 28 of the M6 motorway.

Directions by public transport:
By train to Leyland station (on West Coast main line).
Buses from Preston and Chorley bus stations.

Charges: Adult £4.50, Child (4-15)/OAP £2.50, Family £12 (2 adults/3children). Group discounts available

Facilities: A D F G L P R S T

Registration	Date	Chassis	Body	New to	Fleet No	Status
note t	1896	Horse bus	O14/12R	Edinburgh & District Tramways		R
XW 9892	1925	Tilling-Stevens TS7	Tilling B30R	Thomas Tilling	0172	R
YT 3738	1927	Leyland Lioness PLC1	Thurgood C22F	King George V		R
KGU 284	1949	Leyland Titan 7RT	Park Royal H30/26R	London Transport	RTL326	R
JRN 29	1956	Leyland Tiger Cub PSUC1/2	Burlingham C41F	Ribble Motor Services	963	R

Registration	Date	Chassis	Body	New to	Fleet No	Status
ED 217	1956	Foden PVD6	East Lancs H30/28R	Warrington Corporation	112	R
301 LJ+	1962	Sunbeam MF2B	Weymann H37/28D	Bournemouth Corporation	301	R
+ trolleybus						

Notes:

note t   unregistered

301 LJ   on loan from Bournemouth Heritage Transport Collection

Castle Point Transport Museum
Canvey Island

Contact address: 105 Point Road, Canvey Island, Essex SS8 7TP

Phone: 01268 684272

Web site: www.castlepointtransportmuseum.co.uk

Affiliation: NARTM

Brief description: This historic former Canvey & District bus depot, built in 1935, houses approximately 35 commercial vehicles spanning the years 1944 to 1988. Exhibits include buses, coaches, lorries, fire engines and military vehicles. They can be seen in varying stages from the totally restored to those in need of complete restoration. Completely run by volunteers, membership of the society is available at £10 per annum.

Events planned: Please see enthusiast press or web site for details, plus
11 October 2009 — 30th Annual Show

Opening days/times: Open on 1st/3rd Sundays, April to mid October.

Directions by car: A130 to Canvey Island; follow brown tourism signs on reaching the island.

Directions by public transport: By rail to South Benfleet, then by bus to Leigh Beck, Canvey Island.

Charges: Free admission. Donations welcome. A charge is made on the Transport Show day in October.

Facilities: B(e) P T

Other information: Hot drinks available.

Registration	Date	Chassis	Body	New to	Fleet No	Status
FOP 429	1944	Daimler CWA6	Duple O33/26R	Birmingham Corporation Tramways	1429	R
JVW 430	1944	Bristol K5G	ECW L27/28R	Eastern National Omnibus Co	3885	RP
MPU 52	1947	Leyland Titan PD1A	ECW L27/26R	Eastern National Omnibus Co	3991	RP
CFV 851	1948	Bedford OB	Duple C29F	Seagull Coaches of Blackpool		R
LYR 997	1949	AEC Regent III O961	Weymann H30/26R	London Transport	RT2827	RP
NEH 453	1949	Leyland Titan OPD2/1	Northern Counties L27/26RD	Potteries Motor Traction Co	L453	R
ONO 49	1950	Bristol L5G	ECW B35R	Eastern National Omnibus Co	4029	R
PTW 110	1950	Bristol L6B	ECW FC31F	Eastern National Omnibus Co	4107	RP
WNO 478	1953	Bristol KSW5G	ECW O33/28R	Westcliff-on-Sea Motor Services		R
XVX 19	1954	Bristol Lodekka LD5G	ECW H33/25R	Eastern National Omnibus Co	4208	R
381 BKM	1957	AEC Reliance MU3RV	Harrington C41F	Maidstone & District Motor Services	C381	RP
PHJ 954	1958	Leyland Titan PD3/6	Massey L35/32R	Southend Corporation	315	RP
217 MHK	1959	Bristol MW6G	ECW DP41F	Eastern National Omnibus Co	480	R
236 LNO	1959	Bristol Lodekka LDL6LX	ECW H37/33R	Eastern National Omnibus Co	1541	RP
VLT 44	1959	AEC Routemaster R2RH	Park Royal H36/28R	London Transport	RM44	R
SGD 407	1960	Leyland Titan PD3/2	Alexander H41/31F	Glasgow Corporation	L405	RP
373 WPU	1961	Guy Arab IV	Massey L34/33R	Moore Bros of Kelvedon		R
138 CLT	1962	AEC Routemaster R2RH	Park Royal H36/28R	London Transport	RM1138	R
28 TKR	1962	AEC Reliance 2MU3RV	Harrington C29F	Maidstone & District Motor Services	C28	R
918 NRT	1963	AEC Regent V MD3RV	Massey H33/28R	Lowestoft Corporation	8	RP
SDX 57	1963	AEC Regent V 2D2RA	Neepsend H37/28R	Ipswich Corporation	57	RP
NTW 942C	1965	Bristol Lodekka FLF6G	ECW H38/32F	Eastern National Omnibus Co	2849	R

Note: Please be aware that vehicles on display can vary from time to time as not all museums display their entire 'fleet'. Visitors wishing to see a particular vehicle should make enquiries prior to their visit.

Registration	Date	Chassis	Body	New to	Fleet No	Status
GJN 509D	1966	Leyland Leopard PSU3/1R	Marshall B49D	Southend Corporation	209	R
AVX 975G	1968	Bristol Lodekka FLF6LX	ECW H38/32F	Eastern National Omnibus Co	2614	RP
CPU 979G	1968	Bristol VRTSL6LX	ECW H39/31F	Eastern National Omnibus Co	3000	RP
GNM 232N	1975	Bristol LHS6L	Plaxton C33F	Epsom Coaches		RP
YEV 308S	1978	Leyland National 11351A/1R	Leyland National B49F	Eastern National Omnibus Co	1850	R
KYV 447X	1982	Leyland Titan TNLXB2RR	Leyland H44/24D	London Transport	T447	R

Notes:

JVW 430	renumbered 1274 in 1954
FOP 429	originally H33/26R; later operated by Eastern National Omnibus Co and Southend Corporation (244)
MPU 52	renumbered 1121 in 1954
LYR 997	in Osbornes of Tollesbury livery
ONO 49	renumbered 309 in 1954 and 1107 in 1964
PTW 110	renumbered 328 in 1954
WNO 478	built as H33/28R; numbered 1423 in 1954; passed to Eastern National Omnibus Co in 1955; renumbered 2380 in 1964 and coverted to open-top in 1965/6
XVX 19	renumbered 1431 in 1954 and 2400 in 1964
VLT 44	in Southend Transport livery
236 LNO	renumbered 2510 in 1964
217 MHK	renumbered 1402 in 1964
AVX 975G	delivered as CH37/18F; fitted with bus seats in 1975 and renumbered 2946

Cavan & Leitrim Railway
Dromod

Contact address: Cavan & Leitrim Railway, Narrow Gauge Station, Station Road, Dromod, Co Leitrim, Eire

Phone/fax: 00353 71 9638599

E-mail: dromod@eircom.net

Web site (railway): http://www.irish-railway.com

Brief description: Half mile 3ft gauge steam railway with a collection of railway vehicles (steam, diesel, carriages, wagons and railcars) together with a selection of vintage road vehicles, military equipment and vintage aircraft.

Opening days/times:
Open Saturday, Sundays and Mondays April-September. Rest of year by request, please phone, write or e-mail

Directions by car: to Dromod on N4 from Dublin. R202 from Dromod, 500yd.

Directions by public transport: Train to Dromod Irish Rail station from Dublin Connolly (Dublin-Sligo line). Narrow gauge station next to main line

Charges: Adult 8 Euro, Child 5 Euro, Family 17 Euro, OAP 5 Euro

Facilities: B(e) C D E G R (on request) S T

Registration	Date	Chassis	Body	New to	Fleet No	Status
KID 154	1947	Leyland Tiger PS1	Northern Ireland Road Transport Board B34R	Northern Ireland Road Transport Board	A8520	A
FCI 323	1950	Bristol LL5G	ECW B39R	Crosville Motor Services	KG156	RP
ZJ 5904	1950	Leyland Tiger OPS3/1	CIE	CIE	P164	R
IY 7383	1951	GNR Gardner	Park Royal/GNR B33R	Great Northern Railway (Ireland)	G389	R
IY 8044	1952	GNR Gardner	Park Royal/GNR B33R	Great Northern Railway (Ireland)	G396	A
ZO 6960	1953	Leyland Titan OPD2/1	CIE H37/31R	CIE	R541	RP
ZU 5000	1953	Leyland Royal Tiger PSU1/9	Saunders Roe B44C	Irish Army		RP
ZY 1715	1955	AEC Regal IV 9622E	Park Royal/GNR B40F	Great Northern Railway (Ireland)	345	R
ILI 98	1958	Bristol SC4LK	ECW B35F	Eastern National Omnibus Co	455	RP
OST 502	1959	AEC Reliance 2MU3RV	Alexander B41F	Highland Omnibuses	B24	RP
3945 UE	1960	Leyland Tiger Cub PSUC1	Park Royal B45F	Stratford-upon-Avon Blue Motors	45	A
71 AHI	1960	Leyland Tiger Cub PSUC1/2	Metro-Cammell B41F	Western Welsh Omnibus Co	1274	A
AZD 203	1964	Leyland Leopard L2	CIE B45F	CIE	E140	R
BLH 123B	1964	Bedford VAS2	Duple (Midland) B30F	London County Council	3159	RP

Registration	Date	Chassis	Body	New to	Fleet No	Status
EZH 155	1965	Leyland Leopard PSU3/4R	CIE B—F	CIE	C155	A
EZH 170	1966	Leyland Leopard PSU3/4R	CIE B45F	CIE	C170	R
UZH 258	1966	Leyland Leopard PSU3/4R	CIE B55F	CIE	C258	R
ZS 8621	1971	Daimler Fleetline CRG6LX	Park Royal H—/—F	West Midlands PTE	4130	A
177 IK	1972	Leyland Leopard PSU5/4R	CIE B48F	CIE	M177	A
78 D 140	1978	Bedford SB5	Marshall B40F	Royal Navy		R
78 D 824	1978	Bristol RELL6G	Alexander (Belfast) B52F	Ulsterbus	2193	R
85 D 2412	1978	Bedford SB5	Marshall B40F	Royal Air Force		A
643 MIP	1981	Volvo B58-56	Duple C53F	North West Coachlines of Kirkham		A

Notes:

KID 154	originally registered GZ 7588		EZH 155	converted to mobile workshop
FCI 323	originally registered LFM 737		ZS 8621	originally registered YOX 130K; converted as playbus
ZJ 5904	converted to recovery vehicle by CIE in 1971		177 IK	DAF engine fitted early 1980s
ZO 6960	sole survivor of a batch of six Airport buses		78 D 140	originally registered 42 RN 98
ZY 1715	converted to 3ft-gauge railway carriage 1971		78 D 824	originally registered POI 2193
ILI 98	originally registered 9579 F		85 D 2412	originally registered 48 AC 14
71 AHI	originally registered UKG 274		643 MIP	originally registered GRN 896W
AZD 203	worked on hire to County Donegal Railways			

Cobham Bus Museum

Contact address: Redhill Road, Cobham, Surrey, KT11 1EF

Phone: 01932 868665

Web site: www.lbpt.org

E-mail: info@lbpt.org

Affiliation: AIM, NARTM

Brief description: This well-established museum is home to the London Bus Preservation Trust Ltd. It was formed by a small group of enthusiasts in 1966. The collection has grown steadily over the years and now over 30 preserved buses, coaches and service vehicles are located at Cobham.

Events planned:
5 April 2009 — Spring Gathering at Wisley Airfield and Cobham Bus Museum.
Also 25 May (to be confirmed), 31 August, 25 October 2009. Please see the enthusiast press for details.

Opening days/times: Open days as advertised.
Viewing possible on Wednesdays and at weekends 11.00 to 17.00 but please telephone in advance to confirm.

Directions by car: From M25 junction 10 take A3 north and turn left on to A245. Museum is 1 mile on left.

Directions by public transport: Museum bus service from Weybridge station on main events. Network of special services on Spring Gathering and other event days.
Infrequent bus service at other times to Brooklands Road/Byfleet.

Charges: £10 on Annual Open Day, £5 on other event days.

Facilities: B B(e) G P R(limited) S T

Registration	Date	Chassis	Body	New to	Fleet No	Status
note ca	1875	Horse bus	LGOC Knife Board	LGOC		R
note cb	1890	Horse bus	Garden seat	Andrews Star Omnibus Co		R
XO 1048	1923	AEC 405 (NS)	(chassis only)	London General Omnibus Co	NS174	RP
XX 9591	1925	Dennis 4 ton	Dodson O24/24RO	Dominion Omnibus Co		R
UU 6646	1929	AEC Regal 662	LGOC B30R	London General Omnibus Co	T31	R
GJ 2098	1930	AEC Regent 661	Thomas Tilling H27/25RO	Thomas Tilling	ST922	R

Note: Please be aware that vehicles on display can vary from time to time as not all museums display their entire 'fleet'. Visitors wishing to see a particular vehicle should make enquiries prior to their visit.

Registration	Date	Chassis	Body	New to	Fleet No	Status
GN 8242	1931	AEC Regal 662	Weymann B30F	Queen Line Coaches of London	T357	A
GO 5170	1931	AEC Renown 664	LGOC B35F	London General Omnibus Co	LT1059	A
AGX 520	1933	AEC Regent 661	Chalmers -	London Transport	738J	R
AXM 693	1934	AEC Regent 661	LPTB H30/26R	London Transport	STL441	RP
CGJ 188	1935	AEC Q O762	Birmingham RC&W B35C	London Transport	Q83	R
CXX 171	1936	AEC Regal O662	Weymann C30F	London Transport	T448	RP
DLU 92	1937	AEC Regent O661	LPTB H30/26R	London Transport	STL2093	A
EGO 426	1937	AEC Regent O661	LPTB H30/26R	London Transport	STL2377	R
ELP 228	1938	AEC Regal O662	LPTB C30F	London Transport	T504	R
FJJ 764	1939	Leyland Tiger FEC	(chassis only)	London Transport	TF67	
HGC 130	1945	Guy Arab II	Park Royal UH30/26R	London Transport	G351	R
HLX 410	1948	AEC Regent III O961	Weymann H30/26R	London Transport	RT593	R
JXC 288	1949	Leyland Tiger PS1	Mann Egerton B30F	London Transport	TD95	R
KGK 803	1949	Leyland Titan 7RT	Park Royal H30/26R	London Transport	RTL139	R
KGU 142	1949	AEC Regent III O961	(chassis only)	London Transport	RT2213	R
MYA 590	1949	Leyland Comet CPO1	Harrington C29F	Scarlet Pimpernel of Minehead		R
UMP 227	1949	AEC Regal IV	Park Royal B40F	AEC (prototype)		RP
LUC 210	1951	AEC Regal IV 9821LT	Metro-Cammell DP35F	London Transport	RF10	RP
LYR 826	1952	AEC Regent III O961	Park Royal H30/26R	London Transport	RT2775	RP
LYR 910	1952	AEC Regent III O961	Park Royal H30/26R	London Transport	RT3491	R
MLL 740	1953	AEC Regal IV 9822E	Park Royal RC37C	British European Airways		R
MXX 283	1953	AEC Regal IV 9821LT	Metro-Cammell B41F	London Transport	RF395	R
MXX 334	1953	Guy Special NLLVP	ECW B26F	London Transport	GS34	R
NLE 672	1953	AEC Regal IV 9821LT	Metro-Cammell B41F	London Transport	RF672	R
CDX 516	1954	AEC Regent III 9613E	Park Royal H30/26R	Ipswich Corporation	16	R
SLT 58	1958	Leyland Routemaster	Weymann H34/30R	London Transport	RML3	R
461 CLT	1962	AEC Routemaster	Park Royal H32/25RD	London Transport	RMC1461	R
EGN 369J	1971	AEC Swift 4MP2R	Park Royal B33D	London Transport	SMS369	R
JPA 190K	1972	AEC Reliance 6U2R	Park Royal DP45F	London Country Bus Services	RP90	R
OJD 172R	1976	Leyland Fleetline FE30AGR	(chassis only)	London Transport	DMS2172	R
WYW 6T	1979	MCW Metrobus DR101/8	MCW H43/28D	London Transport	M6	R

Notes:

note ca	two-horse bus
note cb	three light garden seat; on loan to North of England Open Air Museum
XX 9591	restored as London General Omnibus Co D142
GJ 2098	on loan to BMMO during World War 2
AGX 520	former STL169 converted to LT service van
CXX 171	used as an ambulance during World War 2
DLU 92	original metal-framed Park Royal body replaced in 1949
ELP 228	used as an ambulance during World War 2
HGC 130	only remaining example of a London utility bus
MYA 590	converted from petrol to diesel in 1966
UMP 227	operated by London Transport in 1950
JXC 288	toured Europe and USSR 1963-7
LYR 910	fitted with AEC 11.3-litre engine in 1998
LYR 826	toured USA and Canada when new
SLT 58	prototype Leyland Routemaster; renumbered RM3 in 1961
OJD 172R	shortened chassis

Note: Please be aware that vehicles on display can vary from time to time as not all museums display their entire 'fleet'. Visitors wishing to see a particular vehicle should make enquiries prior to their visit.

Coventry Transport Museum

Contact address: Coventry Transport Museum, Millenium Place, Hales Street, Coventry CV1 1PN
Phone: 024 7623 4270
Fax: 024 7623 4284
E-mail: enquiries@transport-museum.com
Brief Description: The museum has over 260 cars and commercial vehicles, over 120 motorcycles and around 300 bicycles. Various tableaux chart the development of the motor vehicle from the early years and Coventry's contribution to this can be seen in the many marques on display. Other exhibits include the Thrust 2 and Thrust SSC land speed record car, several thousand die-cast models and a walk through audio visual display of the Coventry Blitz experience.
Opening days/times: Open all year, 10.00-17.00 (last admission 016.30) except 24/25/26 December.
Directions by car: Coventry ring road circles the city centre and is encountered whichever direction you come from. Once on it follow the brown 'Transport Museum' signs and turn off at junction 1. Nearest car park (pay & display) is signposted and is in Tower Street at the back of the Museum.
Directions by public transport: The Museum is opposite Pool Meadow bus/coach station. Use Travel West Midlands bus 17 or 27 from Coventry railway station to Broadgate (5min walk downhill to Museum from Broadgate).
Facilities: R, T, L, D, S, G, F, Be, H
Note: The vehicles are frequently stored off site while new developments are built. Please phone to check which vehicles are on display

Registration	Date	Chassis	Body	New to	Fleet No	Status
SR 1266	1916	Maudslay Subsidy A	(chassis only)			A
EKV 966	1944	Daimler CWA6	Roe H31/25R	Coventry Corporation	366	R
JNB 416	1948	Maudslay Marathon II	Trans-United C33F	Hackett's of Manchester		R
KOM 150	1950	Daimler CVD6	Wilsdon -	Birmingham Post & Mail		R
SRB 424	1953	Daimler CD650	Willowbrook L27/28RD	Tailby & George ('Blue Bus Services') of Willington		R
PBC 734	1954	Karrier Bantam Q25	Reading C14F	Mablethorpe Homes of Leicester		R
333 CRW	1963	Daimler CVG6	Metro-Cammell H34/29R	Coventry Corporation	333	R
PDU 125M	1973	Daimler Fleetline CRG6LX	East Lancs O44/30F	Coventry Corporation	125	R
K232 DAC	1993	Peugeot J5	C11F	Peugeot UK		A

Notes:

SR 1266	to be restored as replica of 1921 Hickman-bodied bus for Coventry Corporation
EKV 966	rebodied 1951; converted to mobile repair workshop (O2) in 1960
KOM 150	built as mobile print shop for the Birmingham Post and Mail and currently used as museum promotional vehicle
PBC 734	welfare bus
PDU 125M	originally H44/30F; converted to open-top in 1986
K232 DAC	prototype electric minibus

Dover Transport Museum
Whitfield

Contact address: Willingdon Road, Port Zone White Cliffs Business Park, Whitfield, Dover, CT16 2HJ
Phone: 01304 822409
Affiliation: NARTM, Transport Trust, AIM, ASTRO

Brief description: The museum displays local transport and social history. Road vehicles of all types. A maritime room, railway room, bygone shops and a garage. Hundreds of transport models including a working model tramway.

Events planned: 7 June 2009 — rally and running day in conjunction with East Kent Light Railway.
Enquiries and entries to David Atkins on 01303 248999 or dave@opentopbus.co.uk

Opening days/times: All year round — Sundays 10.00 to 17.00 (except when Chrisatmas Day falls on a Sunday)

Easter to end September — Sundays and Bank Holidays 10.00 to 17.00; Wednesday,Thursdays and Fridays 14.00 to 17.00.
Last entry 45 minutes before closing
Open at other times for pre-arranged groups.
Directions by car: Approximately one mile from the A2 Whitfield roundabout on the Dover bypass.
Directions by public transport: Dover Priory station then bus to Old Park, Whitfield.
Charges: Adult £4, Senior Citizen £3.50, Child £2.50, Family £9.
Facilities: B(e) D E G P R T

Registration	Date	Chassis	Body	New to	Fleet No	Status
CC 9305	1930	Dennis G	Roberts T19	Llandudno UDC	4	R
MFN 888	1957	Guy Arab IV	Park Royal H33/28RD	East Kent Road Car Co		R
569 KKK	1960	AEC Reliance 2MU3RA	Duple C41C	Ayers Coaches of Dover		R
GJG 751D	1966	AEC Regent V 2D3RA	Park Royal O40/32F	East Kent Road Car Co		R
GJG 757D	1966	AEC Regent V 2D3RA	Park Royal H40/32F	East Kent Road Car Co		A
FKM 706L	1972	Leyland Atlantean PDR1A/1Sp	MCW O45/33F	Maidstone & District Motor Services	5706	A
NPD 145L	1973	Leyland National 1151/1R/0402	Leyland National B30D	London Country Bus Services	LNC45	A
WKO 137S	1978	Bristol VRTSL3/6LXB	ECW H43/31F	Maidstone & District Motor Services	5137	R
BJG 674V	1980	Bristol VRTSL3/6LXB	ECW O43/31F	East Kent Road Car Co	7674	A
B147 EDP	1984	MCW Metrobus DR102/44	MCW DPH39/27F	Reading Transport	147	A

Notes:
GJG 751D   originally H40/32F; used as promotional vehicle
FKM 706L   originally H45/33F
NPD 145L   originally B49F; rebuilt after acquisition by East Kent (1145) in 1984
              and subsequently converted to rally control/hospitality unit
BJG 674V   originally H43/31F; converted to open-top in 2001

East Anglia Transport Museum
Carlton Colville

Contact address: Chapel Road, Carlton Colville, Lowestoft, Suffolk, NR33 8BL
Phone: 01502 518459
Web site: www.eatm.org.uk
Affiliation: NARTM, London Trolleybus Preservation Society, Transport Trust.
Brief description: A working transport museum on a fiver-acre site, first opened in 1972 and run entirely by volunteers. Tram and trolleybus services operate regularly within a developing street scene and the tramway has a woodland section. There is also a narrow-gauge railway. A wide variety of other vehicles on display and sometimes operated includes buses, lorries, steam rollers, battery-electrics, tower wagons and a London taxi. The museum is a registered charity.
Events planned:
25/26 April 2009 — Steam & Vintage Weekend. Free bus service to Lowestoft.
12 July 2009 — Vintage and modern bus weekend. Free bus service to Lowestoft and Beccles.
12/13 September 2009 — Trolleybus Weekend. Free bus service to Lowestoft and Beccles.
Opening days/times: April to end of September:
Sundays and Bank Holidays — 11.00 to 17.00;
Thursdays and Saturdays (June to Sept) — 14.00 to 17.00;
Daily, except Mondays (late July and Aug) — 14.00 to 17.00.
Last entry 1 hour before closing.
Directions by car: Follow the brown signs from the A12, A146 and A1117. Free car parking.
Directions by public transport:
Monday to Saturday: First Eastern Counties bus 102 from Lowestoft bus station to Carlton Colville Church, then 10min walk.
Bus X2 fromLowestoft to Norwich, to Carlton Crown PH then 5min walk.

Note: Please be aware that vehicles on display can vary from time to time as not all museums display their entire 'fleet'. Visitors wishing to see a particular vehicle should make enquiries prior to their visit.

By train to Oulton Broad South then 35min walk or bus 606 or 607.

Bus service 606 or 607 links Oulton Broad North and Oulton Broad South railway stations with the museum (Chapel Road bus stop), (Mondays to Saturdays only). For more details of this or other public transport information please ring the travel line on 08459 583358.

Charges: £6 adults, £5 Senior Citizens, £4.50 children. Admission includes free rides within the museum.

Facilities: B(e) D E F G H P R S T

Other information: Regular tram, train and trolleybus rides

Registration	Date	Chassis	Body	New to	Fleet No	Status
AH 79505+	1926	Garrett O type	Strachan & Brown B26D	NESA Copenhagen	5	RP
KW 1961	1927	Leyland Lion PLSC3	Leyland B35F	Blythe & Berwick of Bradford		A
WX 3567	1930	Gilford 168SD	Fielding & Bottomley C26D	Oade of Heckmondwike		RP
ALJ 986+	1935	Sunbeam MS2	Park Royal O40/29R	Bournemouth Corporation	202	R
CUL 260+	1936	AEC 664T	Metro-Cammell H40/30R	London Transport	260	R
EXV 201+	1938	Leyland LPTB70	Leyland H40/30R	London Transport	1201	R
FXH 521+	1940	Metro-Cammell	Metro-Cammell H40/30R	London Transport	1521	R
GBJ 192	1947	AEC Regent II O661	ECW H30/26R	Lowestoft Corporation	21	R
BDY 809+	1948	Sunbeam W	Weymann H30/26R	Hastings Tramways Co	34	RP
KAH 408	1948	Bristol L4G	ECW B35R	Eastern Counties Omnibus Co	LL108	A
note d+	1948	Berna	Hess B37D	Biel (Switzerland)	39	R
EX 6566	1950	Leyland Titan PD2/1	Leyland H30/26R	Great Yarmouth Corporation	66	R
KXW 234	1950	AEC Regent III O961 RT	Weymann H30/26R	London Transport	RT3125	R
LLU 829	1950	Leyland Titan 7RT	Park Royal H30/26R	London Transport	RTL1050	R
NBB 628+	1950	BUT 9641T	Metro-Cammell H40/30R	Newcastle Corporation	628	A
ERV 938+	1951	BUT 9611T	Burlingham H28/26R	Portsmouth Corporation	313	R
SG 2030+	1952	Henschel HIII/s	Uerdingen B32T	Solingen (Germany)	1	R
DRC 224+	1953	Sunbeam F4	Willowbrook H32/28R	Derby Corporation	224	R
LCD 52+	1953	BUT 9611T	Weymann H30/26R	Brighton Corporation	52	R
ONE 744+	1956	BUT 9612T	Burlingham H33/26R	Manchester Corporation	1344	R
YTE 826+	1956	BUT 9612T	Bond H32/28R	Ashton-under-Lyne Corporation	87	A
YLJ 286+	1959	Sunbeam MF2B	Weymann H35/28D	Bournemouth Corporation	286	R
557 BNG	1962	Bristol Lodekka FL6G	ECW H37/33RD	Eastern Counties Omnibus Co	LFL57	R
AEX 85B	1964	AEC Reliance 2MU3RA	Pennine B39F	Great Yarmouth Corporation	85	RP
YRT 898H	1969	AEC Swift 2MP2R	ECW B45D	Lowestoft Corporation	4	R
OCK 985K	1972	Bristol VRTSL6LX	ECW H39/31F	Ribble Motor Services	1985	R
D103 DAJ	1986	Mercedes-Benz L608D	Reeve-Burgess B20F	Hartlepool Transport	103	R
note ea+	1989	ZiU 682G1	ZiU B27T	ILPAP Athens	5088	R

+ trolleybus

Notes:

AH 79505	Danish registration
ALJ 986	new as H31/25RD, numbered 112; rebuilt and renumbered in 1958
note d	unregistered
SG 2030	German registration
LCD 52	built 1950 but not used until 1953; preserved in livery of subsequent operator Maidstone Corporation
OCK 985K	acquired by Eastern Counties Omnibus Co (VR385) in 1985
D103 DAJ	acquired by Lincolnshire Road Car Co (13) in 1990; preserved in LRCC RoadRunner livery
note ea	unregistered

Grampian Transport Museum
Alford

Contact address: Alford, Aberdeenshire AB33 8AE

Phone: 01975 562292

Fax: 01975 562180

E-mail: info@g-t-m.freeserve.co.uk

Web site: www.gtm.org.uk

Brief description: Dramatic displays, working exhibits and video presentations trace the history of travel and transport.

Opening days/times: April to October inclusive, 10.00 to 17.00 (10.00-16.00 in October).

Directions by car: On A944 west from Aberdeen (27 miles).

Directions by public transport: Stagecoach bus services from Aberdeen.

Charges: £5 Adults, £4.40 Senior Citizens, £2.40 Children, £13.Family.

Facilities: A B(e) C D E FG H L M P R S T

Registration	Date	Chassis	Body	New to	Fleet No	Status
JFM 238D	1966	Bristol Lodekka FS6G	ECW H33/27RD	Crosville Motor Services	DFG238	R
NRG 154M	1974	Leyland Atlantean AN68/1R	Alexander H45/29D	Grampian Regional Transport	154	R

Notes:
JFM 238D — last rear-entrance Bristol built
NRG 154M — used as a video theatre

Imperial War Museum
London

Contact address: Lambeth Road, London SE1 6HZ

Phone:
020 7416 5320
0891 600140 (recorded information)

E-mail: website: www.iwm.org.uk

Brief description: Revel in the history of the nation, through the world wars and much more besides. Regular exhibitions and displays of considerable educational value. The one bus in the collection fills a significant gap in transport history and is on display in museum atrium.

Opening days/times: Daily 10.00 to 18.00 (closed 24, 25 and 26 December)

Directions by car: South of Waterloo station, close to the Elephant & Castle. Parking difficult but coach park at Vauxhall Bridge and disabled parking by prior arrangement only — phone 020 7416 5397.

Directions by public transport:
Underground to Lambeth North, Waterloo or Elephant & Castle.
Rail to Waterloo.
Bus routes 1, 3, 12, 53, 59, 68, 148, 155, 159, 168, 171, 172, 176, 188, 344, 453, 468 and C10 with 45, 63, 100 nearby.

Charges: Free entry to main displays.

Facilities: A C D G H R T

Registration	Date	Chassis	Body	New to	Fleet No	Status
LN 4743	1911	LGOC B	LGOC O18/16RO	London General Omnibus Co	B43	R

Notes:
LN 4743 — named 'Ole Bill' after wartime cartoon character

Ipswich Transport Museum

Contact address: Old Trolleybus Depot, Cobham Road, Ipswich IP3 9JD

Phone: 01473 715666

Web site: www.ipswichtransportmuseum.co.uk.html

Affiliation: NARTM, ASTRO, SEMS, AFSM

Brief description: The collection includes most forms of road transport from the last 200 years, including bicycles, horse-drawn vehicles, trucks and service vehicles. There are displays of vehicles and other products of Ipswich engineering companies including six mobile cranes.

Events planned: Please see enthusiast press or web site for details

Opening days/times: April to November: Sundays and Bank Holidays 11.00 to 16.00. School holidays, Monday to Friday 13.00 to 16.00

Directions by car: From A12/A14 junction with A1189 (Nacton and Ipswich East) head towards Ipswich on Nacton Road. Turn right into Lindburgh Road. Museum is on left in Cobham Road.

Directions by public transport: By train to Ipswich. Take any bus to Tower Ramparts bus station. Then Ipswich Buses route 2.

Charges: Adult £4, Child £2.50, Concessions £2.50, Family £10. Special event rates may apply

Facilities: A B(e) D G P R T, picnic area

Registration	Date	Chassis	Body	New to	Fleet No	Status
DX 3988+	1923	Railless	Short B30D	Ipswich Corporation	2	R
DX 5610+	1926	Ransomes Sims & Jefferies D	Ransomes Sims & Jefferies B31D	Ipswich Corporation	9	A
DX 5617+	1926	Ransomes Sims & Jefferies D	(chassis only)	Ipswich Corporation	16	R
DX 5629+	1926	Garrett O type	Strachan & Brown B31D	Ipswich Corporation	26	A
DX 6591	1927	Tilling Stevens B9B	Eastern Counties B36R	Eastern Counties Road Car Co	78	A
VF 2788	1928	ADC 425A	Eastern Counties B36R	United Automobile Services	J379	A
DX 7812	1929	Tilling Stevens B10A2	(chassis only)	Eastern Counties Road Car Co	116	R
VF 8157	1930	Chevrolet LQ	Bush & Twiddy C14D	Final of Hockwold	4	R
WV 1209	1932	Bedford WLB	Waveney B20F	Alexander of Devizes		A
PV 817+	1933	Ransomes Sims & Jefferies	Ransomes Sims & Jefferies H24/24R	Ipswich Corporation	46	A
CVF 874	1939	Bristol L5G	ECW B35R	Eastern Counties Omnibus Co	LL574	A
CAH 923	1940	Dennis Ace	ECW B20F	Eastern Counties Omnibus Co	D23	A
PV 8270+	1948	Karrier W	Park Royal H30/26R	Ipswich Corporation	105	RP
KAH 407	1949	Bristol L4G	ECW B35R	Eastern Counties Omnibus Co	LL407	R
KNG 374	1949	Bristol K6B	ECW L27/28R	Eastern Counties Omnibus Co	LK374	R
PV 9371	1949	Bedford OB	Duple C27F	Mulleys Motorways of Ixworth	26	R
ADX 1	1950	AEC Regent III 9612E	Park Royal H30/26R	Ipswich Corporation	1	R
ADX 196+	1950	Sunbeam F4	Park Royal H30/26R	Ipswich Corporation	126	R
MAH 744	1951	Bristol LSX4G	ECW B42F	Eastern Counties Omnibus Co	LL744	R
BPV 9	1953	AEC Regal IV 9822E	Park Royal B42D	Ipswich Corporation	9	A
ADX 63B	1964	AEC Regent V 2D2RA	Massey H37/28R	Ipswich Corporation	63	R
APW 829B	1964	Bristol MW6G	ECW C39F	Eastern Counties Omnibus Co	LS829	R
GNG 125C	1965	Bristol Lodekka FS5G	ECW H33/27RD	Eastern Counties Omnibus Co	LFS125	RP
DPV 68D	1966	AEC Regent V 2D2RA	Neepsend H37/28R	Ipswich Corporation	68	A
JRT 82K	1971	AEC Swift 2MP2R	Willowbrook B40D	Ipswich Corporation	82	R
MRT 6P	1976	Leyland Atlantean AN68/1R	Roe H43/29D	Ipswich Borough Transport	6	R
XNG 770S	1978	Leyland National 11351/1R	Leyland National B53F	Eastern Counties Omnibus Co	LN770	A

+ trolleybus

Notes:

DX 3988	believed the oldest trolleybus on display anyehere in the world
DX 5610	changed from solid to pneumatic tyres in 1930
DX 6591	new with charabanc body; rebuilt in 1934
VF 2788	original United body replaced in 1934
DX 7812	rebodied twice while with Eastern Counties
VF 8157	body swapped with that of VF 9126; acquired by Mulleys Motorways of Ixworth in 1940
PV 817	first Ipswich double-decker
CVF 874	originally numbered LL74
CAH 923	originally fitted with Gardner 4LK engine
PV 8270	originally fitted with wooden seats
KNG 374	Gardner 5LW engine fitted by Eastern Counties
ADX 1	Ipswich Corporation's first motor bus
MAH 744	Bristol LS prototype

Note: Please be aware that vehicles on display can vary from time to time as not all museums display their entire 'fleet'. Visitors wishing to see a particular vehicle should make enquiries prior to their visit.

Isle of Wight Bus Museum
Newport (IoW)

Contact address: Seaclose Quay, Newport, Isle of Wight, PO30 2EF

Phone: 01983 533352

Affiliation: NARTM

Brief description: The collection ranges from a former Ryde Pier electric tram rebuilt in 1911 and a 1927 Daimler CK to a 1984 Olympian. Many of the vehicles are of Southern Vectis origin.

Events planned: 18th October 2009 — Running day (an additional running day is planned for a Sunday in May).

Opening days/times:
Saturdays: 11 April; 12 September
Sundays: 5, 12, 19, 26 April; 3 May-19 July (EXCEPT 14 June); 6 September-25 October.
Tuesdays: 7 April-14 July; 8 September-27 October
Wednesdays: 27 May; 24 June-15 July; 2-30 September
Thursdays: 28 May-16 July; 10-24 September Good Friday: 10 April
Bank Holiday Mondays: 13 April; 4, 25 May
Daily: 21 July-3 September
Times on all dates 10.30-16.00
Times subject to confirmation when going to press (phone 01983 533352 or 562069)

Directions by car: Bus museum is adjacent to Boat Museum (both signposted) off Fairlee Road through Seaclose Park to Quay past Travel Inn.

Directions by public transport: Bus to Newport bus station. Walk 12min to north of town, passing Church, then via Quay Street and Quay.

Charges: £4 Adult, £3.50 Senior Citizen, £2.50 child.

Facilities: B(e) D G S

Other information: Car parking nearby. Refreshments and toilets at adjacent Boat Museum.
Some vehicles are stored away from the museum. Please enquire for details.

Registration	Date	Chassis	Body	New to	Fleet No	Status
DL 5084	1927	Daimler CK	Dodson B26R	Dodson Bros ('Vectis')	11	A
NG 1109	1931	REO Pullman	Taylor Ch26D	Reynolds of Overstrand		R
AUF 666	1934	Leyland Titan TD3	Beadle H28/26R	Southdown Motor Services	966	RP
CDL 792	1938	Bedford WTB	Duple C26F	Shotters of Brightstone		R
EUF 196	1938	Leyland Titan TD5	Beadle L26/26R	Southdown Motor Services	196	A
DDL 50	1940	Bristol K5G	ECW O30/26R	Southern Vectis Omnibus Co	703	R
EDL 657	1947	Bristol K5G	ECW L27/28R	Southern Vectis Omnibus Co	721	RP
FDL 676	1949	Bedford OB	Duple C29F	Southern Vectis Omnibus Co	216	R
GDL 764	1950	Leyland Titan PD2/1A	Leyland L27/26R	Seaview Services		R
MDL 954	1956	Bristol LD6G	ECE O33/27R	Southern Vectis Omnibus Co	544	R
ODL 400	1957	Bedford SBG	Duple C41F	Moss Motor Tours of Sandown		RP
PDL 515	1958	Bristol MW6G	ECW C39F	Southern Vectis Omnibus Co	315	RP
PDL 519	1958	Bristol Lodekka LD6G	ECW H—/—R	Southern Vectis Omnibus Co	559	A
VJW 882	1958	Commer Avenger TS3	Duple C37F	Don Everall of Wolverhampton		R
SDL 268	1959	Bristol Lodekka LD6G	ECW H33/27R	Southern Vectis Omnibus Co	563	R
ADL 459B	1964	Bedford SB3	Duple C41F	Paul's Tours of Ryde	9	RP
CDL 479C	1965	Bristol Lodekka FLF6G	ECW H38/32F	Southern Vectis Omnibus Co	611	R
FDL 927D	1966	Bristol MW6G	ECW B43F	Southern Vectis Omnibus Co	806	RP
KDL 885F	1968	Bristol RESH6G	Duple C45F	Southern Vectis Omnibus Co	301	R
NDL 490G	1969	Bristol VRTSL6LX	ECW H39/31F	Southern Vectis Omnibus Co	622	A
SDL 638J	1971	Bristol VRTSL6LX	ECW H39/31F	Southern Vectis Omnibus Co	628	R
TDL 564K	1971	Bristol RELL6G	ECW OB53F	Southern Vectis Omnibus Co	864	R
TDL 566K	1972	Bristol RELL6G	ECW B53F	Southern Vectis Omnibus Co	866	A
XDL 122L	1972	Bristol RELH6G	ECW C49F	Southern Vectis Omnibus Co	302	R
NDL 637M	1973	Bristol VRTSL6LX	ECW H39/31F	Southern Vectis Omnibus Co	637	R
RDL 309X	1982	Leyland Leopard PSU3G/4R	ECW C49F	Southern Vectis Omnibus Co	309	A
A700 DDL	1984	Leyland Olympian ONLXB/1R	ECW H45/32F	Southern Vectis Omnibus Co	700	A

Notes:
AUF 666   rebodied in 1949

DDL 50	converted to open-top in 1959; used as tree-lopper from 1969
MDL 954	originally H33/27R; converted to open-top in 1973 and renumbered OT4
PDL 519	originally H33/27R

Keighley Bus Museum
Keighley

Contact address: 47 Brantfell Drive, Burnley, Lancs BB12 8AW

Phone: 01282 413179

Web site: www.kbmt.org.uk

Affiliation: AIM, FBHVC, NARTM, Y&HMC

Brief description: A collection of 50 buses, coaches and ancillary vehicles. Some 60% are owned by the Trust and others by private individuals. The Trust aims to establish a permanent home for the collection in central Keighley.

Events planned:

5 July 2009 — Keighley Festival of Transport
Other events not yet finalised. Please see enthusiast press.

Opening days/times: Tuesday evenings 19.00-22.00, and most Saturdays and Sundays (please check in advance) at Riverside, off Dalton Lane adjacent to railway station.

Car parking: Dalton Lane.

Directions by public transport: Keighley (5min from main line station) and 10min walk from bus station. Frequent buses from Keighley (zone routes 708/711, alight at Dalton Mills).

Charges: Special events: £2 Adult, £1 concession. Otherwise free but donations welcome.

Facilities: B(e) P T

Registration	Date	Chassis	Body	New to	Fleet No	Status
WT 7101+	1924	Straker Clough	Brush H-/-RO	Keighley Corporation Tramways	5	R
KW 2260	1927	Leyland Lion PLSC3	Leyland B35R	Bradford Corporation	325	A
KY 9106	1931	AEC Regent I O661	Metro-Cammell	Bradford Corporation	046	A
TF 6860	1931	Leyland Lion LT3	Leyland B36R	Rawtenstall Corporation	61	RP
ANW 682	1934	AEC Regent 661	Roe H30/26R	Leeds City Transport	139	R
CWX 671	1938	Bristol K5G	Roe L27/28R	Keighley West Yorkshire Services	KDG26	R
FWX 914+	1948	Sunbeam F4	East Lancs H37/29F	Bradford City Transport	844	R
MNW 86	1948	Leyland Tiger PS1	Roe B36R	Leeds City Transport	28	R
JWU 886	1951	Bristol LL5G	ECW B39R	West Yorkshire Road Car Co	SGL16	R
LYR 533	1951	AEC Regent III O961	Park Royal H30/26R	London Transport	RT3314	R
MTE 635	1951	AEC Regent III 6812A	Weymann H33/26R	Morecambe & Heysham Corporation	73	RP
UUA 214	1955	Leyland Titan PD2/11	Roe H33/25R	Leeds City Transport	214	A
GJX 331	1956	Daimler CVG6	Roe H37/26R	Halifax Corporation	119	R
VTU 76	1956	Daimler CVG6	Northern Counties H35/23C	SHMD Board	76	RP
XLG 477	1956	Atkinson Alpha PL745H	Northern Counties B34C	SHMD Board	77	A
7514 UA	1959	Daimler CVG6-30	Roe H38/32R	Leeds City Transport	514	A
XYJ 418	1961	AEC Routemaster R2RH	Park Royal H36/28R	London Transport	RM736	R
PJX 232	1962	Leyland Leopard L1	Weymann B44F	Halifax Joint Omnibus Committee	232	R
WJY 758	1962	Leyland Atlantean PDR1/1	Metro-Cammell O44/31F	Plymouth Corporation	158	R
WBR 246	1963	Atkinson Alpha PM746HL	Marshall B45D	Sunderland Corporation	46	RP
6203 KW	1964	AEC Regent V 2D3RA	Metro-Cammell H40/30F	Bradford City Transport	203	A
6204 KW	1964	AEC Regent V 2D3RA	Metro-Cammell H40/30F	Bradford City Transport	204	A
6220 KW	1964	AEC Regent V 2D3RA	Metro-Cammell H40/30F	Bradford City Transport	220	R
CUB 331C	1965	Leyland Atlantean PDR1/1	Weymann H41/29F	Leeds City Transport	331	RP
ENW 980D	1966	AEC Regent V 2D2RA	Roe H39/31R	Leeds City Transport	980	RP
HNW 131D	1966	Daimler Fleetline CRG6LX	Roe H45/33F	Leeds City Transport	131	RP
KVH 473E	1966	Daimler Fleetline CRG6LX	Roe H44/31F	Huddersfield Corporation	473	R

Note: Please be aware that vehicles on display can vary from time to time as not all museums display their entire 'fleet'. Visitors wishing to see a particular vehicle should make enquiries prior to their visit.

Registration	Date	Chassis	Body	New to	Fleet No	Status
NWU 265D	1966	Bristol Lodekka FS6B	ECW H33/27RD	York - West Yorkshire Services	YDX221	R
TWW 766F	1967	Bristol RELH6G	ECW C47F	West Yorkshire Road Car Co	CRG6	R
YLG 717F	1967	Bristol RESL6G	Northern Counties B43F	SHMD Board	117	A
LAK 309G	1969	Leyland Titan PD3A/12	Alexander H41/29F	Bradford City Transport	309	R
LAK 313G	1969	Leyland Titan PD3A/12	Alexander H41/29F	Bradford City Transport	313	RP
TKU 467K	1971	Leyland Atlantean PDR2/1	Alexander H47/29D	Bradford City Transport	467	A
WFM 801K	1972	Leyland National 1151/2R/0403	Leyland National B44D	Crosville Motor Services	SNL801	R
XAK 355L	1972	Daimler Fleetline CRL6	Alexander H43/31F	Bradford City Transport	355	RP
GWY 690N	1975	Leyland Leopard PSU4B/4R	Plaxton C45F	West Yorkshire PTE	64	A
OJD 192R	1977	Leyland Fleetline FE30AGR	MCW H45/32F	London Transport	DMS2192	A
DNW 840T	1978	Leyland National 10351B/1R	Leyland National B44F	West Yorkshire Road Car Co	1002	RP
JUM 505V	1980	MCW Metrobus DR101/7	MCW H43/30F	West Yorkshire PTE	7505	RP
NKU 245X	1981	Leyland National 2 NL116AL11/1R	Leyland National B52F	Yorkshire Traction Co	245	RP
A577 NWX	1984	Leyland Olympian ONLXB/1R	ECW H45/32F	West Riding Automobile Co	577	RP
D275 OOJ	1987	Freight Rover Sherpa	Carlyle B20F	Carlyle (demonstrator)		RP
+ trolleybus						

Notes:

WT 7101	solid tyres
KY 9106	former double-decker converted to gritter; on loan from Bradford Museums Service
TF 6860	used as a tow bus and snowplough 1950-63
CWX 671	rebodied 1950; now based at Transdev's Burnley depot
FWX 914	rebodied 1963; chassis ex Mexborough & Swinton Traction Co
JWU 886	single-block experimental Gardner engine
UUA 214	driver trainer 1972-8
XYJ 418	originally registered WLT 736
WJY 758	converted to open-top in 1975; restored as Keighley Corporation Tramways 59
NWU 265D	renumbered 3821 in 1971
KWT 642D	renumbered 1810 in 1971
TWW 766F	renumbered 1019 in 1971; restored in later guise as 2508
WFM 801K	second production Leyland National; operated as a single-door bus with Greater Manchester Buses (South)

Lincolnshire Road Transport Museum
North Hykeham

Contact address: Whisby Road, North Hykeham, Lincoln LN6 3QT

Phone: 01522 689497

Web site: www.lvvs.org.uk

Affiliation: NARTM

Brief description: An impressive collection of over 60 vehicles including classic cars, commercials, buses and motor cycles, mostly with Lincolnshire connections. Sixty years of road transport history is represented in the museum hall, which was built in 1993. New storage buildings are planned very shortly. The LVVS celebrates its 50th year in 2009.

Events planned: Please see enthusiast press and web site.

12 April 2009 — Easter Sunday open day

1 November 2009 — Autumn open day

Opening days/times:

May to October: Monday to Friday 12.00 to 16.00; Sunday 10.00 to 16.00;

November to April: Sunday 13.00 to 16.00. Other times by appointment.

Directions by car: Just off A46 Lincoln by-pass on Whisby Road, which links A46 to B1190.

Directions by public transport: 1 mile from North Hykeham railway station.

Whisby Road is just off Doddington Road, served by several bus routes from city centre.

Charges: £2 adult. Accompanied children free. Other charges may apply at special events — please see web site.

Facilities: A B(e) D P T

Other information: Refreshments available on open days. Please check beforehand if you wish to se aparticular vehicle as a few are rotated with other accommodation.

Registration	Date	Chassis	Body	New to	Fleet No	Status
KW 474	1927	Leyland Lion PLSC1	Leyland B31F	Blythe & Berwick of Bradford		R
TE 8318	1929	Chevrolet LQ	Spicer C14D	Jardine of Morcambe		R
VL 1263	1929	Leyland Lion LT1	Applewhite B32R	Lincoln Corporation	5	R
WH 1553	1929	Leyland Titan TD1	Leyland L27/24RO	Bolton Corporation	54	R
KW 7604	1930	Leyland Badger TA4	Plaxton B20F	Bradford Education Committee	023	R
TF 818	1930	Leyland Lion LT1	Roe B30F	Lancashire United Transport	202	R
FW 5698	1935	Leyland Tiger TS7	Burlingham B35F	Lincolnshire Road Car Co	1411	R
RC 2721	1935	SOS DON	Brush B—F	Trent Motor Traction Co	321	RP
FHN 833	1940	Bristol L5G	ECW B35F	United Automobile Services	BLO133	RP
BFE 419	1941	Leyland Titan TD7	Roe H30/26R	Lincoln Corporation	64	R
VV 8934	1945	Daimler CWD6	Duple H30/26R	Northampton Corporation	129	RP
AHE 163	1946	Leyland Titan PD1	Roe H31/25R	Yorkshire Traction	726	RP
DBE 187	1946	Bristol K6A	ECW H30/26R	Lincolnshire Road Car Co	2115	R
GUF 727	1947	Leyland Tiger PS1/1	ECW B32R	Southdown Motor Services	677	R
DFE 383	1948	Guy Arab III	Guy H30/26R	Lincoln Corporation	23	R
HPW 133	1949	Bristol K5G	ECW H30/26R	Eastern Counties Omnibus Co	LKH133	R
OHK 432	1949	Daimler CVD6	Roberts H30/26R	Colchester Corporation	4	R
ONO 59	1949	Bristol K5G	ECW L—/—RD	Eastern National Omnibus Co	4038	A
FFU 860	1950	AEC Regal III 9621E	Willowbrook DP35F	Enterprise of Scunthorpe	60	R
KDT 393	1951	AEC Regent III 9613A	Roe H31/25R	Doncaster Corporation	122	R
FDO 573	1953	AEC Regent III 9613E	Willowbrook H32/28RD	J. W. Camplin & Sons ('Holme Delight') of Donington		RP
JDN 668	1954	AEC Regent III 6812A	Roe H33/25RD	York Pullman Bus Co	64	R
OLD 714	1954	AEC Regent III O961 RT	Weymann H30/26R	London Transport	RT4494	R
LFW 326	1955	Bristol Lodekka LD6B	ECW H33/25RD	Lincolnshire Road Car Co	2318	R
OVL 465	1960	Bristol MW5G	ECW B45F	Lincolnshire Road Car Co	2245	R
RFE 416	1961	Leyland Titan PD2/41	Roe H33/28R	Lincoln Corporation	89	R
952 JUB	1964	AEC Regent V 2D2RA	Roe H39/31R	Leeds City Transport	952	RP
CVL 850D	1966	Bristol RELH6G	ECW C47F	Lincolnshire Road Car Co	1431	RP
EVL 549E	1967	Leyland Panther PSUR1/1R	Roe DP45F	Lincoln Corporation	41	RP
UVL 873M	1973	Bristol RELL6L	Alexander B48F	Lincoln Corporation	73	RP
NFW 36V	1980	Bristol VRTLL3/6LXB	East Lancs H50/36F	Lincoln City Transport	36	A
PFE 542V	1980	Bristol VRTSL3/6LXB	ECW H43/31F	Lincolnshire Road Car Co	1958	R

Notes:

KW 474	restored as Lincoln Corporation No 1
FW 5698	originally numbered 370; rebodied in 1949
FHN 833	later renumbered BG147
VV 8934	utility body
DBE 187	originally numbered 661; rebuilt by ECW in the mid-1950s
DFE 383	Ruston Hornsby air-cooled engine
ONO 59	renumbered 1427 in 1954 and 2255 in 1964; subsequently converted to caravan
FFU 860	passed to Lincolnshire Road Car Co (860) in 1950
CVL 850D	later renumbered 2231

Note: Please be aware that vehicles on display can vary from time to time as not all museums display their entire 'fleet'. Visitors wishing to see a particular vehicle should make enquiries prior to their visit.

London Transport Museum
London

Contact address: 39 Wellington Street, London WC2E 7BB.

Phone: 020 7565 7299 — 24hr recorded information; 020 7379 6344 — Admin etc

Fax: 020 7565 7250

E-mail: enquiry@ltmuseum.co.uk

Web site: www.ltmuseum.co.uk

Affiliation: HRA, NARTM, TT

Brief description: Lively new galleries tell the story of London's transport system and how it shaped the lives of people living and working in London, including current and future transport developments. The Design for Travel gallery showcases original artworks and advertising posters.

Opening days/times:
Museum:
Saturday to Thursday — 10.00-18.00 (last admission 17.15)
Friday — 11.00-21.00 (last admission 20.15)
Closed 24-26 December
Museum shop:
Saturday to Tuesday — 10.00-18.30
Wednesday, Thursday and Saturday — 10.00-19.00
Friday — 11.00-21.00
Check website for Christmas opening
Upper Deck Café Bar:
Monday to Thursday — 10.00-21.30
Friday — 11.00-21.30
Saturday — 10.00-21.30
Sunday — 10.00-18.00
Closed 25/26 December

Access by public transport: Tube: Covent Garden, Holborn, Leicester Square stations
Main line: Charing Cross
Bus: to Strand or Aldwych

Facilities for the disabled: Full disabled access including toilets. Reduced admission for registered disabled and person accompanying them

Registration	Date	Chassis	Body	New to	Fleet No	Status
note m	1829	horse bus	LGOC	George Shillibeer		R
note n	1875	horse bus	Thomas Tilling -24-	Thomas Tilling		R
LA 9928	1911	LGOC B	LGOC O18/16RO	London General Omnibus Co	B340	R
EXV 253+	1939	Leyland LPTB70	Leyland H40/30R	London Transport	1253	R
FJJ 774	1939	Leyland FEC	LPTB B34F	London Transport	TF77	R
737 DYE	1963	AEC Routemaster 2R2RH	Park Royal H36/28R	London Transport	RM1737	R
EGP 1J	1970	Daimler Fleetline CRG6LXB	Park Royal H44/24D	London Transport	DMS1	R
+ trolleybus						

Notes:
note m   unregistered reconstruction
note n   unregistered; 'knifeboard' type

Manchester Museum of Transport
Cheetham

Contact address: Boyle Street, Cheetham, Manchester M8 8UW

Phone/Fax: 0161 205 2122

E-mail: email@gmts.co.uk

Web site: www.gmts.co.uk or www.manchester.bus.museum

Affiliation: NARTM

Brief description:
The museum houses over 70 buses and coaches from the Greater Manchester area, from an 1876 horse bus to a 1990 Metrolink tram. Travel back to a time of twopenny singles and coach trips to Blackpool. Extensive displays of photos, uniforms and models complement the vehicles, and visitors may enter many of the vehicles and view the museum's workshop.

Events planned:
28/29 March 2009 — Spring Transport Festival
19 April 2009 — London Bus Event
16/17 May 2009 — Bolton Event
27 June 2009 — Busmen's Holiday (retired employee event)
6 September 2009 — September Rally
31 October/1 November 2009 — SELNEC 40
5/6 December 2009 — The Christmas Cracker

Opening days/times: Wednesdays, Saturdays, Sundays & Bank Holidays: 10.00-16.30 all year (please phone for Christmas/New Year opening)

Directions by car:
From M62/M60 junction 18, follow 'Castlefields' signs to Cheetham Hill; from City, follow A665 (Cheetham Hill Road) — Museum signposted.
Due to limited parking on special event days it is suggested to park at either MEN Arena, or any other central area car park and travel on one of the free buses linking Victoria station with the museum

Directions by public transport:
Bus 135 or 59 to Queen's Road.

Charges: £4 adult, £2 concession (over 60, students and unemployed). Free under 16 and registered disabled. Season tickets available. School parties free

Facilities: B(e) C D F G H P R S T

Other information: Archives available for study by arrangement.

Note: Please be aware that vehicles on display can vary from time to time as not all museums display their entire 'fleet'. Visitors wishing to see a particular vehicle should make enquiries prior to their visit.

Registration	Date	Chassis	Body	New to	Fleet No	Status
note b	1876	Horse bus O18/14RO	Manchester Carriage Co	Manchester Carriage Co	2	R
DB 5070	1925	Tilling-Stevens TS6 Petrol-Electric	Brush O54RO	North Western Road Car Co	170	R
CK 3825	1927	Leyland Lion PLSC1	Leyland B31F	Ribble Motor Services	295	R
VM 4439	1928	Leyland Tiger TS1	Metro-Cammell/Crossley B—R	Manchester Corporation	138	A
VY 957	1929	Leyland Lion PLSC1	Ribble B32R	York Corporation	2	R
VR 5742	1930	Leyland Tiger TS2	Manchester Corporation Car Works B30R	Manchester Corporation	28	R
ANB 851	1934	Crossley Mancunian	Crossley/MCT H28/26R	Manchester Corporation	436	A
AXJ 857	1934	Leyland Titan TD3	(chassis only)	Manchester Corporation	526	R
JA 7585	1935	Leyland Tiger TS7	English Electric B35C	Stockport Corporation	185	A
RN 7824	1936	Leyland Cheetah LZ2	Brush C31F	Ribble Motor Services	1568	RP
EFJ 92	1938	Bedford WTB	Heaver C25F	Taylor of Exeter		RP
AJA 152	1939	Bristol K5G	Willowbrook L27/26R	North Western Road Car Co	432	R
BBA 560	1939	AEC Regent O661	Park Royal H26/22R	Salford Corporation	235	R
JP 4712	1940	Leyland Titan TD7	Leyland L24/24R	Wigan Corporation	70	RP
FTB 11	1941	Leyland Titan TD7	Northern Coachbuilders L27/26R	Leigh Corporation	84	A
BJA 425	1946	Bristol L5G	Willowbrook B38R	North Western Road Car Co	270	R
HTB 656	1946	Leyland Tiger PS1	Roe B35R	Ramsbottom UDC	17	R
HTF 586	1947	Bedford OB	Scottish Motor Traction C29F	Warburton Bros of Bury		R
CDB 224	1948	Leyland Titan PD2/1	Leyland L27/26R	North Western Road Car Co	224	R
CWH 717	1948	Leyland Titan PD2/4	Leyland	Bolton Corporation	367	R
DBU 246	1948	Leyland Titan PD1/3	Roe H31/25R	Oldham Corporation	246	RP
JND 791	1948	Crossley DD42/8S	Crossley H32/26R	Manchester Corporation	2150	R
JNA 467	1949	Leyland Titan PD1/3	Metro-Cammell H32/26R	Manchester Corporation	3166	RP
LMA 284	1949	Foden PVSC6	Lawton C35F	Coppenhall of Comberbach		R
BEN 177	1950	AEC Regent III 9613A	Weymann H30/26R	Bury Corporation	177	R
CWG 206	1950	Leyland Tiger PS1	Alexander C35F	W. Alexander & Sons	PA164	R
FBU 827	1950	Crossley DD42/8	Crossley H30/26R	Oldham Corporation	368	RP
LTC 774+	1950	Crossley Empire TDD42/2	Crossley H30/26R	Ashton-under-Lyne Corporation	80	RP
EDB 549	1951	Leyland Titan PD2/1	Leyland O30/20R	Stockport Corporation	295	R
EDB 562	1951	Leyland Titan PD2/1	Leyland H30/26R	Stockport Corporation	308	A
EDB 575	1951	Crossley DD42/7	Crossley H30/26R	Stockport Corporation	321	R
JND 646	1951	Leyland Titan PD2/3	Metro-Cammell H32/26R	Manchester Corporation	3245	R
JVU 755+	1951	Crossley Dominion TDD64/1	Crossley H36/30R	Manchester Corporation	1250	R
NNB 125	1953	Leyland Royal Tiger PSU1/13	Northern Counties B41C	Manchester Corporation	25	R
UMA 370	1955	Atkinson PD746	Northern Counties H35/24C	SHMD Board	70	R
JBN 153	1956	Leyland Titan PD2/13	Metro-Cammell H34/28R	Bolton Corporation	77	R
NDK 980	1956	AEC Regent V D2RA6G	Weymann H33/28R	Rochdale Corporation	280	R
PND 460	1956	Leyland Titan PD2/12	Metro-Cammell H36/28R	Manchester Corporation	3460	R
DJP 754	1957	Leyland Titan PD2/30	Northern Counties H33/28R	Wigan Corporation	115	R
NBU 494	1957	Leyland Titan PD2/20	Roe H31/29R	Oldham Corporation	394	R
116 JTD	1958	Guy Arab IV	Northern Counties H41/32R	Lancashire United Transport	21	R
122 JTD	1958	Guy Arab IV	Northern Counties H41/32R	Lancashire United Transport	27	R
SDK 442	1958	Leyland Worldmaster RT3/2	Plaxton C41F	Ellen Smith of Rochdale		RP
TNA 496	1958	Leyland Titan PD2/40	Burlingham H37/28R	Manchester Corporation	3496	R
TNA 520	1958	Leyland Titan PD2/34	Burlingham H37/28R	Manchester Corporation	3520	R
UNB 629	1960	Leyland Atlantean PDR1/1	Metro-Cammell H45/33F	Manchester Corporation	3629	R
YDK 590	1960	AEC Reliance 2MU3RA	Harrington C37F	Yelloway Motor Services of Rochdale		R
HEK 705	1961	Leyland Titan PD3A/2	Massey H41/29F	Wigan Corporation	57	A
3655 NE	1962	Leyland Tiger Cub PSUC1/12	Park Royal DP38D	Manchester Corporation	55	A
TRJ 112	1962	Daimler CVG6	Metro-Cammell H37/28R	Salford City Transport	112	R
414 CLT	1963	AEC Routemaster 2R2RH	Park Royal H36/28R	London Transport	RM1414	R
4632 VM	1963	Daimler CVG6K	Metro-Cammell H37/28R	Manchester Corporation	4632	R
REN 116	1963	Leyland Atlantean PDR1/1	Metro-Cammell H41/33F	Bury Corporation	116	A
8860 VR	1964	AEC Regent V 2D3RA	Neepsend H41/32R	A. Mayne & Son of Manchester		R
BND 874C	1965	Leyland Panther Cub PSURC1/1	Park Royal B43D	Manchester Corporation	74	R

Registration	Date	Chassis	Body	New to	Fleet No	Status
DBA 214C	1965	Leyland Atlantean PDR1/1	Metro-Cammell H43/33F	Salford City Transport	214	R
DDB 174C	1965	Daimler Fleetline CRG6LX	Alexander H44/31F	North Western Road Car Co	174	R
PTC 114C	1965	AEC Renown 3B3RA	East Lancs H41/31F	Leigh Corporation	15	R
PTE 944C	1965	Leyland Titan PD2/37	Roe H37/28F	Ashton-under-Lyne Corporation	44	R
FRJ 254D	1966	Leyland Titan PD2/40	Metro-Cammell H36/28F	Salford City Transport	254	R
HVM 901F	1968	Leyland Atlantean PDR1/1	Park Royal H45/28D	Manchester City Transport	1001	R
KDB 408F	1968	Leyland Leopard PSU4/1R	East Lancs B43D	Stockport Corporation	408	RP
KJA 871F	1968	Leyland Titan PD3/14	East Lancs H38/32R	Stockport Corporation	71	R
MJA 891G	1969	Leyland Titan PD3/14	East Lancs H38/32R	Stockport Corporation	91	R
MJA 897G	1969	Leyland Titan PD3/14	East Lancs O38/32F	Stockport Corporation	97	R
TTD 386H	1969	Leyland Titan PD3/14	East Lancs H41/32F	Ramsbottom UDC	11	R
SRJ 328H	1970	Leyland Atlantean PDR2/1	MCW H47/31D	SELNEC PTE	1205	RP
TXJ 507K	1972	Leyland National 1151/2R/0202	Leyland National B46D	SELNEC PTE	EX30	R
VNB 101L	1972	Leyland Atlantean AN68/1R	Park Royal H43/32F	SELNEC PTE	7001	R
XVU 352M	1974	Seddon Pennine IV-236	Pennine B19F	Greater Manchester PTE	1722	R
GNC 276N	1975	Seddon-Lucas	Pennine B19F	Greater Manchester PTE	EX62	R
HVU 244N	1975	AEC Reliance 6U3ZR	Plaxton C49F	Yelloway Motor Services of Rochdale		R
XBU 17S	1978	Leyland Fleetline FE30AGR	Northern Counties H43/32F	Greater Manchester PTE	8017	A
ORJ 83W	1981	MCW Metrobus DR102/21	MCW H43/30F	Greater Manchester PTE	5083	A
A706 LNC	1984	Leyland Atlantean AN68D/1R	Northern Counties H43/32F	Greater Manchester PTE	8706	A
B65 PJA	1984	Leyland Olympian ONLXB/1R	Northern Counties H43/30F	Greater Manchester PTE	3065	A
C208 FVU	1986	MCW Metrobus DR132/8	Northern Counties CH43/29F	Greater Manchester PTE	5208	RP
C255 FRJ	1986	Leyland Olympian ONLXB/1R	Northern Counties CH43/26F	Greater Manchester PTE	3255	A
D63 NOF	1986	Freight Rover 400 Special	Carlyle B18F	Manchester Minibuses ('Bee Line Buzz Co')	63	A
D676 NNE	1987	MCW Metrorider MF151/3	MCW B23F	Greater Manchester Buses	1676	R
M939 XKA	1994	Mercedes-Benz 609D	Devon Conversions DP16FI	Greater Manchester Accessible Transport		R

+ trolleybus

Notes:

note b	largest surviving horse bus
CK 3825	body rebuilt 1981
VM 4439	body new 1935
VY 957	body rebuilt 1983; restored to Ribble livery
VR 5742	rebodied 1937
ANB 851	rebodied 1938
BBA 560	training bus with dual controls, 1948-70; renumbered 98 in 1950
AJA 152	rebodied 1951
FTB 11	utility body, originally L27/28R; refurbished by Thurgood in the 1950s
BJA 425	originally numbered 125; rebodied 1958 with 1952 body
CWH 717	originally H30/26R; converted to tower wagon 1963
LMA 284	body new 1954
EDB 549	originally H30/26R; converted to open top in 1968
EDB 562	used as driver-training bus 1968-78
UMA 370	only Atkinson double-decker bodied; originally H35/25C
122 JTD	Gardner 6LX engine from new
TNA 520	fully automatic transmission when new; converted to semi-automatic in 1963
SDK 442	rebodied 1970
UNB 629	originally H43/34F; re-seated in 1954 using trolleybus seats
414 CLT	loaned to Manchester Corporation when new in February 1963
HVM 901F	first 'Mancunian' double-decker
KJA 871F	restored as Greater Manchester PTE 5871
MJA 891G	last open-rear-platform double-decker delivered to a British operator

Note: Please be aware that vehicles on display can vary from time to time as not all museums display their entire 'fleet'. Visitors wishing to see a particular vehicle should make enquiries prior to their visit.

MJA 897G   originally H38/32F; converted to open-top in 1982
TTD 386H   last half-cab double-decker delivered to a British operator
SRJ 328H   'Mancunian' style ordered by Salford City Transport
VNB 101L   first SELNEC Standard double-decker

Midland Road Transport Group
Butterley

Contact address: 21 Ash Grove, Mastin Moor, Chesterfield S43 3AW

Phone: Midland Road Transport Group — 01246 473619
Midland Railway 01773 747674, Visitor Information Line (01773) 570140.

Website: www.mrtg.org.uk

Brief Description: A large purpose-built museum building housing a collection of buses, lorries and fork lift trucks fully or partially restored. Situated at the Swanwick Junction site of the Midland Railway Centre. All vehicles are all privately-owned by individual preservaionists who co-operated together to provide finances to build the museum which was completed in 2004

Events planned:
12 July 2009 — 3rd Annual Road Transport Rally

Opening days/times:
The Centre is open daily except for 25/26 December. Please contact for Road Transport Group opening

Directions by car: To Swanwick Junction.
From the north, M1 Jcn 28, follow A38 southbound to B600, turn left to Somercotes, right on to B6016 through Riddings. Follow signs to Codnor/Heanor and turn right onto Coach Road at the bottom of descent from Riddings. Half mile along this narrow lane, take right fork after speed bumps.
From the south, M1 Jcn 26, follow A610 northbound to Codnor, turn right and right again onto B6016 Alfreton/Somercotes. Travel along for three miles and turn left onto Coach Road at bottom of hill after wooded areas on B6016.

Directions by public transport: Trent Barton service H1 from Derby, Heanor or Alfreton. Half mile walk from end of Coach Road, ask for Riddings Dale

Facilities: R, S, T

Registration	Date	Chassis	Body	New to	Fleet No	Status
ESV 811	1947	AEC Regal III O963	Weymann B30D	CARRIS of Lisbon	141	RP
HVO 937	1947	AEC Regent II O661	Weymann H30/26R	Mansfield District Traction Co	126	R
KRR 255	1949	AEC Regal III 9621E	Weymann B35F	Mansfield District Traction Co	9	R
BNU 679G	1969	Bristol VRTSL6LX	ECW H43/32F	Midland General Omnibus Co	315	RP
PNU 114K	1971	Leyland Atlantean PDR1A/1	Northern Counties H44/28D	Chesterfield Corporation	114	RP
RCH 629L	1972	Bristol VRTSL6LX	ECW H43/34F	Trent Motor Traction Co	629	R
SHN 80L	1973	Bristol RELH6G	ECW DP49F	United Automobile Services	6080	R
UOA 322L	1973	Leyland National 1151/1R/0401	Leyland National B52F	Eastern National Omnibus Co	1702	A
NNU 123M	1973	Daimler Fleetline CRL6-30	Roe H42/29D	Chesterfield Corporation	123	R
NNU 124M	1973	Daimler Fleetline CRL6-30	Roe H42/29D	Chesterfield Corporation	124	R
LRA 801P	1975	Bristol VRTSL3/501	ECW H43/34F	Midland General Omnibus Co	801	R
PRA 109R	1976	Leyland Leopard PSU3C/4R	Alexander C49F	Trent Motor Traction Co	109	R
UHG 353Y	1982	Leyland Atlantean AN68D/2R	East Lancs H49/36F	Blackpool Transport	353	R
D278 FAS	1987	Leyland Tiger TRCTL11/3RH	Alexander C49F	Highland Scottish Omnibuses	Z278	R

Notes:
ESV 811   original Portugese registration II-14-49
UOA 322L   originally registered WNO 551L
LRA 801P   original Leyland 501 engine replaced by Gardner unit in 1980
D278 FAS   later acquired by Western Scottish Omnibuses (438)

Note: Please be aware that vehicles on display can vary from time to time as not all museums display their entire 'fleet'. Visitors wishing to see a particular vehicle should make enquiries prior to their visit.

Milestones — Hampshire's Living History Museum, Basingstoke

Contact address: Leisure Park, Churchill Way, Basingstoke, Hants, RG21 6YR

Phone: 01256 477766 / 0845 603 5635

Website: www.milestones-museum.com

Affiliation: NARTM, HLF, Hampshire CC

Brief description: Step indoors into a huge award winning living history museum. Explore a network of full size streets from late Victorian times to 1945. See period shops, vintage vehicles, a village green and even a working pub!

Opening days/times:
Tuesday – Friday and Bank Holiday Mondays 10am to 5pm. Saturday and Sunday 11am to 5pm. Last admission 4pm. Closed Mondays, Christmas Day, Boxing Day and New Year's Day.

Directions by car: From M3 junction 6, take the Ringway Road (West) and follow the brown signs for Leisure Park and Milestones. At Thornycroft Roundabout, take first exit into Churchill Way West, signed Milestones. At West Ham Roundabout, follow brown sign for Milestones. Directions by public transport: Centre Shuttle bus runs between the Leisure Park and the town-centre railway station. Bus stops outside the museum.

Charges: Adult £7.50 Concessions £6.75 Children £ 4.50 Family £22. Under 5s Free. Reduced prices available for pre-booked groups of 15 or more. Schools programmes available. (Prices valid until 1 April 2009)

Facilities: A D F P R T

Registration	Date	Chassis	Body	New to	Fleet No	Status
BK 2986	1919	Thornycroft J	Dodson O18/16R	Portsmouth Corporation	10	R
RV 3411	1933	Leyland Titan TD2	English Electric/ Portsmouth Corporation	Portsmouth Corporation	17	R
RV 4649+	1934	AEC 661T	English Electric H26/24R	Portsmouth Corporation	201	RP
EY 5218	1935	Thornycroft GC/SC6		Jones of Menai Bridge		
RV 6368	1935	Leyland Titan TD4	English Electric O26/24R	Portsmouth Corporation	8	R
+ trolleybus						

Notes:

BK 2986	body c1910, ex LGOC B type; on loan from Portsmouth City Museum
RV 3411	converted to tower wagon in 1955; on loan from Portsmouth City Museum
RV 4649	on loan from Portsmouth City Museum
RV 6368	originally H26/24R; on loan from Portsmouth City Museum

Museum of Transport Glasgow

Contact address: Kelvin Hall, 1 Bunhouse Road, Glasgow G3 8DP

Phone: 0141 287 2720 (school bookings on 0141 565 4112/3)

Fax: 0141 287 2692

Web site: www.glasgowmuseums.com

Affiliation: NARTM

Brief description: The museum displays many items of transport history dating from the 1860s.
Opening days/times: Monday to Thursday and Saturday, 10.00 to 17.00; Friday and Sunday 11.00 to 17.00 (closed 25/26, 31 December and 1/2 January)

Directions by car: From M8 junctions 17 or 19

Directions by public transport: Buses 9, 16, 18, 62, from City Centre (Dumbarton Road) to Kelvin Hall; Underground to Kelvin Hall; nearest main-line railway station is Partick.

Charges: Free admission

Facilities: D F G H R T

Other information: Guided tours, exhibitions and events also held.

Note: All vehicles are now on loan/stored at the Glasgow Vintage Vehicle Trust in Bridgton, Glasgow, due to the inventory and decant project that is currently underway as part of the Riverside Museum project.

Registration	Date	Chassis	Body	New to	Fleet No	Status
EGA 79	1949	Albion Venturer CX37S	Croft H30/26R	Glasgow Corporation	B92	R
FYS 988+	1958	BUT RETB1	Burlingham B50F	Glasgow Corporation	TBS13	R
FYS 998	1958	Leyland Atlantean PDR1/1	Alexander H44/34F	Glasgow Corporation	LA1	R
+ trolleybus						

Notes:
FYS 988   exhibited at the 1958 Commercial Motor Show

North of England Open Air Museum
Beamish

Contact address: Beamish, Co Durham, DH9 0RG

Phone: 0191 370 4000

Fax: 0191 370 4001

E-mail: museum@beamish.org.uk

Web site: www.beamishmuseum.co.uk

Brief description: Beamish is an open-air museum which vividly recreates life in the North of England in the early 1800s and early 1900s Buildings from throughout the region have been brought to Beamish, rebuilt and furnished as they once were. Costumed staff welcome visitors and demonstrate the past way of life in The Town, Colliery Village, Home Farm, Railway Station, Pockerley Manor and 1825 Railway. A one-mile circular period tramway carries visitors around the Museum and a replica 1913 Daimler bus operates between The Town and Colliery Village.

Events planned: Please see web site for details

Opening days/times: 2009
Summer: 4 April to 1 November: (open every day 10.00-17.00)
Winter: 2 November to 26 March 2010: 10.00 to 16.00 (closed Mondays, Fridays and Christmas Day).
Reduced operations in winter.
Last admission always 15.00.

Directions by car: Follow A1(M) to junction 63 (Chester-le-Street exit). Take A693 towards Stanley and follow Beamish Museum signs.

Directions by public transport: Buses 709 from Newcastle, 720 from Durham and 775/778 from Sunderland all serve Beamish.

Charges: — 2009 rates, under 5s free
Summer: Adult £16, Child £10, Over 60s/Students £13.
Winter: £6 per person.
Group rates available in summer for parties of 20 or more.

Facilities: B E F G H M P R T

Other information: Free leaflet available in advance for visitors with disabilities and mobility limitations.
Some vehicles not on display. Please telephone for information

Registration	Date	Chassis	Body	New to	Fleet No	Status
WT 7108+	1924	Straker Clough T29	Brush B32F	Keighley Corporation Tramways	12	A
UP 551	1928	BMMO SOS QL	Brush B37F	Northern General Transport Co	338	RP
VK 5401	1931	Dodge UF30A	Robson B14F	Batey of Rookhope		RP
LTN 501+	1948	Sunbeam S7	Northern Coachbuilders H39/31R	Newcastle Corporation	501	R
J 2503	1988	Renault	Osborne O18/14RO	Beamish of the North of England Open Air Museum		R

+ trolleybus

Notes:
UP 551   replica body, built 1997
VK 5401   undergoing restoration off-site
LTN 501   on loan to the Trolleybus Museum at Sandtoft
J 2503   replica of 1913 Daimler

North West Museum of Road Transport

Contact address: The Old Bus Depot, 51 Hall Street, St Helens, WA10 1DU
Phone: 01744 451681
E-mail: email@hallstreetdepot.co.uk
Website: www.hallstreetdepot.co.uk
Affiliation: NARTM
Brief description: A collection of over 70 historic vehicles representing the transport heritage of the northwest of England.
Events planned: Please see the enthusiast press for details
Opening days/times: Saturdays, Sundays and bank holidays 11.00-16.00 (April-October), 12.00-16.00 (November-March).
Charges: £3.50 Adult, £2 child/concession, £10 family.
Facilities: Fully disabled access including toilets, drinks machine, shop

Registration	Date	Chassis	Body	New to	Fleet No	Status
AFY 971	1934	Leyland Titan TD3	English Electric O26/25R	Southport Corporation	43	A
ATD 683	1935	Leyland Lion LT7	Massey B30R	Widnes Corporation	39	A
RV 6360	1935	Leyland Titan TD4	English Electric O26/24R	Portsmouth Corporation	117	R
EWM 358	1945	Daimler CWA6	Duple UH30/26R	Southport Corporation	62	A
ANQ 778	1946	AEC Regent III O961	Commonwealth Engineering H-/-RD	Dept of Road Transport & Tramways of Sydney	1984	A
DED 797	1946	Leyland Titan PD1	Alexander H30/26R	Warrington Corporation	16	A
FFY 404	1947	Leyland Titan PD2/3	Leyland O30/26R	Southport Corporation	87	R
KTD 768	1948	Leyland Titan PD2/1	Lydney L27/26R	Leigh Corporation	16	R
NTF 466	1952	Daimler CVG5	Northern Counties B32F	Lancaster City Transport	466	R
MXX 421	1953	AEC Regal IV 9821LT	Metro-Cammell B39F	London Transport	RF444	R
RFM 641	1953	Guy Arab IV	Massey H30/26R	Chester Corporation	1	R
CDJ 878	1954	Leyland Titan PD2/9	Davies H30/26R	St Helens Corporation	E78	A
434 BTE	1957	Crossley Regent V D3RV	East Lancs H31/28RD	Darwen Corporation	17	R
GDJ 435	1957	AEC Regent V MD3RV	Weymann H33/26R	St Helens Corporation	H135	RP
KRN 422	1957	Leyland Titan PD2/10	Crossley H33/29R	Preston Corporation	31	R
FHF 456	1959	Leyland Atlantean PDR1/1	Metro Cammell H44/33F	Wallasey Corporation	6	A
KDJ 999	1959	AEC Regent V 2D3RA	East Lancs H41/32F	St Helens Corporation	K199	A
LDJ 985	1960	Leyland Titan PD2A/27	Weymann H30/25RD	St Helens Corporation	K175	RP
562 RTF	1961	Leyland Titan PD2/40	East Lancs H37/28R	Widnes Corporation	31	R
574 TD	1962	Guy Arab IV	Northern Counties H41/32R	Lancashire United Transport	110	R
PSJ 480	1962	Leyland Titan PD2A/27	Massey H37/27F	Wigan Corporation	35	RP
TRJ 109	1962	AEC Reliance 2MU3RV	Weymann B45F	Salford City Transport	109	RP
201 YTE	1963	Leyland Titan PD2/37	East Lancs O37/28F	Lancaster City Transport	201	R
TDJ 612	1963	AEC Reliance 2MU3RA	Marshall B45F	St Helens Corporation	212	R
4227 FM	1964	Bristol Lodekka FS6G	ECW H33/27RD	Crosville Motor Services	DFG157	R
AJA 139B	1964	Bedford VAL14	Strachans B52F	North Western Road Car Co	139	RP
DTJ 139B	1964	Leyland Titan PD2/40	Roe H37/28R	Ashton-under-Lyne Corporation	39	RP
HTF 644B	1964	Leyland Titan PD2/40	East Lancs H37/28R	Widnes Corporation	38	R
JTD 300B	1964	Guy Arab V	Northern Counties H41/32F	Lancashire United Transport	166	A
BCK 367C	1965	Leyland Titan PD3/6	Leyland/Preston Corporation H38/32F	Preston Corporation	61	A
BED 731C	1965	Leyland Titan PD2/40 Special	East Lancs H34/30F	Warrington Corporation	50	R
BED 732C	1965	Leyland Titan PD2/40 Special	East Lancs H34/30F	Warrington Corporation	51	RP
FFM 135C	1965	Guy Arab V	Massey H41/32F	Chester Corporation	35	R
UTC 768D	1966	Leyland Leopard L2	Plaxton C43F	Lancashire United Transport	216	R
MDJ 555E	1967	Leyland Titan PD2A/27	East Lancs H37/28R	St Helens Corporation	55	A
OBU 163F	1967	Leyland Atlantean PDR1/1	Roe H43/324F	Oldham Corporation	163	R

Note: Please be aware that vehicles on display can vary from time to time as not all museums display their entire 'fleet'. Visitors wishing to see a particular vehicle should make enquiries prior to their visit.

Registration	Date	Chassis	Body	New to	Fleet No	Status
RFM 453F	1967	Leyland Tiger Cub PSUC1/11	Massey B40D	Chester Corporation	53	R
SMK 701F	1967	AEC Routemaster R2RH/1	Park Royal H40/32R	London Transport	RML2701	R
HCK 204G	1968	Leyland Panther PSUR1A/1R	MCW B47D	Preston Corporation	204	RP
KJA 299G	1968	Bristol RESL6G	Marshall B43F	North Western Road Car Co	299	R
DFM 347H	1969	Guy Arab V	Northern Counties H41/32F	Chester Corporation	47	R
EFM 181H	1970	Bristol RELL6G	ECW B53F	Crosville Motor Services	SRG181	A
JFM 650J	1970	Daimler Fleetline CRG6LX	Northern Counties H43/29F	Chester Corporation	50	A
NWA 257K	1972	Daimler Fleetline CRG6LXB	Alexander H43/31F	Sheffield Transport	257	A
DKC 301L	1972	Leyland Atlantean AN68/1R	Alexander H43/32F	Merseyside PTE	1301	A
PDJ 269L	1972	AEC Swift 3MP2R	Marshall B42D	St Helens Corporation	269	A
RTC 645L	1972	Leyland National 1151/1R/0101	Leyland National B52F	Widnes Borough Transport	1	R
HEN 868N	1975	Leyland Leopard PSU3C/2R	Northern Counties B47F	Chester City Transport	68	A
LED 71P	1976	Bristol RESL6G	East Lancs B41D	Warrington Borough Transport	71	R
LED 73P	1976	Bristol RESL6G	East Lancs B41D	Warrington Borough Transport	73	R
FWA 475V	1980	Leyland National 2 NL106L11/1R	Leyland National B44F	South Yorkshire PTE	1075	R
GEK 14V	1980	Leyland Atlantean AN68A/1R	East Lancs H45/31F	Warrington Borough Transport	14	A
MNC 487W	1980	Leyland Fleetline FE30AGR	Northern Counties H43/32F	Greater Manchester PTE	8144	R
XLV 140W	1980	Leyland National 2 NL116AL11/1R	Leyland National B49F	Merseyside PTE	6140	R
YMA 99W	1981	Dennis Dominator DD121B	Northern Counties H43/29F	Chester City Transport	99	RP
A323 GLV	1983	Leyland Atlantean AN68D/1R	Alexander H43/32F	Merseyside PTE	1003	R
A910 SYE	1983	Leyland Titan TNLXB2RR	Leyland H44/26D	London Transport	T910	R
H35 HBG	1991	Leyland Lynx LX2R11C15Z4R	Leyland B51F	Halton Transport	35	R

Notes:

AFY 971	originally H26/25R
RV 6360	originally H26/24R; renumbered 6 following open-top conversion
ANQ 778	Australian registration
FFY 404	originally H30/26R
PSJ 480	originally registered JJP 502
201 YTE	originally H37/28F
BCK 367C	rebuilt from Leyland PD2 by Preston Corporation
DFM 347H	last Guy Arab delivered to a British operator

Nottingham Transport Heritage Centre
Ruddington

Contact address: Mere Way, Ruddington, Nottingham NG11 6NX

Phone: 0115 940 5705

Web site: http://www.nthc.co.uk

Affiliation: NARTM

Brief description: The centre offers exhibits covering road and rail transport, and provides the opportunity to experience travel of a bygone age.

Events planned: Please see enthusiast press for details.

Opening days/times: Easter to mid-October: Sundays and Bank Holiday Mondays (10.45-17.00).

Directions by car: 3 miles south of Nottingham just off A52 ring-road and main A60 road via small roundabout at Ruddington.

Directions by public transport: Buses from Nottingham pass near museum

Charges: Not finalised at time of publication, all rides inclusive of steam train rides.

Facilities: B B(e) D E G H P R S T

Registration	Date	Chassis	Body	New to	Fleet No	Status
VO 8846	1932	Leyland Lion LT5	Willowbrook DP32F	South Notts Bus Co of Gotham	17	A
DJF 349	1947	Leyland Titan PD1	Leyland H30/26R	Leicester City Transport	248	RP
JVO 230	1948	Leyland Titan PD1A	Duple L29/26F	Barton Transport of Chilwell	507	R
MAL 310	1951	Leyland Royal Tiger PSU1/11	Duple DP45F	South Notts Bus Co of Gotham	42	A
OTV 161	1953	AEC Regent III 9613E	Park Royal H30/26R	Nottingham City Transport	161	R

Registration	Date	Chassis	Body	New to	Fleet No	Status
PFN 865	1959	AEC Regent V 2LD3RA	-	East Kent Road Car Co		R
866 HAL	1960	AEC Reliance 2MU3RV	Plaxton C41F	Barton Transport of Chilwell	866	RP
CUV 218C	1965	AEC Routemaster R2RH/1	Park Royal H32/25RD	London Transport	RCL2218	R
KVO 429P	1975	Leyland National 11351/2R	Leyland National B50F	Trent Motor Traction Co	429	A
ORC 545P	1976	Leyland Atlantean AN68/1R	ECW O—/—F	Northern General Transport Co	3299	R
ARC 666T	1979	Leyland Atlantean AN68A/1R	Northern Counties H47/31D	Nottingham City Transport	666	R

Notes:

PFN 865	recovery vehicle; originally fitted with Park Royal FH40/32F body
KVO 429P	originally B44D
ORC 545P	originally H45/27D and registered MPT 299P; used as promotional vehicle

Oxford Bus Museum
Long Hanborough

Contact address: Station Yard, Long Hanborough, Witney, Oxfordshire, OX29 8LA

Phone: 01993 883617 (Answerphone)

Web site: www.oxfordbusmuseum.org.uk

Affiliation: NARTM

Brief description: Over 40 buses dating from 1915 to 1994, mainly from City of Oxford Motor Services and other local companies. The collection includes many vehicles of AEC manufacture plus cars, fire engines and support vehicles. Morris Motors Museum incorporated.

Events planned: Please see enthusiast press or website for details.

Opening days/times: Wednesdays, Sundays and Bank Holiday Mondays, 10.30 to 16.30. Saturdays open from Easter until the last Saturday in October, 10.30-16.30 (last entries 15.30). Bus rides at 15.00 on the first Sunday of each month from the first Sunday in April to the first Sunday in October inclusive.

Directions by car: The entrance is on the south side of the A4095 (Witney-Bicester), between the villages of Bladon and Long Hanborough.

Directions by public transport: Museum is adjacent to Hanborough railway station on the Oxford–Worcester line, Sunday train services (journey time Oxford 10mins, London Paddington 70mins). Stagecoach bus service from George Street Oxford, weekdays, hourly to Long Hanborough village centre (1 mile). Service from Witney to Woodstock, weekdays, passes the entrance.

Charges: Adults £4, Children £2, OAP £3, Family (2+2) £9.

Facilities: B(e) D P R S T

Other information: School parties welcome by arrangement — please telephone 01865 774233 for booking.

Registration	Date	Chassis	Body	New to	Fleet No	Status
BM 2856	1913	Commer WP3	Commer CH14	Lord Lonsdale		R
DU 4838	1915	Daimler Y	City of Oxford Electric Tramways B32R	City of Oxford Electric Tramways	39	A
note e	1916	Daimler Y	(chassis only)			A
note f	1916	Daimler Y	(chassis only)			A
note ac	1917	Daimler Y	O18/16RO	City of Oxford Electric Tramways		A
YL 740	1925	Morris Commercial 1 ton	CH14			R
JO 5032	1932	AEC Regal 642	(chassis only)	City of Oxford Motor Services	GC41	R
JO 5403	1932	AEC Regent 661	Brush O28/24R	City of Oxford Motor Services	GA16	R
DBW 613	1948	Bedford OB	Duple C29F	Oliver of Long Hanborough		A
JVF 528	1949	Bedford OB	Duple C29F	Bensley of Martham		R
NJO 703	1949	AEC Regal III 9621A	Willowbrook DP32F	City of Oxford Motor Services	703	R
OFC 393	1949	AEC Regent III 9612A	Weymann H30/26R	City of Oxford Motor Services	H892	A
OFC 205	1950	AEC Regal III 6821A	Duple C32F	South Midland Motor Services	66	A
PWL 413	1950	AEC Regent III 9613A	Weymann L27/26R	City of Oxford Motor Services	L166	R
SFC 610	1952	AEC Regal IV 9821S	Willowbrook C37C	City of Oxford Motor Services	610	RP
TWL 928	1953	AEC Regent III 9613S	Park Royal H30/26R	City of Oxford Motor Services	H928	R

Note: Please be aware that vehicles on display can vary from time to time as not all museums display their entire 'fleet'. Visitors wishing to see a particular vehicle should make enquiries prior to their visit.

Registration	Date	Chassis	Body	New to	Fleet No	Status
956 AJO	1957	AEC Regent V MD3RV	Park Royal H33/28R	City of Oxford Motor Services	H956	R
756 KFC	1960	AEC Reliance 2MU3RV	Park Royal B44F	City of Oxford Motor Services	756	R
14 LFC	1961	Morris FF	Wadham C27F	Morris Motors		RP
304 KFC	1961	Dennis Loline II	East Lancs H35/28F	City of Oxford Motor Services	304	R
305 KFC	1961	Dennis Loline II	East Lancs H35/28F	City of Oxford Motor Services	305	R
850 ABK	1962	AEC Reliance 2MU3RA	Duple C43F	Don Motor Coach Co of Southsea		RP
FWL 371E	1967	AEC Renown 3B3RA	Northern Counties H38/27F	City of Oxford Motor Services	371	RP
NAC 416F	1967	Leyland Atlantean PDR1A/1	Northern Counties H44/31F	Stratford-upon-Avon Blue Motors	10	A
UFC 430K	1971	Daimler Fleetline CRL6	Northern Counties H43/27D	City of Oxford Motor Services	430	A
EUD 256K	1972	AEC Reliance 6MU4R	Plaxton B47F	Chiltern Queens of Woodcote		A
VER 262L	1972	AEC Reliance 6U3ZR	Alexander C53F	Premier Travel of Cambridge	262	RP
HUD 476S	1977	Bristol VRTSL3/6LXB	ECW H43/27D	City of Oxford Motor Services	476	R
BBW 21V	1980	Leyland Leopard PSU3E/4R	Duple C49F	City of Oxford Motor Services	21	R
JUD 597W	1980	Ford R1014	Plaxton C45F	House of Watlington		R
BBW 214Y	1982	Leyland Olympian ONLXB/1R	ECW H45/28D	City of Oxford Motor Services	214	A
B106 XJO	1985	Ford Transit 160D	Carlyle B16F	South Midland	SM6	R
C724 JJO	1986	Ford Transit 190D	Carlyle B20F	City of Oxford Motor Services	724	R
D122 PTT	1987	Ford Transit VE6	Mellor B16F	Thames Transit	122	R
L247 FDV	1994	Iveco 49-10	Mellor B13D	Bayline	2111	R

Notes:

BM 2856	on loan to museum
DU 4838	body new 1920
note ac	body ex London, built 1906
JO 5032	passed to Mascot Motors in Jersey and subsequently converted to lorry
JO 5403	originally H28/24R
JVF 528	restored in Mulleys livery
OFC 205	displayed as an unrestored vehicle
305 KFC	sectioned museum display showing body construction method
14 LFC	originally used for transporting Morris Motors band
850 ABK	acquired by Chiltern Queens of Woodcote in 1964
NAC 416F	acquired by City of Oxford Motor Services (905) in 1970
L247 FDV	bi-mode minibus

Scottish Vintage Bus Museum
Lathalmond

Contact address: M90 Commerce Park, Lathalmond, Fife, KY12 OSJ

Phone: 01383 623380

E-mail: website: www.busweb.co.uk/svbm

Affiliation: NARTM

Brief description: The collection of over 170 buses was, in the main, operated or manufactured in Scotland, from the late 1920s to the early 1980s. Vehicles are generally owned by private individuals or groups. A fully-equipped workshop enables comprehensive restoration to be undertaken. The 42-acre site is a former Royal Navy depot.

Events planned: Please see enthusiast press for details.

Opening days/times: Easter to end of September, Sundays 13.00 to 17.00

Directions by car: Use M90 junction 4. Take B914 Dollar road. Left B915 Dunfermline (2 miles). 2 miles to M90 Commerce Park on right.

Directions by public transport: Nearest bus/train Dunfermline. No public transport to site.

Charges: Sunday opening £3. Other charges apply at special events.

Facilities: B B(e) D E P R S T

Registration	Date	Chassis	Body	New to	Fleet No	Status
CD 7045	1922	Leyland G7	Short O27/24R	Southdown Motor Services	135	R
GE 2446	1928	Leyland Titan TD1	Leyland L27/24RO	Glasgow Corporation	111	R
RU 8678	1929	Leyland Lion PLSC3	Leyland B35F	Hants & Dorset Motor Services	268	RP

Registration	Date	Chassis	Body	New to	Fleet No	Status
SO 3740	1929	Leyland Tiger TS2	Alexander B32F	Scottish General (Northern) Omnibus Co		R
VD 3433	1934	Leyland Lion LT5A	Alexander B36F	Central SMT Co		R
WG 1620	1934	Gilford Hera L176S	(chassis only)	W. Alexander & Sons	Y49	R
AAA 756	1935	Albion Victor PK114	Abbott C20C	King Alfred Motor Services		R
WG 3260	1935	Leyland Lion LT5A	Alexander B35F	W. Alexander & Sons	P705	A
WS 4522	1935	Leyland Tiger TS7	Cowieson B—R	Scottish Motor Traction Co		RP
CS 3364	1936	Leyland Cheetah LZ2	Alexander B37F	Western SMT Co		A
ATF 477	1937	Leyland Tiger TS7T	Fowler B39F	Singleton of Leyland		A
AUX 296	1939	Sentinel-HSG	Cowieson B32R	Sentinel (demonstrator)		RP
WG 8107	1939	Leyland Tiger TS8	Alexander -	W. Alexander & Sons	P528	RP
WG 8790	1939	Leyland Tiger TS8	Alexander B39F	W. Alexander & Sons	P573	RP
HF 9126	1940	Leyland Titan TD7	Metro Cammell	Wallasey Corporation	74	A
WG 9180	1940	Leyland Titan TD7	Leyland L27/26R	W. Alexander & Sons	R266	R
DSG 169	1942	Leyland Titan TD5	Alexander L27/26R	Scottish Motor Traction Co	J66	R
CDR 679	1943	Guy Arab II	Duple H30/26R	Plymouth Corporation	249	R
JWS 594	1943	Guy Arab II	Duple/Nudd H31/24R	London Transport	G77	R
BRS 37	1945	Daimler CWD6	Duple H30/26R	Aberdeen Corporation	155	R
ACB 904	1947	Guy Arab II	Northern Coachbuilders	Blackburn Corporation	76	RP
AWG 623	1947	AEC Regal I O662	Alexander C31F	W. Alexander & Sons	A36	R
AWG 639	1947	AEC Regal I O662	Alexander C35F	W. Alexander & Sons	A52	R
GSU 378	1947	Albion Venturer CX19	Comeng H33/28R	DRTT of Sydney	1877	R
XG 9304	1947	Leyland Titan PD1A	Northern Counties L27/26R	Middlesbrough Corporation	52	A
AWG 393	1948	Guy Arab III	Cravens H30/26R	W. Alexander & Sons	RO607	R
BMS 405	1948	Daimler CVD6	Burlingham C33F	W. Alexander & Sons	D10	A
BWG 39	1948	Bedford OB	Scottish Motor Traction C25F	W. Alexander & Sons	W218	RP
CU 4740	1948	Leyland Tiger PS1	Burlingham C33F	Hall Bros of South Shields		A
ESG 652	1948	Guy Arab III	Metro Cammell B35R	Edinburgh Corporation	739	R
FSC 182	1949	Daimler CVG6	Metro Cammell H31/25R	Edinburgh Corporation	135	R
CWG 283	1950	Leyland Tiger PS1	Alexander C35F	W. Alexander & Sons	PA181	R
DCS 616	1950	Daimler CVD6	Massey O32/28RD	Hunter (A1) of Dreghorn	16A	R
EVA 324	1950	Guy Arab III	Guy B33R	Central SMT Co	K24	R
GVD 47	1950	Guy Arab III	Duple H31/26R	Hutchinson's Coaches of Overtown		R
SJ 1340	1950	Bedford OB	Duple C29F	Gordon of Lamlash		RP
SS 7486	1950	Bedford OB	Duple C29F	Stark's Motor Services of Dunbar		A
SS 7501	1950	Bedford OB	Duple C29F	Fairbairn of Haddington		R
AYJ 379	1951	Daimler CVD6	Croft H30/26R	Dundee Corporation	127	R
DGS 536	1951	Leyland Tiger PS1/1	McLennan C39F	A. & C. McLennan of Spittalfield		R
DGS 625	1951	Leyland Tiger PS1/1	McLennan C39F	A. & C. McLennan of Spittalfield		R
DMS 820	1951	Leyland Tiger OPS2/1	Alexander C35F	W. Alexander & Sons	PB7	A
DMS 823	1951	Leyland Tiger OPS2/1	Alexander C35F	W. Alexander & Sons	PB10	RP
DWG 526	1951	Leyland Royal Tiger PSU1/15	Leyland C41C	W. Alexander & Sons	PC30	A
BMS 222	1952	Leyland Royal Tiger PSU1/15	Alexander C41C	W. Alexander & Sons	PC1	R
JVB 908	1952	Leyland Royal Tiger PSU1/13	Mann Egerton HD24/26F	Homeland of Croydon		RP
CYJ 252	1953	AEC Regent III 9613E	Alexander H32/26R	Dundee Corporation	137	R
FGS 59D	1953	Bedford SB	Mulliner B36F	Royal Navy		RP
GM 6384	1954	Leyland Titan PD2/10	Leyland L27/28R	Central SMT Co	L484	RP
LFS 480	1954	Leyland Titan PD2/20	Metro-Cammell H34/29R	Edinburgh Corporation	480	R
ETS 964	1955	Daimler CVG6	Metro-Cammell H36/28R	Dundee Corporation	184	RP
FWG 846	1955	Bristol LS6G	ECW B45F	W. Alexander & Sons	E11	RP
HRG 209	1955	AEC Regent V D2RV6G	Crossley H35/29R	Aberdeen Corporation	209	A
TYD 888	1955	AEC Reliance MU3RV	Duple C43F	Wakes of Sparkford		R
UFF 178	1955	AEC Regent V D2RV6G	Crossley H35/29R	Aberdeen Corporation	207	A
ABV 33A	1957	Leyland Titan PD2/12	Metro Cammell H—/—RD	Trent Motor Traction Co	1012	RP
OFS 777	1957	Leyland Titan PD2/20	Metro-Cammell H34/29R	Edinburgh Corporation	777	R

Note: Please be aware that vehicles on display can vary from time to time as not all museums display their entire 'fleet'. Visitors wishing to see a particular vehicle should make enquiries prior to their visit.

Registration	Date	Chassis	Body	New to	Fleet No	Status
OFS 798	1957	Leyland Titan PD2/20	Metro-Cammell H34/29R	Edinburgh Corporation	798	RP
OWS 620	1957	Bristol Lodekka LD6G	ECW H33/27R	Scottish Omnibuses	AA620	RP
FAS 982	1959	Albion Victor FT39KAN	Reading B35F	Jersey Motor Transport Co	5	R
SWS 671	1959	AEC Reliance 2MU3RV	Alexander C38F	Scottish Omnibuses	B671	R
SWS 715	1959	AEC Reliance 2MU3RV	Park Royal C41F	Scottish Omnibuses	B715	A
EDS 50A	1960	AEC Routemaster R2RH	Park Royal H36/28R	London Transport	RM560	R
EDS 320A	1960	AEC Routemaster R2RH	Park Royal H36/28R	London Transport	RM606	RP
NMS 366	1960	AEC Reliance 2MU3RV	Alexander C41F	W. Alexander & Sons	AC155	RP
RAG 578	1960	Daimler CVG6LX	Northern Counties FH41/32F	T. Hunter (A1) of Kilmarnock		R
VSC 86	1960	Leyland Tiger Cub PSUC1/3	Weymann B47F	Edinburgh Corporation	86	R
WAJ 112	1960	Albion Nimbus NS3N	Plaxton C29F	Watson of Huntingdon		A
XSL 945A	1960	Bristol MW6G	Alexander C41F	Western SMT Co	T1590	A
XSN 25A	1960	Bristol MW6G	Alexander C41F	Western SMT Co	T1591	A
EDS 288A	1961	AEC Routemaster R2RH	Park Royal H36/28R	London Transport	RM 910	R
RAG 411	1961	Bristol Lodekka LD6G	ECW H33/27RD	Western SMT Co	1645	R
RCS 382	1961	Leyland Titan PD3A/3	Alexander L35/32RD	Western SMT Co	1684	R
RMS 714	1961	Leyland Tiger Cub PSUC1/2	Alexander C41F	W. Alexander & Sons (Fife)	PD225	R
YSG 101	1961	Leyland Leopard PSU3/2R	Alexander B33T	Edinburgh Corporation	101	R
YYJ 914	1961	Leyland Tiger Cub PSUC1/2	Alexander C41F	Stark's Motor Services of Dunbar	H8	A
7424 SP	1962	AEC Reliance 2MU3RV	Alexander C41F	W. Alexander & Sons (Fife)	FAC4	R
LDS 201A	1962	AEC Routemaster 2R2RH	Park Royal H36/28R	London Transport	RM1607	R
NSJ 502	1962	AEC Reliance 2MU3RV	Alexander C41F	W. Alexander & Sons (Northern)	NAC205	R
UCS 659	1963	Albion Lowlander LR3	Northern Counties H40/31F	Western SMT Co	N1795	R
AFS 91B	1964	AEC Reliance 4MU3RA	Alexander B53F	Scottish Omnibuses (Eastern Scottish) B91		R
ARG 17B	1964	AEC Reliance 2MU3RA	Alexander C41F	W. Alexander & Sons (Northern)	NAC246	RP
ASC 665B	1964	Leyland Titan PD3/6	Alexander H41/29F	Edinburgh Corporation	665	R
AWA 124B	1964	Bedford SB13	Duple C41F	J. O. Andrew of Sheffield		R
BXA 464B	1964	Bristol Lodekka FS6G	ECW H33/27RD	W. Alexander & Sons (Fife)	FRD199	R
CSG 29C	1965	Bristol Lodekka FLF6G	ECW -	Scottish Omnibuses (Eastern Scottish) AA29		R
CSG 43C	1965	Bristol Lodekka FLF6G	ECW H38/32F	Scottish Omnibuses (Eastern Scottish) AA43		RP
DMS 325C	1965	Leyland Leopard PSU3/3R	Alexander -	W. Alexander & Sons (Midland)	MPE40	RP
DMS 359C	1965	Leyland Leopard PSU3/3R	Alexander -	W. Alexander & Sons (Midland)	MPE73	R
ESF 801C	1965	Leyland Atlantean PDR1/1	Alexander H43/31F	Edinburgh Corporation	801	R
EWS 130D	1966	AEC Reliance 2U3RA	Alexander C—F	Scottish Omnibuses (Eastern Scottish) ZB130		A
EWS 168D	1966	Bristol RELH6G	Alexander C38Ft	Scottish Omnibuses (Eastern Scottish) XA168		RP
EWS 812D	1966	Leyland Atlantean PDR1/1	Alexander H43/31F	Edinburgh Corporation	812	R
FFV 447D	1966	AEC Reliance 2U3RA	Plaxton C45F	J. Abbott & Sons of Blackpool		R
GRS 343E	1967	Albion Viking VK43AL	Alexander DP40F	W. Alexander & Sons (Northern)	NNV43	R
HDV 639E	1967	Bristol MW6G	ECW C39F	Western National Omnibus Co	1434	R
HGM 335E	1967	Bristol Lodekka FLF6G	ECW H44/34F	Central SMT Co	BL335	R
JSC 869E	1967	Leyland Atlantean PDR1/1	Alexander H41/31F	Edinburgh Corporation	869	RP
JSC 900E	1967	Leyland Atlantean PDR2/1	Alexander O47/35F	Edinburgh Corporation	900	R
LUS 524E	1967	AEC Reliance 2U3RA	Willowbrook C49F	David MacBrayne of Glasgow	150	R
KGM 664F	1968	Leyland Leopard PSU3/1R	Alexander B53F	Central SMT Co	T64	A
LFS 288F	1968	Bristol VRTLL6LX	ECW O47/33F	Scottish Omnibuses (Eastern Scottish) AA288		R
LFS 294F	1968	Bristol VRTLL6LX	ECW H47/36F	Scottish Omnibuses (Eastern Scottish) AA294		RP
NTY 416F	1968	AEC Reliance 6MU3R	Plaxton C45F	J. Rowell of Prudhoe		RP
VMP 8G	1968	Albion Viking VK43AL	Alexander DP40F	Road Transport Industry Training Board16		RP
NAG 120G	1969	Bristol REMH6G	Alexander C42Ft	Western SMT Co	T2214	RP
XFM 42G	1969	Guy Arab V	Northern Counties H40/31F	Chester Corporation	42	R
SSF 237H	1970	Bedford VAL70	Duple C53F	Edinburgh Corporation	237	A
TMS 585H	1970	Leyland Leopard PSU3/1R	Alexander C49F	Road Transport Industry Training Board84		A
TGM 214J	1971	Daimler Fleetline CRG6LX	ECW H43/34F	Central SMT Co	D14	R
XWS 165K	1971	Bedford J2	Plaxton C20F	Ian Glass of Haddington		R
BFS 1L	1972	Leyland Atlantean AN68/1R	Alexander H45/30D	Edinburgh Corporation	1	R
BWG 833L	1972	Leyland Leopard PSU3/3R	Alexander B53F	W. Alexander & Sons (Midland)	MPE133	A
YSD 350L	1972	Leyland Leopard PSU3/3R	Alexander B41F	Western SMT Co	L2390	R
BFS 463L	1973	Bedford YRQ	Alexander DP45F	Scottish Omnibuses (Eastern Scottish) C463		A

Registration	Date	Chassis	Body	New to	Fleet No	Status
BWS 105L	1973	Seddon Pennine IV-236	Seddon DP25F	Edinburgh Corporation	105	R
HDZ 5488	1974	Leyland Leopard PSU3/3R	Alexander	W. Alexander & Sons (Fife)	FPE59	R
SCS 333M	1974	Leyland Leopard PSU3/3R	Alexander B53F	Western SMT Co	L2464	R
SCS 366M	1974	Leyland Leopard PSU3/3R	Alexander B53F	Western SMT Co	L2497	R
LSX 16P	1975	Volvo Ailsa AB57	Alexander H44/35F	W. Alexander & Sons (Fife)	FRA16	A
MSF 750P	1976	Seddon Pennine VII	Alexander C42Ft	Scottish Omnibuses (Eastern Scottish)	XS750	R
NCS 16P	1976	Leyland Fleetline FE30AGR	Alexander H43/31F	Hill (A1) of Stevenston		RP
SMS 120P	1976	Daimler Fleetline CRG6LXB	Alexander H44/31F	W. Alexander & Sons (Midland)	MRF120	RP
NDL 656R	1977	Bristol VRTSL3/6LXB	ECW H43/31F	Southern Vectis Omnibus Co	656	RP
OSJ 629R	1977	Leyland Leopard PSU3C/3R	Alexander B53F	Western SMT Co	L2629	RP
RRS 46R	1977	Leyland Leopard PSU3E/4R	Duple C49F	W. Alexander & Sons (Northern)	NPE46	R
XMS 252R	1977	Leyland Leopard PSU3C/4R	Alexander B53F	W. Alexander & Sons (Midland)	MPE252	A
CSG 773S	1978	Volvo Ailsa B55-10	Alexander H43/32F	Scottish Omnibuses (Eastern Scottish)	VV773	R
CSG 792S	1978	Seddon Pennine VII	Plaxton C45F	Scottish Omnibuses (Eastern Scottish)	S792	A
GLS 265S	1978	Leyland Leopard PSU3E/4R	Alexander C49F	W. Alexander & Sons (Midland)	MPE265	R
LIL 9929	1979	Bedford VAS5	Plaxton C29F	Blood Transfusion Service		RP
JSF 928T	1979	Seddon Pennine VII	Alexander DP49F	Scottish Omnibuses (Eastern Scottish)	S928	RP
JSX 595T	1979	Leyland Atlantean AN68A/1R	Alexander H45/30D	Lothian Region Transport	595	R
JTU 588T	1979	Leyland National 10351B/1R	Leyland National B—D	Crosville Motor Services	SNL588	RP
RLS 469T	1979	Ford R1014	Alexander B45F	W. Alexander & Sons (Midland)	MT69	RP
WTS 266T	1979	Volvo Ailsa B55-10	Alexander H44/31D	Tayside Regional Council	266	R
DSD 936V	1979	Seddon Pennine VII	Alexander C49F	Western SMT Co	S2936	R
SSX 602V	1980	Seddon Pennine VII	Alexander B53F	Scottish Omnibuses (Eastern Scottish)	S602	R
ESF 647W	1980	Guy Victory Mk 2	Alexander H60/24D	China Motor Bus	LV36	R
LMS 374W	1980	Leyland Leopard PSU3F/4R	Alexander B53F	W. Alexander & Sons (Midland)	MPE374	RP
RHS 400W	1980	Wales & Edwards	JSP B12F	South of Scotland Electricity		R
FES 831W	1981	Volvo B58-61	Duple B59F	Stagecoach of Perth		RP
YFS 310W	1981	Leyland National 2 NL116L11/1R	Leyland National B48F	Scottish Omnibuses (Eastern Scottish)	N310	A
HSC 173X	1981	Leyland Cub CU435	Duple B31F	Lothian Region Transport	173	RP
RRM 386X	1981	Leyland National 2 NL116AL11/1R	Leyland National B52F	Cumberland Motor Services	386	R
GSC 667X	1982	Leyland Olympian ONTL11/1R	Alexander H47/28D	Lothian Region Transport	667	R
KSX 102X	1982	Leyland National 2 NL116AL11/2R	Leyland National B40D	Lothian Region Transport	102	R
ULS 716X	1982	Leyland Leopard PSU3G/4R	Alexander C49F	W. Alexander & Sons (Midland)	MPE416	RP
ULS 717X	1982	Leyland Leopard PSU3G/4R	Alexander C49F	W. Alexander & Sons (Midland)	MPE417	RP
NFS 176Y	1982	Leyland Leopard PSU3G/4R	Alexander C49F	W. Alexander & Sons (Fife)	FPE176	RP
A108 CFS	1983	Leyland National 2 NL116L11/2R	Leyland National B40D	Lothian Regional Transport	108	R
B349 LSO	1985	Leyland Olympian ON5LXCT/1R	Alexander H45/32F	W. Alexander & Sons (Northern)	NLO49	A
C777 SFS	1985	Leyland Olympian ONTL11/2R	ECW H51/32D	Lothian Region Transport	777	R

Notes:

CD 7045	rebodied 1928; on loan from Southdown Motor Services
SO 3740	passed to W. Alexander & Sons in 1930; numbered P63 in 1932 and rebodied in 1934
VD 3433	rebodied 1945
WG 3260	rebodied 1945
WG 8107	breakdown vehicle; originally C35F
ETJ 108	breakdown vehicle
HF 9126	originally H28/26R; acquired by Lancashire County Constabulary in 1952 and converted for use as mobile control post
DSG 169	Alexander body to Leyland design; converted to open-top in 1959 and restored in 1980/1
JWS 594	originally London Transport G77 (GLL577); rebuilt and rebodied 1953
CDR 679	original Roe utility body converted to platform lorry in 1963; present utility body from VV 9135
GSU 378	not registered
ACB 904	recovery vehicle
SS 7486	passed to Scottish Omnibuses (C22) in 1964
DCS 616	rebodied in 1958 as H32/28RD
GVD 47	acquired by McGill's Bus Service of Barrhead in 1952

Note: Please be aware that vehicles on display can vary from time to time as not all museums display their entire 'fleet'. Visitors wishing to see a particular vehicle should make enquiries prior to their visit.

AYJ 379	on loan from Dundee Museums	
FGS 59D	originally registered 51 51 RN	
UFF 178	originally registered HRG 207	
ABV 33A	originally registered KCH 112	
ETS 964	on loan from Travel Dundee	
FAS 982	originally registered J 1359	
EDS 50A	originally registered WLT 560; acquired by Stagecoach in 1985	
EDS 320A	originally registered WLT 606; acquired by Kelvin Scottish Omnibuses (1919) in 1986	
XSL 945A	originally registered OCS 712	
XSN 25A	originally registered OCS 713	
EDS 288A	originally registered WLT 910; acquired by Kelvin Scottish Omnibuses (1929) in 1986	
YYJ 914	originally registered ESS 989	
NSJ 502	originally registered SRS 117	

LDS 201A	originally registered 607 DYE; acquired by Stagecoach in 1986
CSG 29C	converted to breakdown vehicle
DMS 325C	converted to breakdown vehicle
DMS 359C	converted to breakdown vehicle
HDV 639E	first vehicle operated by Stagecoach
JSC 900E	originally H47/35F
LFS 288F	originally H47/36F
HDZ 5488	recovery vehicle; originally registered XXA 859M
NDL 656R	acquired by Lowland Scottish Omnibuses (856) in 1991
LIL 9929	originally registered CJU 998T
JTU 588T	later fitted with Gardner engine and renumbered SNG588
ESF 647W	original Hong Kong registration CH 9399
RHS 400W	battery-electric bus
FES 831W	first new vehicle delivered to Stagecoach (as C50Ft)

Tameside Transport Collection
Mossley

Contact address: Roaches Industrial Estate, Manchester Road, Mossley, Greater Manchester

Brief description: A working museum comprising a small but varied collection of vehicles ranging from 1929 to the 1960s. There is in addition a display of transport-related items.

Opening days/times: Last weekend of each month (except December), 10.00 to 15.00; visits at other times by prior appointment.

Directions by car: From Ashton-under-Lyne take A635 (Huddersfield) through Mossley. Museum is 1 mile on right-hand side, adjacent to Claybank Terrace.

Directions by public transport:
Bus service 350 Ashton–Oldham, alight at the Royal George and walk towards Mossley.
Bus service 354 Ashton–Uppenmill, alight before Royal George.
By rail to Mossley station (approximately 1 mile walk towards Greenfield).

Charges: No charge but donations welcome.

Facilities: D R T

Other information: Car parking is limited.

Registration	Date	Chassis	Body	New to	Fleet No	Status
DNF 204	1937	Crossley Mancunian	Metro-Cammell/Crossley B32R	Manchester Corporation	129	RP
DBN 978	1949	Crossley SD42/7	Crossley B32R	Bolton Corporation	8	R
JND 728	1950	Daimler CVG6	Metro-Cammell H32/26R	Manchester Corporation	4127	RP
FRJ 511	1951	Daimler CVG6	Metro-Cammell H30/24R	Salford City Transport	511	R
422 CAX	1961	AEC Regent V MD3RV	Massey L31/28R	Bedwas & Machen UDC	5	R
105 UTU	1962	Leyland Titan PD2/37	Northern Counties H36/28F	SHMD Board	5	RP
7209 PW	1962	Bedford J2SZ2	Plaxton C20F	H. & I. Jarvis of Downham Market	4	R
WRJ 179	1963	Leyland Titan PD2/40	Metro-Cammell H36/28F	Salford City Transport	179	R
BWO 585B	1964	AEC Regent V 2MD3RA	Massey L31/28R	Bedwas & Machen UDC	8	A
NMA 328D	1966	Daimler Fleetline CRG6LX	Northern Counties H—/—F	SHMD Board	28	RP

Notes:
422 CAX converted to driver trainer by Rhymney Valley UDC 1976
BWO 585B last AEC to receive lowbridge body
NMA 328D used as exhibition bus 1983-92; originally H43/31F

Note: Please be aware that vehicles on display can vary from time to time as not all museums display their entire 'fleet'. Visitors wishing to see a particular vehicle should make enquiries prior to their visit.

The Transport Museum, Wythall

Contact address: The Transport Museum, Chapel Lane, Wythall, Worcestershire, B47 6JX

Phone: 01564 826471

E-mail: enquiries@thetransportmuseum.org.uk

Web site: www.thetransportmuseum.org.uk

Affiliations: AIM, NARTM, Transport Trust, MLA West Midlands

Brief description: The collection is based on buses built and/or operated locally, plus others of significant PSV history. In addition, there is a unique collection of battery-operated road vehicles and a miniature passenger-carrying steam railway on site. Museum developed and run by volunteers. New exhibition hall opened in 2007, thanks to Heritage Lottery Fund.

Events planned:
Major operating days: 12 April 2009, 3/4, 24 May 2009, 30/31 August 2009;
25 May 2009 — Two Museums Day, half hourly buses to Aston Manor Transport Museum
21 June 2009 — Father's Day, additional service to Avoncroft Museum of Historic Buildings
26 July 2009 — 1970s Family Day
11 October 2009 — Wumpty Forty (40 years since West Midlands PTE took over)

Opening days/times: Saturdays, Sundays and Bank Holidays 11.00 to 16.30 (10.30 to 17.00 on event days), March to end November. Also Wednesdays May-August 13.00-16.30. Last admission 30min before closing time

Directions by car: Wythall is on the main A435 Birmingham-Evesham road. The museum is next to Wythall old church. From M42 use junction 3 and head towards Birmingham.

Directions by public transport: Museum services operate on event days (including ex-Hill St, Birmingham 10.30 and 11.00 on 13 April;
4, 25 May, 31 August, 11 October.
Bus services serve Wythall from Birmingham and Solihull. Neither operates on Sundays
Wythall rail station is 25min walk from museum.

Charges: £3.00 (£4 on major operating days). Admission ticket can be upgraded to all-day riding ticket at additional charge of £4 — £5 on 25 May when it includes admission to Aston Manor Transport Museum

Facilities: B(e) E P S T

Other information: Refreshments available on event days

Registration	Date	Chassis	Body	New to	Fleet No	Status
O 9926	1913	Tilling Stevens TTA2	Thomas Tilling O18/16RO	BMMO ('Midland Red')	26	RP
HA 3501	1925	SOS Standard	Ransomes Sims & Jefferies B32F	BMMO ('Midland Red')	501	A
CN 2870	1927	SOS Q	Brush B37F	Northern General Transport Co	321	RP
CC 7745	1928	SOS QL	Brush B37F	Royal Blue of Llandudno		A
OV 4090	1931	Morris Commercial Dictator	Metro-Cammell B34F	Birmingham Corporation Tramways	90	A
OV 4486	1931	AEC Regent 661	Metro-Cammell H27/21R	Birmingham Corporation Tramways	486	A
OC 527	1933	Morris Commercial Imperial	Metro-Cammell H—/—R	Birmingham Corporation Tramways	527	A
AHA 582	1935	SOS DON	Brush B36F	BMMO ('Midland Red')	1703	A
CVP 207	1937	Daimler COG5	Metro-Cammell H30/24R	Birmingham City Transport	1107	R
RC 4615	1937	AEC Regal O662	Willowbrook B34F	Trent Motor Traction Co	714	R
GHA 333	1940	SOS SON	(chassis only)	BMMO ('Midland Red')	2414	RP
GHA 337	1940	SOS SON	Brush B38F	BMMO ('Midland Red')	2418	RP
HHA 637	1946	BMMO S6	Metro-Cammell B40F	BMMO ('Midland Red')	3036	A
FFY 402	1947	Leyland Titan PD2/3	Leyland O30/26R	Southport Corporation	85	RP
GUE 247	1948	Leyland Tiger PS1	Northern Coachbuilders B34F	Stratford-upon-Avon Blue Motors	41	A
HOV 685	1948	Leyland Titan PD2/1	Brush H30/24R	Birmingham City Transport	1685	R
JRR 404	1948	Leyland Titan PD1	Duple L29/26F	Barton Transport of Chilwell	473	RP
KAL 579	1948	Daimler CVD6	Massey H33/28RD	W. Gash & Sons of Newark	DD2	R
FDM 724	1949	Foden PVD6	Massey H30/26R	E. H. Phillips of Holywell		A
FJW 616+	1949	Sunbeam F4	Park Royal H28/26R	Wolverhampton Corporation	616	R
HDG 448	1949	Albion Venturer CX19	Metro-Cammell H30/26R	Cheltenham District Traction Co	72	R
HWO 334	1949	Guy Arab III	Duple L27/26R	Red & White Services	34	R
JOJ 245	1950	Leyland Tiger PS2/1	Weymann B34F	Birmingham City Transport	2245	R
JOJ 533	1950	Guy Arab III Special	Metro Cammell H30/24R	Birmingham City Transport	2533	R
JUE 349	1950	Leyland Tiger PS2/3	Northern Counties H35/28F	Stratford-upon-Avon Blue Motors	33	RP

Registration	Date	Chassis	Body	New to	Fleet No	Status
KFM 775	1950	Bristol L5G	ECW B35R	Crosville Motor Services	KG126	R
NHA 744	1950	BMMO S12	Brush B44F	BMMO ('Midland Red')	3744	RP
NHA 795	1950	BMMO D5B	Brush H30/26RD	BMMO ('Midland Red')	3795	A
ORB 277	1950	Daimler CVD6	Duple C35F	Tailby & George ('Blue Bus Services') of Willington		R
MXX 23	1952	AEC Regal IV 9821LT	Metro-Cammell B41F	London Transport	RF381	R
JOJ 976	1953	Guy Arab IV	Metro-Cammell H30/25R	Birmingham City Transport	2976	R
PDH 808	1953	Leyland Royal Tiger PSU1/13	Park Royal DP40F	Walsall Corporation	808	R
RDH 505	1953	Leyland Titan PD2/12	Roe FH33/23RD	Walsall Corporation	815	A
SHA 431	1953	Leyland Titan PD2/12 Special	Leyland H30/26RD	BMMO ('Midland Red')	4031	R
FRC 956	1954	Leyland Titan PD2/12	Leyland H32/26RD	Trent Motor Traction Co	1256	R
UHA 255	1955	BMMO S14	BMMO B44F	BMMO ('Midland Red')	4255	R
XHA 482	1956	BMMO D7	Metro-Cammell H37/26RD	BMMO ('Midland Red')	4482	R
XHA 496	1956	BMMO D7	Metro-Cammell	BMMO ('Midland Red')	4496	A
SUK 3	1957	Guy Arab IV	Metro-Cammell H33/27R	Wolverhampton Corporation	3	R
UTU 596J	1957	Guy Otter NLLODP	Mulliner B26F	Douglas Corporation	9	R
VVP 911	1958	Bedford SB3	Duple C41F	Sandwell Motor Co of Birmingham		R
WDF 569	1959	Leyland Tiger Cub PSUC1	Willowbrook DP41F	Soudley Valley Coaches of Cinderford		R
819 HHA	1959	BMMO C5	BMMO C37F	BMMO ('Midland Red')	4819	RP
871 KHA	1960	BMMO D9	BMMO H40/32RD	BMMO ('Midland Red')	4871	R
943 KHA	1960	BMMO D10	BMMO H43/35F	BMMO ('Midland Red')	4943	R
802 MHW	1961	Bristol Lodekka FSF6G	ECW H34/26F	Cheltenham District Traction Co	6037	R
3016 HA	1962	BMMO D9	BMMO O40/32RD	BMMO ('Midland Red')	5016	R
5073 HA	1962	BMMO S15	BMMO B40F	BMMO ('Midland Red')	5073	R
5212 HA	1962	Leyland Leopard PSU3/4R	Willowbrook B53F	BMMO ('Midland Red')	5212	A
SBF 233	1962	Leyland Titan PD2/28	Northern Counties -	Harper Bros of Heath Hayes	25	R
248 NEA	1963	Daimler CVG6-30	Metro-Cammell H41/33R	West Bromwich Corporation	248	R
6545 HA	1964	BMMO S16	BMMO B52F	BMMO ('Midland Red')	5545	R
BHA 399C	1965	BMMO D9	BMMO H40/32RD	BMMO ('Midland Red')	5399	R
BHA 656C	1965	BMMO CM6T	BMMO C44Ft	BMMO ('Midland Red')	5656	R
BON 474C	1965	Daimler Fleetline CRG6LX	Marshall B37F	Birmingham City Transport	3474	R
CUV 219C	1965	AEC Routemaster R2RH/1	Park Royal H36/29RD	London Transport	RCL2219	R
EHA 767D	1966	BMMO S17	BMMO/Plaxton B52F	BMMO ('Midland Red')	5767	R
GHA 415D	1966	Daimler Fleetline CRG6LX	Alexander H44/33F	BMMO ('Midland Red')	6015	R
GRY 60D	1966	Leyland Titan PD3A/1	Park Royal H41/33R	Leicester City Transport	60	R
HBF 679D	1966	Leyland Titan PD2A/27	Metro-Cammell H36/28RD	Harper Bros of Heath Hayes	27	R
Q124 VOE	1966	Leyland Leopard PSU4/4R	Plaxton -	Midland Red Omnibus Co	5826	A
JHA 868E	1967	BMMO S21	BMMO DP49F	BMMO ('Midland Red')	5868	R
KHW 306E	1967	Bristol RELL6L	ECW B53F	Cheltenham District Traction Co	1000	R
NJW 719E	1967	Daimler Roadliner SRC6	Strachan B54D	Wolverhampton Corporation	719	R
KOX 780F	1968	Daimler Fleetline CRG6LX	Park Royal H43/33F	Birmingham City Transport	3780	R
NEA 101F	1968	Daimler Fleetline CRG6LX	Metro-Cammell H42/31F	West Bromwich Corporation	101	R
NOV 796G	1968	Daimler Fleetline CRG6LX	Park Royal H43/29D	Birmingham City Transport	3796	R
XDH 56G	1968	Daimler Fleetline CRC6-36	Northern Counties H51/34D	Walsall Corporation	56	R
SHA 645G	1969	Leyland Leopard PSU4A/4R	Plaxton C36F	BMMO ('Midland Red')	6145	R
SOE 913H	1969	Daimler Fleetline CRG6LX-33	Park Royal H47/33D	West Midlands PTE	3913	RP
UHA 956H	1969	BMMO S23	BMMO/Plaxton B51F	BMMO ('Midland Red')	5956	R
XDH 516G	1969	Daimler Fleetline CRG6LX	Northern Counties H41/27D	Walsall Corporation	116	R
FRB 211H	1970	Bristol VRTSL6LX	ECW H39/31F	Midland General Omnibus Co	322	R
UHA 941H	1970	BMMO S23	BMMO B51F	BMMO ('Midland Red')	5941	A
UHA 981H	1970	BMMO S23	BMMO/Plaxton B51F	BMMO ('Midland Red')	5981	R
AHA 451J	1971	Leyland Leopard PSU4B/4R	Plaxton C36F	BMMO ('Midland Red')	6451	R
OWE 271K	1972	Bristol VRTSL6LX	East Lancs H43/30F	Sheffield Transport	271	R
PDU 135M	1973	Daimler Fleetline CRG6LX	East Lancs H44/30F	Coventry Transport	135	RP
NOB 413M	1974	Bristol VRTSL6LX	MCW H43/33F	West Midlands PTE	4413	R
PHA 370M	1974	Ford R1014	Plaxton/Midland Red DP23F	Midland Red Omnibus Co	370	R
JOV 613P	1975	Daimler Fleetline CRG6LX	Park Royal H43/33F	West Midlands PTE	4613	R
99-64-HB	1976	Den Oudsten LOK	Den Oudsten B35D	VAD of Ermele (Netherlands)	5656	A
KON 311P	1976	Leyland Fleetline FE30ALR	MCW H43/33F	West Midlands PTE	6311	R
NOE 544R	1976	Leyland National 11351A/1R	Leyland National B49F	Midland Red Omnibus Co	544	R

Registration	Date	Chassis	Body	New to	Fleet No	Status
SDA 757S	1977	Leyland Fleetline FE30AGR	East Lancs H43/33F	West Midlands PTE	6757	R
WDA 835T	1978	MCW Metrobus DR102/1	MCW H43/30F	West Midlands PTE	6835	RP
WDA 956T	1978	Leyland Fleetline FE30AGR	MCW/WMT B37F	West Midlands PTE	1956	R
DOC 26V	1980	Leyland National 2 NL116L11/1R	Leyland National B50F	West Midlands PTE	7026	R
D553 NOE	1986	Ford Transit	Carlyle B18F	West Midlands Travel	553	R

+ trolleybus

Notes:

RC 4615	rebodied 1950
GHA 333	converted to works tug with AEC engine c1960
FFY 402	originally H30/26R
KAL 579	rebodied 1958
JUE 349	rebodied 1963
PDH 808	originally B42F
XHA 496	converted to breakdown vehicle in 1972
UTU 596J	originally registered WMN 485
943 KHA	entered service 1961
3016 HA	originally H40/32RD; converted to open-top by Marshall ('Obsolete Fleet') London (OM5)
5073 HA	originally DP40F; re-seated in 1969

SBF 233	rebuilt as towing tender in 1981
Q124 VOE	rebuilt as towing tender in1977
PHA 370M	originally B45F; shortened as B27F by Midland Red in 1979 and re-seated as DP23F by Midland Red (West) in 1983.
99-64-HB	Netherlands registration
KON 311P	Gardner engine fitted in 1981; reverted to Leyland 680 in 2005
WDA 835T	exhibited at 1978 Commercial Motor Show
WDA 956T	originally double-decker (H43/33F) numbered 6956; rebuilt and renumbered in 1994
DOC 26V	later renumbered 1026

Trolleybus Museum at Sandtoft

Contact address: Belton Road, Sandtoft, Doncaster DN8 5SX

Phone: 01724 711391

E-mail: enquiries@sandtoft.org.uk

Web site: www.sandtoft.org.uk

Affiliation: NARTM

Brief description: Home of the nation's trolleybuses

Events planned:

11-13 April 2009 — Trolley Weekend;

2-4 May 2009 — May Day Trolleydays;

23-25 May 2009 — 40th Anniversarry Extravaganza Weekend;

13/14 June 2009 — Trolley Weekend;

27/28 June 2009 — Trolley Weekend;

11/12 July 2009 — Huddersfield Weekend (40 years since the end of Huddersfield trolleybus)

25/26 July 2009 — The Gathering;

8/9 August 2009 — Blues and Twos Weekend

29-31 August 2009 — European Weekend;

12/13 September 2009 — Trolley Weekend;

26/27 September 2009 — Trolley Weekend;

18 October 2009 — St Leger Rally;

15 November 2009 — Twilight Trolleybuses;

12/13 December 2009 — Santa Weekend

Opening days/times: 11.00 to 17.00 on the above dates.

Directions by car: From M180 junction 2, take A161 southbound to Belton. Turn right and museum is 2 miles on right-hand side.

Directions by public transport: Free bus from Doncaster Interchange station stand C5 at 12.30 on 24 March, 5, 26 May, 26/27 July, 25 August, 14 September and 19 October
(please telephone to check operation)

Note: Please be aware that vehicles on display can vary from time to time as not all museums display their entire 'fleet'. Visitors wishing to see a particular vehicle should make enquiries prior to their visit.

Charges: Adult £4.50, Child/Senior Citizen £2.50, Family £12.
Except: 29/30 July — Adult £6.00, Child/Senior Citizen £4.00.

Facilities: A B(e) D E F G H L P R S T

Other information: Coach tours and private party visits can be accommodated at other times by prior arrangement

Registration	Date	Chassis	Body	New to	Fleet No	Status
note h	1902	Rob Blackwell & Co	-	Reading Corporation	'William'	A
WW 4688+	1927	Garrett O type	Garrett B32C	Mexborough & Swinton Traction Co	34	A
KW 6052+	1929	English Electric A	English Electric B32F	Bradford Corporation	562	A
note t+	1929	Guy BTX	Ransomes B—C	Hastings Tramways Co		RP
TV 4484+	1931	Ransomes Sims & Jefferies D6	(chassis only)	Nottingham City Transport	346	A
1425 P+	1932	Fabrique Nationale	Fabrique Nationale B26SD	Liege (Belgium)	425	R
TV 9333+	1934	Karrier E6	Brush H—/—R	Nottingham City Transport	367	RP
ALJ 973+	1935	Sunbeam MS2	Park Royal H31/25D	Bournemouth Corporation	99	R
CU 3593+	1937	Karrier E4	Weymann H29/26R	South Shields Corporation	204	R
FW 8990+	1937	AEC 661T	Park Royal H30/26R	Cleethorpes Corporation	54	RP
AVH 470	1938	Karrier E6	(chassis only)	Huddersfield Corporation	470	A
ARD 676+	1939	AEC 661T	Park Royal H30/26R	Reading Corporation	113	R
FTO 614	1939	AEC Regent O661		Nottingham City Transport	802	R
CKG 193+	1942	AEC 664T	Northern Counties H38/32R	Cardiff Corporation	203	R
964 H 87+	1943	Vetra CB60	CTL B17D	Limoges (France)	5	R
GHN 574+	1944	Karrier W	East Lancs H39/31F	Bradford Corporation	792	R
GKP 511+	1944	Sunbeam W	Roe H34/28R	Maidstone Corporation	56	R
RC 8472+	1944	Sunbeam W	Weymann H30/26R	Derby Corporation	172	R
CDT 636+	1945	Karrier W	Roe H34/28R	Doncaster Corporation	375	RP
DKY 706+	1945	Karrier W	East Lancs H37/29F	Bradford Corporation	706	R
GTV 666+	1945	Karrier W	Brush H30/26R	Nottingham City Transport	466	RP
RC 8575+	1945	Sunbeam W	Park Royal H30/26R	Derby Corporation	175	RP
SVS 281	1945	Daimler CWA6	Duple H30/26R	Douglas Corporation	52	R
CVH 741+	1947	Karrier MS2	Park Royal H40/30R	Huddersfield Corporation	541	RP
EDT 703	1947	Leyland Titan PD2/1	Roe H34/28R	Doncaster Corporation	94	RP
HKR 11+	1947	Sunbeam W	Northern Coachbuilders H30/26R	Maidstone Corporation	72	R
JV 9901	1947	AEC Regent III O961	Roe H31/25R	Grimsby Corporation	81	A
HYM 812+	1948	BUT 9641T	Metro-Cammell H40/30R	London Transport	1812	R
JMN 727	1948	AEC Regent III O961	Northern Counties H30/26R	Douglas Corporation	63	R
KTV 493+	1948	BUT 9611T	Roe H31/25R	Nottingham City Transport	493	R
DRD 130+	1949	BUT 9611T	Park Royal H33/26RD	Reading Corporation	144	R
EKU 743+	1949	BUT 9611T	Roe H33/25R	Bradford Corporation	743	A
EKU 746+	1949	BUT 9611T	Roe H33/25R	Bradford Corporation	746	R
EKY 558	1949	Leyland Titan PD2/3	Leyland H33/26R	Bradford Corporation	558	RP
GDT 421	1949	Daimler CVD6	Roe L27/26R	Doncaster Corporation	112	A
LHN 784+	1949	BUT 9611T	East Lancs H37/29F	Bradford Corporation	834	R
ERD 145+	1950	Sunbeam S7	Park Royal H38/30RD	Reading Corporation	174	R
ERD 152+	1950	Sunbeam S7	Park Royal H38/30RD	Reading Corporation	181	R
FET 618+	1950	Daimler CTE6	Roe H40/30R	Rotherham Corporation	44	R
GFU 692+	1950	BUT 9611T	Northern Coachbuilders H30/26R	Cleethorpes Corporation	59	A
JWW 375+	1950	Sunbeam F4	East Lancs H37/29F	Bradford Corporation	845	RP
JWW 376+	1950	Sunbeam F4	East Lancs H37/29F	Bradford Corporation	846	A
JWW 377+	1950	Sunbeam F4	East Lancs H37/29F	Bradford Corporation	847	A
KTV 506+	1950	BUT 9641T	Brush H38/32R	Nottingham City Transport	506	R
BDJ 87+	1951	BUT 9611T	East Lancs H30/26R	St Helens Corporation	387	RP
FKU 758+	1951	BUT 9611T	Weymann H33/26R	Bradford Corporation	758	RP
LYR 542	1951	AEC Regent III O961	Park Royal H30/26R	London Transport	RT3323	RP
NDH 959+	1951	Sunbeam F4	Brush H34/31R	Walsall Corporation	342	R
MDT 222	1953	AEC Regal III 9621A	Roe B39F	Doncaster Corporation	22	R
OTV 137	1953	AEC Regent III 9613E	Park Royal H30/26R	Nottingham City Transport	137	RP
AC-L 379+	1956	Henschel 562E	Ludewig RB17/44T	Aachen (Germany)	22	R
KVH 219+	1956	BUT 9641T	East Lancs H40/32R	Huddersfield Corporation	619	R
FYS 839+	1958	BUT 9613T	Crossley H37/34R	Glasgow Corporation	TB78	R

Registration	Date	Chassis	Body	New to	Fleet No	Status
PVH 931+	1959	Sunbeam S7A	East Lancs H40/32R	Huddersfield Corporation	631	R
XWX 795	1959	AEC Reliance 2MU3RV	Roe C—F	Felix Motors of Doncaster	40	A
9629 WU	1960	AEC Reliance 2MU3RV	Roe DP41F	Felix Motors of Doncaster	41	R
WLT 529	1960	AEC Routemaster R2RH	Park Royal H36/28R	London Transport	RM529	R
VRD 193+	1961	Sunbeam F4A	Burlingham H38/30F	Reading Corporation	193	RP
657 BWB	1962	Leyland Atlantean PDR1/1	Park Royal H44/33F	Sheffield Joint Omnibus Committee	1357	R
433 MDT	1963	Leyland Tiger Cub PSUC1/11	Roe B45F	Doncaster Corporation	33	R
7830 LG 69+	1964	Vetra EH87	B22T	Lyon (France)	1704	A
JTF 920B	1964	AEC Reliance 2MU3RV	East Lancs B—D	Reading Corporation	48	A
66+	1967	Lancia	Dalfa H43/25D	Oporto (Portugal)	140	R
UDT 455F	1968	Leyland Royal Tiger Cub RTC1/2	Roe B45D	Doncaster Corporation	55	R
WWJ 754M	1973	Daimler Fleetline CRG6LXB	Park Royal H43/27D	Sheffield Transport	754	R
8319 JD 13+	1980	Renault ER100	B26D	Marseilles (France)	202	R
C45 HDT+	1985	Dennis Dominator DTA1401	Alexander H47/33F	South Yorkshire PTE	2450	R
D472 OWE	1986	Dennis Dominator DDA910	Alexander DPH45/33F	South Yorkshire PTE	2472	A
D479 OWE	1986	Dennis Dominator DDA910	Alexander DPH45/33F	South Yorkshire PTE	2479	RP

+ trolleybus

Notes:

note h	unregistered wooden-bodied tower wagon, named 'William'; owned by the British Trolleybus Society	LHN 784	rebodied 1962 by Bradford Corporation (834)
		FET 618	rebodied 1957; formerly single-decker
WW 4688	owned by the British Trolleybus Society	JWW 375	rebodied 1962; chassis ex Mexborough & Swinton Traction Co
KW 6052	caravan conversion to be restored		
note t	identity not yet confirmed but possibly Hastings 57	JWW 376	rebodied 1962; chassis ex Mexborough & Swinton Traction Co
1425 P	Belgian registration		
ALJ 973	owned by the British Trolleybus Society	JWW 377	rebodied 1962; chassis ex Mexborough & Swinton Traction Co
CU 3593	owned by the British Trolleybus Society		
ARD 676	owned by the British Trolleybus Society	NDH 959	rebuilt/lengthened 1965; owned by the British Trolleybus Society
FTO 614	converted to tower wagon		
CKG 193	owned by the British Trolleybus Society	AC-L 379	German registration; owned by the British Trolleybus Society
964 H 87	French registration		
GHN 574	originally single-decker; rebodied 1958	FYS 839	owned by the British Trolleybus Society
GKP 511	rebodied 1960	PVH 931	owned by the British Trolleybus Society
SVS 281	originally registered FMN 955	657 BWB	rebodied 1968; renumbered 227 in 1970 following dissolution of JOC
DKY 706	rebodied 1960		
CDT 636	rebodied 1955	7830 LG 69	French registration
EDT 703	original Leyland body replaced 1964 by ex-trolleybus body new 1955	JTF 920B	caravan conversion; originally registered 5148 DP
		66	Portuguese registration
HKR 11	on loan from Maidstone Borough Council	8319 JD 13	French registration
HYM 812	owned by the British Trolleybus Society		

Ulster Folk & Transport Museum
Cultra

Contact address: Cultra, Holywood, Co Down, BT18 OEU

Phone: 028 9042 8428

Website: www.uftm.org.uk

Brief description: A unique collection of wheeled vehicles from cycles to trams, railways, buses and cars. Interpretive exhibitions show the development of road transport. Not all the vehicles listed are always on display. Please enquire before your visit.

Opening days/times: All the year round but closing for a few days at Christmas time. From 10.00 on weekdays and 11.00 on Sundays (please 'phone for details)

Directions by car: On A2 Belfast-Bangor road

Note: Please be aware that vehicles on display can vary from time to time as not all museums display their entire 'fleet'. Visitors wishing to see a particular vehicle should make enquiries prior to their visit.

Directions by public transport: On main Belfast–Bangor railway and bus routes

Charges: £7 (discounts for groups)

Facilities: A D E F G L P R T

Registration	Date	Chassis	Body	New to	Fleet No	Status
CZ 7013	1935	Dennis Lancet	Harkness B31F	Belfast Corporation	102	R
FZ 7883+	1943	AEC 664T	Harkness/Park Royal H36/32R	Belfast Corporation	98	A
FZ 7897+	1948	Guy BTX	Harkness H36/32R	Belfast Corporation	112	R
EOI 4857	1973	Daimler Fleetline CRG6LX-33	Alexander (Belfast) H49/37F	Belfast Corporation	857	R
+ trolleybus						

Notes:
EOI 4857   passed to Citybus (2857) in 1973; rebodied 1976

Western Isles Transport Preservation Group, Isle of Lewis

Contact address: 43b Lower Barvas, Isle of Lewis, HS2 0QY

Phone: 01851 840294 or 07765 131793

Web site: www.witpg.org.uk

Affiliation: NARTM

Brief description: The collection of vehicles can be visited at any time by prior arrangement. At present stored at a variety of locations, the group is planning to bring the collection to a common site incorporating a working museum

Events planned:
15th August 2009 — Annual Motor Show at Stornoway (venue to be arranged).

Opening days/times: Viewing at any time by arrangement

Directions: By air from Glasgow, Inverness or Aberdeen or by ferry via Ullapool or Uig or Oban

Registration	Date	Chassis	Body	New to	Fleet No	Status
JS 1972	1924	Ford Model T	McLeod 8-seat	Mackay of Stornaway		RP
JS 8089	1948	Bedford OB	Duple B30F	Mitchell of Stornaway		A
UGB 138H	1970	Bedford SB5	Duple Midland B40F	Highland Omnibuses	10	RP
DSE 980T	1979	Bedford YRQ	Plaxton C33F	Low of Tonintoul		A
A913 ERM	1984	Bedford YNT	Plaxton B54F	George T. Irving of Dalston		A
F649 FGE	1988	Mercedes-Benz 507D	Steeldrive M16	Craney of Kilsyth		A

Notes:
DSE 980T   originally C45F

Wirral Transport Museum Birkenhead

Contact address: 1 Taylor Street, Birkenhead, Merseyside, L41 5HN

Phone: 0151 666 2756

Affiliation: NARTM

Brief description: The museum houses a collection of buses, tramcars, motor cycles, cars and a model railway. Local enthusiast groups are restoring some of the trams and buses. Trams operate during weekends and some school holidays.

Opening days/times: Weekends 13.00-17.00. Please see web site for further details

Directions by car: Adjacent to Woodside ferry terminal

Directions by public transport: Bus or ferry to Woodside, or train to Hamilton Square station

Registration	Date	Chassis	Body	New to	Fleet No	Status
BG 8557	1944	Guy Arab II	Massey H31/26R	Birkenhead Corporation	242	RP
BG 9225	1946	Leyland Titan PD1A	Massey H30/26R	Birkenhead Corporation	105	RP
HKF 820	1949	AEC Regent III 9612E	Weymann/LCPT H30/26R	Liverpool Corporation	A344	RP
AHF 850	1951	Leyland Titan PD2/1	Metro-Cammell H30/26R	Wallasey Corporation	54	R
CHF 565	1956	Leyland Titan PD2/10	Burlingham H30/26R	Wallasey Corporation	106	RP
FBG 910	1958	Leyland Titan PD2/40	Massey H31/28R	Birkenhead Corporation	10	R
FHF 451	1958	Leyland Atlantean PDR1/1	Metro-Cammell H44/33F	Wallasey Corporation	1	R
101 CLT	1962	AEC Routemaster 2R2RH	Park Royal H36/28R	London Transport	RM1101	R
RCM 493	1964	Leyland Leopard L1	Massey B42D	Birkenhead Corporation	93	R
GCM 152E	1967	Leyland Titan PD2/37	Massey H36/30R	Birkenhead Corporation	152	R
UFM 52F	1968	Bristol RELL6G	ECW DP50F	Crosville Motor Services	ERG52	R
OFM 957K	1972	Daimler Fleetline CRG6LX	Northern Counties O43/29F	Chester Corporation	57	R
THM 692M	1974	Daimler Fleetline CRL6	MCW H—/—D	London Transport	DMS1692	A
CWU 146T	1978	Leyland Fleetline FE30AGR	Roe H—/—F	West Yorkshire PTE	7146	A
B926 KWM	1984	Leyland Atlantean AN68D/1R	Alexander H43/32F	Merseyside PTE	1070	R

Notes:

BG 8557	rebodied 1953
HKF 820	privately owned
CHF 565	carries 1949 body
FHF 451	first production Atlantean in service
FBG 910	driver trainer 1974-81
OFM 957K	originally H43/29F; rebodied 1984 and converted to open-top (renumbered 75) in 1998
THM 692M	mobile classroom; originally H44/24D
CWU 146T	promotional vehicle for The Hamilton Quarter; originally H43/32F

Note: Please be aware that vehicles on display can vary from time to time as not all museums display their entire 'fleet'. Visitors wishing to see a particular vehicle should make enquiries prior to their visit.

Above: Mulliner-bodied Bedford OB MHU 193 spent 30 years with Clifton College of Bristol as a school bus before passing to the Bristol Omnibus Vehicle Collection and taking on the identity of Bristol Tramways 219, an identical Bedford OB also built in 1949 but registered MHU 915. *Bristol Omnibus Vehicle Collection*

Below: Now at the Manchester Museum of Transport and seen operating a free service in the city, SELNEC Leyland National EX30 was new in 1972. *Philip Lamb*

Above: In the postwar Chester fleet Massey- and, later, Northern Counties-bodied Guy Arabs reigned supreme. No 1 (RFM 641) was, as its fleet number suggests, the first of 47 delivered in the period 1953-69 and is today preserved at the North West Museum of Road Transport at St Helens. *Philip Lamb*

Left: Normally based at the North of England Open Air Museum at Beamish, Newcastle 501 (LTN 501), a Northern Coachbuilders-bodied Sunbeam S7, is here seen on loan to the Black Country Living Museum at Dudley. *Philip Lamb*

Right: Liverpool Corporation L255 (VKB 711) is a Leyland Titan PD2/Crossley new in 1956. *Merseyside Transport Trust*

Aldershot & District Bus Interest Group

Contact address: 111 Park Barn Drive, Guildford, Surrey, GU2 6ER

E-mail: bill.tutty@ntlworld.com

Web site: www.adbig.co.uk

Affiliation: NARTM, FBHVC.

Brief description: The group was formed in 1994 to consolidate the collection of preserved ex-Aldershot & District vehicles and other related artefacts that had been saved over the years and to provide a focal point for individuals with an interest in every aspect of the old Aldershot & District Traction Co Ltd. The vehicles, all of which remain in private ownership, range from 1920s Dennis E types through to Dennis, AEC and Bristol buses which entered service with A&D in the 1950s, 1960s and 1970s at the very end of the company's existence. The group works closely with the Dennis Bus Owners Association.

Other information: Monthly meetings. Regular outings and events using the preserved buses. Regular working parties. New members always welcome.

Registration	Date	Chassis	Body	New to	Fleet No	Status
OT 8283	1928	Dennis E	(chassis only)	Aldershot & District Traction Co	D210	A
OT 8592	1928	Dennis E	Strachan & Brown	Aldershot & District Traction Co	D217	A
OT 8898	1928	Dennis E	Strachan & Brown	Aldershot & District Traction Co	D226	A
OT 8902	1928	Dennis E	Dennis B32R	Aldershot & District Traction Co	D235	A
BOT 303	1937	Dennis Lancet II	(chassis only)	Aldershot & District Traction Co	709	A
GAA 580	1948	Dennis Lancet III	Strachans B32R	Aldershot & District Traction Co	944	A
GAA 616	1948	Dennis Lancet III	Strachans C32R	Aldershot & District Traction Co	980	RP
GOU 845	1950	Dennis Lance K3	East Lancs L25/26R	Aldershot & District Traction Co	145	R
HOU 904	1950	Dennis Lancet J10	Strachans B38R	Aldershot & District Traction Co	178	R
LAA 231	1953	Dennis Lancet J10C	Strachans FC38R	Aldershot & District Traction Co	196	RP
LOU 48	1954	Dennis Lance K4	East Lancs L28/28R	Aldershot & District Traction Co	220	R
MOR 581	1954	AEC Reliance MU3RV	Metro-Cammell B40F	Aldershot & District Traction Co	543	R
POR 428	1956	Dennis Falcon P5	Strachans B30F	Aldershot & District Traction Co	282	R
SOU 456	1958	Dennis Loline	East Lancs H37/31RD	Aldershot & District Traction Co	348	RP
SOU 465	1958	Dennis Loline	East Lancs H37/31RD	Aldershot & District Traction Co	357	R
XHO 370	1960	AEC Reliance 2MU3RV	Weymann DP40F	Aldershot & District Traction Co	370	R
462 EOT	1962	Dennis Loline III	Alexander H39/29F	Aldershot & District Traction Co	462	RP
488 KOT	1964	Dennis Loline III	Weymann H39/29F	Aldershot & District Traction Co	488	R
AAA 503C	1965	Dennis Loline III	Weymann H39/29F	Aldershot & District Traction Co	503	R
AAA 506C	1965	Dennis Loline III	Weymann H39/29F	Aldershot & District Traction Co	506	R
AAA 508C	1965	Dennis Loline III	Weymann H39/29F	Aldershot & District Traction Co	508	RP
CCG 296K	1971	Bristol RESL6G	ECW B40D	Aldershot & District Traction Co	651	RP
KCG 627L	1973	Leyland National 1151/1R/0402	Leyland National B49F	Thames Valley & Aldershot Omnibus Co	127	R

Notes:

OT 8283   originally Dennis F; converted to E type

MOR 581   new numbered 250, with Strachans coach body; rebodied 1967

Angus Transport Group

Contact address: The Old Foundry, Bridge Street, Montrose, DD10 8PS

E-mail: ian.forbes@sepa.org.uk

Brief description: A small collection of privately owned vehicles with Scottish origins. Vehicles operate in the summer on a local 'Basin Rambler' free bus service.

Events planned: On Sundays in July and August, 'Basin Rambler' free classic bus service operates around the Montrose basin. Vehicles also attend local and national rallies.

Registration	Date	Chassis	Body	New to	Fleet No	Status
XSA 620	1963	AEC Reliance 2MU3RA	Plaxton B47F	Burkett of Mintlaw	7	R
EWG 22L	1973	Leyland Leopard PSU3/3R	Alexander C49F	W. Alexander & Sons (Midland)	MPE152	RP
RRM 634X	1982	Leyland Leopard PSU3G/4R	ECW C49F	Cumberland Motor Services	634	R
XSS 43Y	1982	Leyland Leopard PSU3G/4R	Alexander B53F	W. Alexander & Sons (Northern)	NPE43	RP
B97 PKS	1985	MCW Metrobus DR102/47	Alexander H45/33F	W. Alexander & Sons (Midland)	MRM97	A

Aycliffe & District Bus Preservation Society

Contact address: 35 Lowther Drive, Newton Aycliffe, Co Durham, DL5 4UL

Affiliation: NARTM

Brief description: A collection of Darlington area service buses, the majority fully restored and in running order.

Opening days/times: Viewing by prior appointment only.

Registration	Date	Chassis	Body	New to	Fleet No	Status
FHN 923	1940	Bristol K5G	-	United Automobile Services	BDO23	A
GHN 189	1942	Bristol K5G	ECW L27/26R	United Automobile Services	BGL29	R
LHN 860	1950	Bristol L5G	ECW B35F	United Automobile Services	BG413	R
304 GHN	1958	Bristol LS6B	ECW C39F	United Automobile Services	BUC4	RP
AHN 451B	1964	Daimler CCG5	Roe H33/28R	Darlington Corporation	7	R
NDL 769G	1969	Bristol LHS6L	Marshall B35F	Southern Vectis Omnibus Co	833	R

Notes:

FHN 923	breakdown vehicle
GHN 189	1949 body fitted in 1954
LHN 860	converted to OMO c1957
304 GHN	now fitted with Gardner engine
NDL 769G	acquired by United Automobile Services (1452) in 1977

Barrow Transport Museum Trust

Contact address: 2 Greengate Lane, Kendal, Cumbria, LA9 5LQ

Phone: 01229 870336

E-mail: dave.caton@talktalk.net

Web site: http://website.lineone.net/~barrow_transport

Affiliation: NARTM

Brief description: The collection comprises vehicles operated by Barrow Corporation and spans the period 1949-88. The storage facility does not permit public access.

Registration	Date	Chassis	Body	New to	Fleet No	Status
EO 9051	1949	Leyland Titan PD2/3	Park Royal	Barrow in Furness Corporation	124	
EO 9177	1950	Leyland Titan PD2/3	Roe H31/28RD	Barrow in Furness Corporation	147	A
CEO 956	1958	Leyland Titan PD2/40	Park Royal H33/28R	Barrow in Furness Corporation	169	R
CEO 957	1958	Leyland Titan PD2/40	Park Royal H33/28R	Barrow in Furness Corporation	170	R
BLV 755A	1963	Leyland Leopard L1	East Lancs B42D	Barrow in Furness Corporation	72	RP
SEO 209M	1974	Leyland National 11351/1R	Leyland National B48F	Barrow in Furness Corporation	9	R
CEO 720W	1981	Leyland National 2 NL116L11/1R	Leyland National B45F	Barrow Borough Transport	20	A

Registration	Date	Chassis	Body	New to	Fleet No	Status
CEO 723W	1981	Leyland National 2 NL116L11/1R	Leyland National B49F	Barrow Borough Transport	23	A
LEO 734Y	1983	Leyland Atlantean AN68D/1R	Northern Counties H43/32F	Barrow Borough Transport	104	RP
VIL 8730	1988	Talbot Pullman	Talbot DP20F	Barrow Borough Transport	100	RP
G571 BHP	1990	Talbot Pullman	Talbot B8FI	non-PSV user in Coventry		R

Notes:

EO 9051	converted as recovery vehicle in 1964
EO 9177	original Park Royal body replaced 1960
BLV 755A	originally registered JEO 772
VIL 8730	originally registered E571 MAC
G571 BHP	used as support vehicle

Bolton Bus Group

Contact address: 69 Hereford Road, Heaton, Bolton BL1 4NJ

Brief description: A small group of enthusiasts formed to preserve examples of Bolton's buses. Some of the vehicles are displayed at Bury Transport Museum, which is temporarily closed until mid-2009.

Registration	Date	Chassis	Body	New to	Fleet No	Status
NBN 436	1959	Leyland Titan PD3/4	East Lancs H41/32F	Bolton Corporation	128	RP
UBN 902	1962	Leyland Titan PD3A/2	East Lancs FH41/32F	Bolton Corporation	169	R
UWH 185	1963	Leyland Atlantean PDR1/1	East Lancs H45/33F	Bolton Corporation	185	R
FBN 232C	1965	Leyland Atlantean PDR1/1	East Lancs H45/33F	Bolton Corporation	232	R
KUS 607E	1967	Leyland Atlantean PDR1/1	Alexander H44/34F	Glasgow Corporation	LA352	RP
TWH 809K	1971	Leyland Atlantean PDR2/1	East Lancs H49/37F	SELNEC PTE	6809	R

Bounty Country Buses

Contact E-mail: gerald@emerton.org.uk

Affiliation: NARTM, HCVS and Leyland Society

Brief description: A carefully assembled and unique collection of country buses, representing the great number of independent operators who established a network of country bus services from the 1920s through to the most profitable years of the 1940s and '50s and beyond, a tribute to their pioneering spirit of taking the country to the town and the town to the countryside, put together by the Emerton family of Nantwich, Cheshire

Opening days/times: Viewing by prior arrangements only

Registration	Date	Chassis	Body	New to	Fleet No	Status
EC 8852	1929	Vulcan Duchess	Vulcan B26D	Fawcett of Milnthorpe	7	R
WX 2658	1929	Dennis 30cwt	Short B16F	Jackson of Westgate on Sea		R
AG 6470	1931	REO FB	Economy B20F	Liddell of Auchinleck		R
ABH 358	1933	Leyland Cub KP3	Duple C20F	Oborne of Aylesbury		RP
WP 6114	1934	Commer Centaur B40	Carmichael B20F	Burnhams of Worcester		R
HL 7538	1936	Leyland Cub KPZ2/1	Roe B24F	West Riding Automobile Co	464	R
ETA 280	1937	Dennis Ace	Dennis HB16F	Hydro Hotel, Torquay		R
DDM 652	1947	Maudslay Marathon II	Duple C33F	Rhyl United Coachways	4	R
GDL 33	1949	Crossley SD42/7	Whitson C33F	Nash of Ventnor		R
JP 7538	1949	Crossley SD42/7	Duple FC35F	Liptrot of Bamfurlong		R
KTB 672	1949	Crossley SD42/7	Burlingham C33F	Warburton of Bury		RP

Registration	Date	Chassis	Body	New to	Fleet No	Status
HUY 655	1950	Bedford OB	Duple C29F	Ketley of Stourport		RP
NKR 529	1950	Crossley SD42/7	Brockhouse FC33F	Molins of Saunderton		R
HDM 473	1951	Bedford SB1	Duple C33F	Owen of Rhyl		A
SVA 438	1958	Bedford C5Z1	Duple Midland B30F	Hutchison of Overtown		RP
TEC 599N	1974	AEC Reliance 6MU4R	Plaxton C45F	Jackson of Kirkby Stephen		R

Notes:

WX 2658	originally registered KR 66
ETA 280	hotel bus with rear luggage compartment
DDM 652	rebodied 1956; previously Santus half-cab
JP 7538	rebodied 1955; previously Bellhouse Hartwell half-cab

Bournemouth Heritage Transport Collection

Phone: 01202 658333

Brief description: The collection comprises vehicles, mainly from Bournemouth Corporation or the Bournemouth area, built between the years 1928 and 1980. Most are owned by the Bournemouth Passenger Transport Association Ltd, which is a registered charity.

Events planned: Please see the enthusiast press for details

Opening days/times: Owing to storage relocation, the collection is not currently open to the public.

Registration	Date	Chassis	Body	New to	Fleet No	Status
RU 2266	1925	Shelvoke & Drewry Tramocar	(chassis only)	Bournemouth Corporation	9	A
VH 6217	1934	AEC Regent 661	Lee Motors -	Huddersfield Corporation	120	R
DKY 712+	1944	Karrier W	East Lancs H37/29F	Bradford Corporation	712	A
JLJ 403	1949	Leyland Tiger PS2/3	Burlingham FDP35F	Bournemouth Corporation	46	R
KEL 110	1949	Leyland Titan PD2/3	Weymann FH33/25D	Bournemouth Corporation	110	R
NNU 234+	1949	BUT 9611T	Weymann FH32/26R	Nottinghamshire & Derbyshire Traction Co	353	RP
KEL 133	1950	Leyland Titan PD2/3	Weymann FH27/21D	Bournemouth Corporation	247	R
KLJ 346+	1950	BUT 9641T	Weymann H31/25D	Bournemouth Corporation	212	R
NLJ 268	1953	Leyland Royal Tiger PSU1/13	Burlingham B42F	Bournemouth Corporation	258	R
NLJ 272	1953	Leyland Royal Tiger PSU1/13	Burlingham B42F	Bournemouth Corporation	262	R
RRU 904	1955	Leyland Tiger Cub PSUC1/1	Park Royal B42F	Bournemouth Corporation	267	R
LJ 147	1959	Leyland Titan PD3/1	Weymann H37/25D	Bournemouth Corporation	147	R
8154 EL	1960	Leyland Titan PD3/1	Weymann H37/25D	Bournemouth Corporation	154	R
8156 EL	1960	Leyland Titan PD3/1	Weymann O37/25D	Bournemouth Corporation	156	R
297 LJ+	1962	Sunbeam MF2B	Weymann H37/28D	Bournemouth Corporation	297	R
6167 RU	1963	Leyland Titan PD3A/1	Weymann H39/30F	Bournemouth Corporation	167	R
AEL 170B	1964	Leyland Atlantean PDR1/1	Weymann H43/31F	Bournemouth Corporation	170	R
ALJ 340B	1964	Daimler Fleetline CRG6LX	MH Cars H44/33F	Bournemouth Corporation	40	R
CRU 103C	1965	Leyland Leopard PSU3/2R	Weymann DP45F	Bournemouth Corporation	103	R
CRU 180C	1965	Daimler Fleetline CRG6LX	Weymann CO43/31F	Bournemouth Corporation	180	R
CRU 197C	1965	Daimler Fleetline CRG6LX	Weymann H43/31F	Bournemouth Corporation	197	R
KRU 55F	1967	Daimler Roadliner SRC6	Willowbrook B49F	Bournemouth Corporation	55	R
ORU 230G	1969	Leyland Atlantean PDR1A/1	Alexander H43/31F	Bournemouth Corporation	230	R
XRU 277K	1972	Leyland Atlantean PDR1A/1	Alexander H43/31F	Bournemouth Corporation	277	RP
DLJ 116L	1973	Daimler Fleetline CRL6	Alexander H43/31F	Bournemouth Corporation	116	R

+ trolleybus

Notes:

VH 6217	converted to tower wagon in 1948
DKY 712	rebodied 1960
NLJ 268	originally B41D; now mobile museum display vehicle

Bristol Omnibus Vehicle Collection

Contact address: 'Combe Barton', High Street, Dinder, Wells BA5 3PL

E-mail: drmichaelwalker@hotmail.com

Brief description: A collection of former of Bristol Omnibus Company vehicles.

Events planned: The vehicles will be attending rallies during the season

Registration	Date	Chassis	Body	New to	Fleet No	Status
HW 6634	1929	Bristol B	Bristol Tramways B32R	Bristol Tramways	559	A
JHT 802	1946	Bristol K6A	ECW H31/28R	Bristol Tramways & Carriage Co	C3386	RP
KHW 630	1948	Leyland Titan PD1	ECW H30/26R	Bristol Tramways& Carriage Co	C4019	RP
LHY 976	1949	Bristol L5G	ECW B33D	Bristol Tramways & Carriage Co	C2736	R
MHU 193	1949	Bedford OB	Mulliner B31F	Clifton College		R
NAE 3	1950	Bristol L6B	ECW FC31F	Bristol Tramways (Greyhound)	2467	RP
NHU 2	1950	Bristol LSX5G	ECW B42D	Bristol Tramways & Carriage Co	2800	R
NHY 947	1951	Bristol LWL6B	ECW FC35F	Bristol Tramways & Carriage Co (Greyhound)	2815	RP
OHY 938	1952	Bristol KSW6B	ECW L27/28RD	Bath Tramways Motor Co	L8089	R
UHY 360	1955	Bristol KSW6B	ECW H32/28R	Bristol Tramways & Carriage Co	C8320	R
UHY 384	1955	Bristol KSW6G	ECW H32/28RD	Bristol Tramways & Carriage Co	8336	R
924 AHY	1958	Bristol MW5G	ECW B45F	Bristol Omnibus Co	2934	R
969 EHW	1959	Bristol Lodekka LD6G	ECW H33/25RD	Bath Electric Tramways	L8515	R
972 EHW	1959	Bristol Lodekka LD6B	ECW H33/25R	Bristol Omnibus Co	LC8518	RP
869 NHT	1961	Bristol Lodekka FS6G	ECW CO33/27R	Bristol Omnibus Co	L8579	RP
BHU 92C	1965	Bristol MW6G	ECW C39F	Bristol Omnibus Co	2138	R
CHU 419C	1965	Bristol Lodekka FLF6G	ECW H38/32F	Bristol Omnibus Co	C7201	RP
FHU 59D	1966	Bristol Lodekka FLF6B	ECW H38/32F	Bristol Omnibus Co	C7246	R
OAE 954M	1973	Bristol RELL6L	ECW B50F	Bristol Omnibus Co	1332	A
AFB 592V	1980	Bristol LH6L	ECW B43F	Bristol Omnibus Co	461	R
A952 SAE	1983	Leyland Olympian ONLXB1/R	Roe H47/29F	Bristol Omnibus Co	9552	A
A954 SAE	1983	Leyland Olympian ONLXB1/R	Roe H47/29F	Bristol Omnibus Co	9554	R

Notes:

HW 6634	new body to be built using remains of original as pattern
JHT 802	1949 body fitted in 1957
MHU 193	restored as Bristol Tramways 219

NHU 2	prototype Bristol LS
A952 SAE	used as exhibition vehicle
A954 SAE	last Bristol-built chassis for Bristol Omnibus Co

Bristol Road Transport Collection

Contact address: 'The Nook', Water Lane, Walls Quarry, Brimscombe, Stroud GL5 2SS

E-mail: william.staniforth@virgin.net

Brief Description: Collection not currently on public display. For enquiries or an appointment to view a particular vehicle, please write to the address shown, enclosing a stamped self-addressed envelope.

Registration	Date	Chassis	Body	New to	Fleet No	Status
FAE 60	1938	Bristol L5G	-	Bristol Tramways & Carriage Co	W75	A
FAM 2	1949	Bristol L6B	Beadle C32R	Wilts & Dorset Motor Services	285	A
HPW 108	1949	Bristol K5G	ECW H30/26R	Eastern Counties Omnibus Co	LKH108	A
JEL 257	1949	Bristol K5G	ECW L27/28R	Hants & Dorset Motor Services	1238	A
LHW 918	1949	Bristol L5G	ECW B35R	Bristol Tramways & Carriage Co	2410	RP

Registration	Date	Chassis	Body	New to	Fleet No	Status
KUO 963	1950	Bristol K6B	ECW L27/28R	Western National Omnibus Co	950	RP
LFM 753	1950	Bristol L6B	ECW DP31R	Crosville Motor Services	KW172	R
CNH 699	1952	Bristol KSW6B	ECW L27/28R	United Counties Omnibus Co	860	A
UHY 359	1955	Bristol KSW6B	ECW H32/28R	Bristol Tramways & Carriage Co	C8319	A
YHT 958	1958	Bristol Lodekka LD6B	ECW O33/25RD	Bristol Omnibus Co	L8462	RP
980 DAE	1959	Bristol MW5G	ECW B45F	Bristol Omnibus Co	2960	A
904 OFM	1960	Bristol SC4LK	ECW C33F	Crosville Motor Services	CSG655	R
507 OHU	1962	Bristol Lodekka FLF6G	ECW H38/32F	Bristol Omnibus Co	7062	RP
RWC 608	1963	Bristol Lodekka FLF6B	ECW O38/32F	Eastern National Omnibus Co	1641	A
RDB 872	1964	Dennis Loline III	Alexander H39/32F	North Western Road Car Co	872	RP
DFE 963D	1966	Bristol Lodekka FS5G	ECW H33/27RD	Lincolnshire Road Car Co	2537	R
GYC 160K	1971	Bristol LH6L	ECW B45F	Hutchings & Cornelius Services of South Petherton		RP
HAX 399N	1975	Bristol LHS6L	Duple C35F	R. I. Davies & Son of Tredegar		RP
KHU 326P	1976	Bristol LH6L	ECW B43F	Bristol Omnibus Co	376	RP
KOU 791P	1976	Bristol VRTSL3/6LXB	ECW H39/31F	Bristol Omnibus Co	5505	A
C416 AHT	1986	Ford Transit 190D	Carlyle B16F	Bristol Omnibus Co	7416	A

Notes:

FAE 60	originally bus 2086, converted to lorry in 1952 and tower wagon in 1956	RWC 608	new as CH38/17F; fitted with Gardner engine in 1978 and converted to open-top, renumbered 2300, in 1978
KUO 963	acquired by Bristol Omnibus Co (L4134) in 1952		
YHT 958	originally H33/25RD		

Bristol Vintage Bus Group

Contact address: 74 Ridgeway Lane, Whitchurch, Bristol BS14 9PJ

Location: Unit G, Flowers Hill Road, Brislington, Bristol

Affiliation: NARTM

Brief description: A small group of enthusiasts formed to preserve examples of mainly Bristol's buses.

Events planned:
9 August 2009 — BVBG/Avon Valley Railway Open Day and Rally
Please see enthusiast press for other events.

Opening days/times: At any time by prior arrangement if someone is available

Directions by car: Flowers Hill Road is off the A4 Bath road, right on the City boundary near the Park & Ride

Directions by public transport: Main bus service to Bath from the Bus Station and Temple Meads railway station stops near Flowers Hill

Charges: No admission charge for viewing or special events

Registration	Date	Chassis	Body	New to	Fleet No	Status
AHU 803	1934	Bristol J5G	BBW B35R	Bristol Tramways & Carriage Co	2355	R
GHT 154	1940	Bristol K5G	BBW H30/26R	Bristol Tramways & Carriage Co	C3336	R
GHT 127	1941	Bristol K5G	ECW O30/26R	Bristol Tramways & Carriage Co	C3315	R
FTT 704	1945	Bristol K6A	ECW L27/28R	Western National Omnibus Co	353	R
LAE 13	1948	Leyland Titan PD1A	ECW H30/26R	Bristol Tramways & Carriage Co	C4044	R
EMW 284	1949	Bristol L6B	Beadle C32R	Wilts & Dorset Motor Services	279	R
JXC 323	1949	Leyland Tiger PS1	Mann Egerton B30F	London Transport	TD130	A
KLB 721	1950	AEC Regent III O961 RT	Park Royal H30/26R	London Transport	RT1599	R
KLJ 749	1950	Bristol LL6G	Portsmouth Aviation DP36R	Hants & Dorset Motor Services	779	R
MOD 978	1952	Bristol LS6G	ECW C39F	Southern National Omnibus Co (Royal Blue)	1291	RP
YHY 80	1957	Bristol LS6G	ECW B43F	Bristol Omnibus Co	2922	RP
363 CLT	1962	AEC Routemaster 2R2RH	Park Royal H36/28R	London Transport	RM1363	R
CWN 629C	1965	Bristol MW6G	ECW B45F	United Welsh Services	134	A

Notes:

AHU 803	originally a petrol-engined coach; rebodied 1947
GHT 127	restored in Brighton, Hove & District livery
FTT 704	original Strachans body replaced in 1955
YHY 80	rebuilt 1972 and renumbered as 3004

British Trolleybus Society

Contact address: 8 Riding Lane, Hildenborough, Tonbridge, Kent, TN11 9HX

Affiliation: NARTM

Brief description: The British Trolleybus Society is a contributing to the Trolleybus Museum at Sandtoft. Vehicles from its collection trolleybuses can be seen from time to time at Sandtoft on display, and are included in the Sandtoft listing.

Events planned: Details given in the section on the trolleybus Museum at Sandtoft.

Registration	Date	Chassis	Body	New to	Fleet No	Status
RD 7127	1935	AEC Regent O661	Park Royal L26/26R	Reading Corporation	47	R

Cardiff & South Wales Trolleybus Project

Contact address: 211 Hillrise, Llanedeyrn, Cardiff CF23 6UQ

Affiliation: NARTM

Brief description: The only trolleybus preservation group in the principality of Wales. A regular newsletter is issued, and new members are always welcome, presently £12.50/annum. Visitors to the workshop can be arranged by writing to the above address for details.

Registration	Date	Chassis	Body	New to	Fleet No	Status
DKY 704+	1945	Karrier W	East Lancs H37/29F	Bradford Corporation	704	A
EBO 919+	1949	BUT 9641T	Bruce H38/29D	Cardiff Corporation	262	RP
KBO 961+	1955	BUT 9641T	East Lancs B40R	Cardiff Corporation	243	RP
DHW 293K	1972	Bristol LH6L	ECW B42F	Bristol Omnibus Co	353	R
+ trolleybus						

Notes:

DKY 704	rebodied 1959
EBO 919	body built on East Lancs frames
DHW 293K	support vehicle

Cardiff Transport Preservation Group

Contact address: 10 Ger Nant, Ystrad Mynach, Hengoed, CF82 7FE

E-mail: mikeystrad73@btinternet.com

Web site: www.ctpg.co.uk   www.the-busdepot-barry.org

Affiliation: NARTM

Brief description: The CTPG is now based at the former Western Welsh depot in Barry, the group is run entirely by volunteers and is always looking for more help with looking after its growing collection of Welsh buses. The collection is not regularly open to the public, but viewing can be arranged via the address, website or e-mail.

Events planned: June 2009 — Barry Festival of Transport; September 2009 — Bus & Coach Wales

Registration	Date	Chassis	Body	New to	Fleet No	Status
LNY 903	1951	Leyland Titan PD2/12	Leyland L27/28R	Caerphilly Corporation	3	A
LKG 678	1956	AEC Regent V MD3RV	Park Royal H33/28R	Western Welsh Omnibus Co	678	A
TAX 235	1958	Bristol Lodekka LD6G	ECW H33/27RD	Red & White Services	L358	R
XNY 416	1958	Guy Arab LUF	Longwell Green B44F	Aberdare UDC	14	A
889 AAX	1961	Leyland Tiger Cub PSUC1/3	Weymann DP44F	Jones of Aberbeeg	98	R
XUH 368	1961	Leyland Titan PD2A/30	Metro Cammell H36/28R	Cardiff Corporation	368	A
GNY 432C	1965	Leyland Titan PD3/4	Massey L35/33RD	Caerphilly UDC	32	RP
EDW 68D	1966	Leyland Atlantean PDR1/1	Alexander H43/31F	Newport Corporation	68	R
JKG 497F	1968	Daimler Fleetline CRG6LX	Park Royal H42/33F	Cardiff Corporation	497	RP
MBO 512F	1968	AEC Swift MP2R	Alexander B47D	Cardiff Corporation	512	RP
OUH 177G	1969	Leyland Leopard PSU3A/4R	Plaxton C49F	Western Welsh Omnibus Co	177	RP
UTG 313G	1969	AEC Regent V 2MD3RA	Willowbrook H34/26F	Pontypridd UDC	8	RP
PKG 532H	1969	Daimler Fleetline CRG6LX	Willowbrook H44/30D	Cardiff Corporation	532	A
TKG 518J	1971	Leyland Leopard PSU4A/2R	Willowbrook -	Western Welsh Omnibus Co	1518	A
PKG 587M	1974	Bristol VRTSL6LX	ECW H43/31F	Cardiff Corporation	587	A
C101 HKG	1986	Ford Transit 190D	Robin Hood B16F	National Welsh Omnibus Services	1	RP
G258 HUH	1990	Leyland Lynx LX2R11C15ZR4	Leyland B49F	Cardiff City Transport Services	258	A
N143 PTG	1996	Optare MetroRider MR15	Optare B31F	Cardiff City Transport Services	143	A

Notes:

TKG 518J	converted as recovery vehicle in 1985 by National Welsh
PKG 587M	converted as display vehicle

Chelveston Preservation Society

Contact address: 36 Moor Road, Rushden, Northants, NN10 9SP

Affiliation: NARTM

Brief description: A private collection owned by a few members has evolved to represent most types of Bristol chassis from a range of former Tilling Group companies.

Registration	Date	Chassis	Body	New to	Fleet No	Status
VV 5696	1937	Bristol JO5G	ECW B35R	United Counties Omnibus Co	450	R
KFM 766	1949	Bristol L5G	ECW B35R	Crosville Motor Services	KG117	A
FRP 692	1950	Bristol KS5G	ECW L27/28R	United Counties Omnibus Co	692	R
FRP 828	1950	Bristol LL5G	ECW B39R	United Counties Omnibus Co	828	A
CNH 860	1952	Bristol LWL6B	ECW B39R	United Counties Omnibus Co	860	R
CNH 862	1952	Bristol LWL6B	ECW DP33R	United Counties Omnibus Co	862	R
HWV 294	1952	Bristol KSW5G	ECW L27/28R	Wilts & Dorset Motor Services	365	A
KNV 337	1954	Bristol KSW6B	ECW L27/28R	United Counties Omnibus Co	964	R
RFU 689	1958	Bristol SC4LK	ECW DP33F	Lincolnshire Road Car Co	2611	R
617 DDV	1960	Bristol MW6G	ECW C39F	Southern National Omnibus Co (Royal Blue)	2250	A
253 KTA	1962	Bristol MW6G	ECW C39F	Western National Omnibus Co (Royal Blue)	2270	A
271 KTA	1962	Bristol SUL4A	ECW C33F	Southern National Omnibus Co	421	RP
HAH 537L	1972	Bristol LH6P	ECW B45F	Eastern Counties Omnibus Co	LH537	RP

Notes:

VV 5696	rebodied 1949
CNH 860	renumbered 426 in 1952; Gardner 5LW engine fitted 1956
CNH 862	renumbered 428 in 1952; Gardner 5LW engine fitted in 1956; reverted to Bristol AVW in 1996

Cherwell Bus Preservation Group

Contact address: 32 Mill Street, Kidlington OX5 2EF

Brief description: A collection of mainly ex-City of Oxford vehicles housed under cover.

Events planned: The operational vehicles will attend a few events during the rally season.

Registration	Date	Chassis	Body	New to	Fleet No	Status
OJO 727	1950	AEC Regal III 9621A	Willowbrook B32F	City of Oxford Motor Services	727	R
191 AWL	1956	AEC Regent V MD3RV	Weymann L30/26R	City of Oxford Motor Services	L191	R
975 CWL	1958	AEC Regent V LD3RA	Park Royal H37/28R	City of Oxford Motor Services	H975	RP
312 MFC	1961	AEC Bridgemaster 2B3RA	Park Royal H43/29F	City of Oxford Motor Services	312	R
332 RJO	1963	AEC Renown 3B3RA	Park Royal H38/27F	City of Oxford Motor Services	332	R
OFC 902H	1970	Bristol VRTSL6LX	ECW H39/31F	City of Oxford Motor Services	902	RP
AUD 310J	1971	Leyland Leopard PSU3B/4R	Plaxton C51F	O. A. Slatter & Sons of Long Hanborough	40	A
TJO 56K	1971	AEC Reliance 6MU4R	Marshall DP49F	City of Oxford Motor Services	56	A
YWL 134K	1972	Leyland Leopard PSU3B/4R	Plaxton C53F	R. Jarvis & Sons of Middle Barton		A
NUD 105L	1973	Bristol VRTSL6LX	ECW CH41/27F	City of Oxford Motor Services	105	A
RBW 87M	1974	Bristol RELH6L	ECW DP49F	City of Oxford Motor Services	87	A
PWL 999W	1980	Leyland Olympian B45/TL11/2R	Alexander H50/32D	Leyland Vehicles (prototype)		A
VJO 201X	1982	Leyland Olympian ONLXB/1R	ECW H47/28D	City of Oxford Motor Services	201	RP
VUD 30X	1982	Leyland Leopard PSU3G/4R	ECW C49F	City of Oxford Motor Services	30	RP
C729 JJO	1986	Ford Transit 190D	Carlyle DP20F	City of Oxford Motor Services	729	RP

Notes:

PWL 999W   Prototype operated by Singapore Bus Service as SBS 5396B; acquired by COMS (999) in 1987

City of Portsmouth Preserved Transport Depot

Contact address: Friends of CPPTD, 58 South View Gardens, Andover, Hampshire SP10 2AQ

Affiliation: NARTM

Brief description: A collection comprising a range of veteran and vintage buses, most of which spent their working lives in the South of England. Suitable premises in the Portsmouth area are being sought for the Museum following closure of the Broad Street site, but the collection's vehicles (currently in storage at two locations) still operate free bus services and attend rallies, carnivals and other events. Please see the enthusiast press for the latest developments.

Registration	Date	Chassis	Body	New to	Fleet No	Status
note a	1876	Horse bus		G. Wheeler of Fawley		RP
RV 6367	1935	Leyland Titan TD4	English Electric O26/24R	Portsmouth Corporation	7	RP
CTP 200	1944	Bedford OWB	Duple (replica) B32F	Portsmouth Corporation	170	RP
DTP 823	1947	Leyland Titan PD1	Weymann H30/26R	Portsmouth Corporation	189	RP
AHC 442	1951	AEC Regent III 9613A	Bruce H30/26R	Eastbourne Corporation	42	R
EHV 65	1951	Bedford OB	Duple B29F	East Ham Borough Council		R
LRV 996	1956	Leyland Titan PD2/12	Metro-Cammell O33/26R	Portsmouth Corporation	4	R
ORV 989	1958	Leyland Titan PD2/40	Metro-Cammell H30/26R	Portsmouth Corporation	112	RP
BBK 236B	1964	Leyland Atlantean PDR1/1	Metro-Cammell H43/33F	Portsmouth Corporation	236	R
BTR 361B	1964	AEC Regent V 2D3RA	Neepsend H37/29R	Southampton Corporation	361	R
GTP 175F	1967	Leyland Panther Cub PSURC1/MCW B42D	Portsmouth Corporation	175	R
TBK 190K	1971	Leyland Atlantean PDR2/1	Seddon B40D	Portsmouth Corporation	190	R
K916 VDV	1994	Iveco 59-12	Mellor B26D	Thames Transit	2040	A

Notes:

note a	unregistered	EHV 65	preserved in Hants & Sussex livery
CTP 200	replica utility body; being restored in wartime livery	LRV 996	originally H33/26R

Colin Billington Collection

Contact Phone: 07990 505373

E-mail: royal_blue@lineone.net

Affiliation: NARTM, WHOTT

Brief Description: A private collection of vehicles, formerly operated by the Western & Southern National Omnibus Companies and their successors, spanning the years 1927 to 1985 many of which have undergone extensive restoration. A particular feature is a collection of Royal Blue coaches which can be seen regularly recreating bygone coach travel to the West Country along the old coach routes. Vehicles also regularly attend rallies and running days.

Opening days/times: Viewing by prior arrangements only

Registration	Date	Chassis	Body	New to	Fleet No	Status
VW 203	1927	Leyland Lion PLSC3	Mumford B—R	National Omnibus & Transport Co	2407	A
YF 714	1927	Guy FBB	Vickers B32R	Great Western Railway	1268	RP
RU 8805	1929	AEC Reliance	Beadle C28R	Elliot Bros (Royal Blue)		A
FJ 8967	1933	Bristol H5G	BBW B—R	Western National Omnibus Co	137	RP
BTA 59	1934	Dennis Mace	Eastern Counties B26F	Southern National Omnibus Co	668	R
FTA 634	1941	Bristol K5G	ECW L27/28R	Western National Omnibus Co	345	RP
JUO 983	1948	Bristol LL6B	ECW FB39F	Southern National Omnibus Co	1218	RP
LTA 748	1950	Bedford OB	Duple C27F	Southern National Omnibus Co (Royal Blue)	1409	RP
LTA 946	1950	Bristol KS6B	ECW L27/28R	Southern National Omnibus Co	1836	RP
LTA 729	1951	Bristol LL6B	Duple C37F	Western National Omnibus Co (Royal Blue)	1250	R
MOD 973	1952	Bristol LS6G	ECW C39F	Southern National Omnibus Co (Royal Blue)	1286	RP
RTT 996	1954	Bristol Lodekka LD6B	ECW H33/27RD	Southern National Omnibus Co	1876	A
519 BTA	1960	Bristol Lodekka FS6G	ECW H33/27RD	Western National Omnibus Co	1967	A
672 COD	1960	Bristol SUS4A	ECW B30F	Western National Omnibus Co	600	R
468 FTT	1960	Bristol Lodekka FLF6G	ECW H38/30F	Western National Omnibus Co	1969	R
JVS 293	1961	Bristol MW6G	ECW C39F	Western National Omnibus Co	2266	A
286 KTA	1962	Bristol SUL4A	ECW C37F	Southern National Omnibus Co	1234	R
BOD 25C	1965	Bristol Lodekka FLF6B	ECW H38/32F	Southern National Omnibus Co	2065	RP
EDV 555D	1966	Bristol SUL4A	ECW B36F	Southern National Omnibus Co	692	RP
HDV 624E	1967	Bristol RELH6G	ECW C45F	Western National Omnibus Co (Royal Blue)	2365	R
MOD 823P	1976	Leyland National 11351A/1R	Leyland National B50F	Western National Omnibus Co	2820	R
XDV 608S	1978	Bristol VRTSL3/6LXB	ECW H43/31F	Western National Omnibus Co	1128	RP
AFJ 708T	1978	Leyland National 11351A/1R	Leyland National B50F	Western National Omnibus Co	2869	R
AFJ 729T	1979	Bristol LH6L	Plaxton C43F	Western National Omnibus Co	3309	A
FDV 790V	1979	Bristol LHS6L	ECW B35F	Western National Omnibus Co	1560	R
FDV 803V	1980	Leyland Leopard PSU3E/4R	Plaxton C45Ft	Western National Omnibus Co	3547	R
LFJ 847W	1980	Bristol VRTSL3/6LXB	ECW H43/31F	Western National Omnibus Co	1203	RP
A686 KDV	1983	Leyland Olympian ONLXB/1R	ECW H45/32F	Devon General Ltd	1814	R
C862 DYD	1985	Ford Transit 190D	Dormobile B16F	Southern National Ltd	300	R

Notes:

VW 203	new with Strachan & Brown B32R body; rebodied 1936
RU 8805	rebodied 1935
FJ 8967	re-engined 1939; rebodied 1942
FTA 634	body rebuilt by ECW in 1941 following bomb damage
JUO 983	rebodied 1958
LTA 946	repatriated from USA in 2002
JVS 293	originally registered 55 GUO
AFJ 708T	converted to B21D + cycles in 1994
A686 KDV	last bus chassis built by Bristol

County Durham Bus Preservation Group

Contact address: 38 Lambton Drive, Heton-le-Hole, Houghton-le-Spring, Tyne & Wear DH5 0EW

E-mail: enquiries.cdbpg@hotmail.co.uk

Affiliation: NARTM

Brief description: The group comprises individuals who own a number of restored vehicles and are in the process of restoring others. The collection is not normally open to the public but may be viewed by prior arrangement

Registration	Date	Chassis	Body	New to	Fleet No	Status
BTN 113	1934	Daimler COS4	Northern Coachbuilders B34R	Newcastle Corporation	173	A
HHN 202	1947	Bristol L5G	ECW B35R	United Automobile Services	BG216	R
HUP 236	1948	Albion Valiant CX39N	ACB C33F	Economic Bus Service of Whitburn	W7	R
LVK 123	1948	Leyland Titan PD2/1	Leyland H30/26R	Newcastle Corporation	123	A
NVK 341	1950	AEC Regent III 9612A	Northern Coachbuilders H30/26R	Newcastle Corporation	341	R
344 XUK	1954	AEC Reliance MU3RV	Roe C41C	Roe (demonstrator)		RP
TUP 859	1956	AEC Regent V MD3RV	Roe H35/28R	Hartlepool Corporation	4	RP
YPT 796	1958	AEC Reliance MU3RV	Roe C41C	Economic Bus Service of Whitburn	W3	R
221 JVK	1962	Leyland Atlantean PDR1/1	Alexander H44/34F	Newcastle Corporation	221	R
EUP 405B	1964	AEC Routemaster 3R2RH	Park Royal H41/31F	Northern General Transport Co	2105	R
FBR 53D	1966	Leyland Panther PSUR/1R	Strachans B47D	Sunderland Corporation	53	R
VOD 101K	1971	Bristol RELL6G	ECW B53F	Western National Omnibus Co	2758	RP
GBB 524K	1972	Leyland Atlantean PDR1A/1	Alexander H48/30D	Tyneside PTE	688	RP
ETY 91L	1972	Daimler Fleetline CRL6	ECW H45/27D	Tyneside Omnibus Co	91L	A
GGR 103N	1974	Leyland Atlantean AN68/2R	Northern Counties H47/36F	OK Motor Services of Bishop Auckland		RP
VPT 598R	1977	Leyland National 11351A/1R	Leyland National B49F	Northern General Transport Co	4598	RP
JPT 906T	1979	Bristol VRTSL3/501	ECW DPH41/29F	Northern General Transport Co	3406	RP
SGR 935V	1979	Bristol VRTSL3/501	ECW H43/31F	Northern General Transport Co	3435	RP
SPT 963V	1980	Leyland Leopard PSU3E/4R	Plaxton C53F	OK Motor Services of Bishop Auckland		RP
AUP 369W	1980	Leyland Atlantean AN68B/1R	Roe H43/30F	Northern General Transport Co	3469	RP
FTN 708W	1981	Leyland National 2 NL116AL11/1R	Leyland National B49F	Northern General Transport Co	4708	RP
UTN 501Y	1983	MCW Metrobus DR102/37	MCW H46/31F	Northern General Transport Co	3501	RP
B207 GNL	1985	Ford Transit 190D	Alexander B16F	Northern General Transport Co	207	A
C771 OCN	1986	MCW Metrobus DR102/55	MCW H46/31F	Northern General Transport Co	3771	A
G251 SRG	1989	DAFSB220LC550	Optare DP48F	Northumbria Motor Services	251	R

Notes:

HHN 202   rebodied 1957 with 1946 body; passed to Durham District Services (DB216) in 1959

344 XUK   originally registered TUG 20

JPT 906T   originally H43/31F

Dave Rogers Collection

Contact E-mail: citybusdave@aol.com

Affiliation: NARTM, Leyland Society

Brief Description: Located near Swindon, the collection represents a passion for Leyland buses and coaches of the 1980s and for vehicles from Hong Kong. Leyland Olympian EUI 530 was the first tri-axle bus returned from Hong Kong to the UK.

Registration	Date	Chassis	Body	New to	Fleet No	Status
UWW 7X	1982	Leyland Olympian ONLXB/1R	Roe H47/29F	West Yorkshire PTE	5007	RP
EUI 530	1983	Leyland Olympian ONTL11/2R	ECW CH49/22F	Leyland (development vehicle)		R
XSU 913	1984	Leyland Olympian ONTL11/2RSp	ECW CH47/30D	South Yorkshire PTE	100	A
D5 CTB	1985	Leyland Olympian ONTL11/3R	ECW CH55/41F	Leyland (demonstrator)		R
E48 TYG	1988	Leyland Royal Tiger Doyen	Leyland C53F	West Riding Automobile Co	48	R
ET 778	1991	Leyland Olympian ON3R49C18Z4	Alexander CH53/41F	Citybus, Hong Kong	152	RP

Notes:

EUI 530	tri-axle chassis fitted with Gardner 6LXCT engine; sold in 1985 to Citybus, Hong Kong (C51), registered DE 4281
XSU 913	built for Ebdon's Tours of Sidcup but delivered in 1986 to South Yorkshire PTE, registered 4475 WE
D5 CTB	tri-axle chassis built as demonstrator for Indonesia but not used; sold in 1987 to Citybus, Hong Kong (C61), registered DU 5866 and later fitted with a Cummins L10 engine
ET 778	Hong Kong registration

Dennis Bus Owners' Association

Contact web site: www.dennisbusowners.co.uk

E-mail: secretary@dennisbusowners.co.uk

Affiliation: NARTM

Brief description: The Association is the focal point for owners and enthusiasts, offering advice and information to assist in the preservation and restoration of buses built by Dennis Bros of Guildford. The vehicles listed are some of those which are preserved. Other Dennis vehicles are listed in the collections of the Aldershot & District Bus Interest Group, Amberley Working Museum, Bounty Country Buses, Buckland Omnibus Co, Cobham Bus Museum, Dover Transport Museum, East Kent Road Car Heritage Trust, Leicester Corporation Bus Preservation Group, Oxford Bus Museum, SELNEC collection, the TH Collection, the Trolleybus Museum at Sandtoft and others. Membership is open to all Dennis bus owners and others interested in the make, details being published on the web site.

Registration	Date	Chassis	Body	New to	Fleet No	Status
CC 8671	1929	Dennis GL	Roberts T19	Llandudno UDC	2	R
MJ 4549	1932	Dennis Lancet I	Short B32F	Smith of Westoning		R
DL 9015	1934	Dennis Ace	Harrington B20F	Southern Vectis Omnibus Co	405	RP
YD 9533	1934	Dennis Ace	Dennis B20F	Southern National Omnibus Co	3560	R
JA 5506	1935	Dennis Lancet I	Eastern Counties B31R	North Western Road Car Co	706	RP
JG 8720	1937	Dennis Lancet II	Park Royal B35R	East Kent Road Car Co		RP
FUF 181	1939	Dennis Falcon	Harrington B30C	Southdown Motor Services	81	A
CFN 154	1948	Dennis Lancet III	Park Royal B31R	East Kent Road Car Co		R
CFN 121	1949	Dennis Lancet III	Park Royal B35R	East Kent Road Car Co		A
EFN 568	1950	Dennis Falcon	Dennis B20F	East Kent Road Car Co		R
EFN 584	1950	Dennis Lancet III	Park Royal C32F	East Kent Road Car Co		A
JDC 599	1958	Dennis Loline	Northern Counties H36/31RD	Middlesbrough Corporation	99	R
RDB 872	1964	Dennis Loline III	Alexander H39/32F	North Western Road Car Co	872	RP
GRD 576D	1966	Dennis Loline III	East Lancs H38/30F	Reading Corporation	76	R
EBB 846W	1980	Dennis Dominator SD130A	Angloco	Tyne & Wear Metropolitan Fire Brigade	319	R
C41 HDT	1985	Dennis Domino SDA1202	Optare B33F	South Yorkshire PTE	41	RP
C46 HDT	1985	Dennis Domino SDA1202	Optare B33F	South Yorkshire PTE	46	RP
C877 JWE	1985	Dennis Dominator DDA910	Alexander H—/—F	South Yorkshire PTE	2457	RP
note da	1989	Dennis Dart 9SDL3002	Duple B39F	Hestair Duple (test vehicle)		A

Notes:

JG 8720	rebodied 1949	note da	unregistered
CFN 154	originally B35R	C877 JWE	originally H46/32F
EBB 846W	Fire Incident Unit		

The Devon General Society

Contact address: 23 Barrack Road, Exeter EX2 5ED

Web site: www.devongeneral.org.uk

Brief description: The Devon General Society was formed in 1982 to promote interest in the former Devon General company and its successors, also to stimulate the preservation of all aspects of the company's past for the benefit of future generations. Approximately 35 former Devon General vehicles are currently preserved privately by society members, The society actively assists them and regularly stages events in Devon whereby these vehicles can be enjoyed.

Events planned: Please see web site

Registration	Date	Chassis	Body	New to	Fleet No	Status
ETT 995	1937	AEC Regent O661	Saunders-Roe H30/26R	Devon General Omnibus & Touring Co	DR705	RP
LTA 629	1950	AEC Regal III 9621A	Duple C32F	Devon General O&TC (Grey Cars)	TCR629	R
NTT 661	1952	AEC Regent III 9613A	Weymann H30/26R	Devon General O&TC	DR661	R
DDV 446	1953	AEC Regent III O662	Weymann H32/26R	Devon General O&TC	DR716	A
ROD 765	1956	AEC Regent V MD3RV	Metro-Cammell H33/26RD	Devon General O&TC	DRD765	R
VDV 798	1957	AEC Reliance MU3RA	Weymann B41F	Devon General O&TC	SR798	A
VDV 817	1957	AEC Regent V MD3RV	Metro-Cammell H33/26R	Devon General O&TC	DR817	R
XTA 839	1958	Albion Nimbus NS3N	Willowbrook B31F	Devon General O&TC	SN839	R
XUO 721	1958	Bristol MW6G	ECW B41F	Western National Omnibus Co (Royal Blue)	2238	R
872 ATA	1959	Leyland Atlantean PDR1/1	Metro-Cammell H44/32F	Devon General O&TC	DL872	RP
913 DTT	1960	Leyland Atlantean PDR1/1	Roe H43/31F	Devon General O&TC	DL913	R
ABV 669A	1961	Leyland Atlantean PDR1/1	Metro-Cammell CO44/31F	Devon General O&TC	DL927	RP
928 GTA	1961	Leyland Atlantean PDR1/1	Metro-Cammell CO44/31F	Devon General O&TC	DL928	RP
931 GTA	1961	Leyland Atlantean PDR1/1	Metro-Cammell O44/31F	Devon General O&TC	DL931	R
932 GTA	1961	Leyland Atlantean PDR1/1	Metro-Cammell CO44/31F	Devon General O&TC	DL932	R
935 GTA	1961	AEC Reliance 2MU3RV	Willowbrook C41F	Devon General O&TC (Grey Cars)	TCR935	R
960 HTT	1962	AEC Reliance 2MU3RV	Willowbrook C41F	Devon General O&TC (Grey Cars)	TCR960	R
1 RDV	1964	AEC Reliance 2MU3RA	Harrington C41F	Devon General O&TC (Grey Cars)	1	R
9 RDV	1964	AEC Reliance 2U3RA	Marshall B49F	Devon General O&TC	9	R
CTT 23C	1965	AEC Reliance 2MU3RA	Park Royal B39F	Devon General O&TC	23	R
CTT 513C	1965	AEC Regent V 2D3RA	Park Royal H40/29F	Devon General O&TC	513	R
CTT 518C	1965	AEC Regent V 2MD3RA	Willowbrook H33/28F	Devon General O&TC	518	R
EOD 524D	1966	AEC Regent V 2D3RA	Metro-Cammell H34/25F	Devon General O&TC	524	R
NDV 537G	1968	Leyland Atlantean PDR1/1	MCW H44/31F	Devon General O&TC	537	R
TUO 74J	1970	AEC Reliance 6MU3R	Willowbrook B41F	Devon General O&TC	74	R
VOD 545K	1971	Bristol VRTSL6LX	ECW H39/31F	Western National Omnibus Co (Devon General)	545	RP
VOD 550K	1971	Bristol VRTSL6LX	ECW H39/31F	Western National Omnibus Co (Devon General)	550	RP
VOD 88K	1972	Bristol LHS6L	Marshall B33F	Western National Omnibus Co (Devon General)	88	R
ATA 563L	1973	Bristol VRTSL6LX	ECW H43/31F	Western National Omnibus Co (Devon General)	563	R
VDV 123S	1978	Bristol VRTSL3/6LXB	ECW H43/31F	Western National Omnibus Co (Devon General)	584	A
A680 KDV	1983	Leyland Olympian ONLXB/1R	ECW H45/32F	Devon General Ltd	1804	R
C526 FFJ	1986	Ford Transit 190D	Carlyle B16F	Devon General Ltd	526	R
C760 FFJ	1986	Ford Transit 190D	Carlyle B16F	Devon General Ltd	760	R

Notes:

ETT 995	rebuilt 1953 using prewar mechanical components and rebodied
XUO 721	originally C39F Royal Blue coach; rebuilt 1973 as bus numbered 2902 in Devon General fleet
ABV 669A	originally registered 927 GTA
931 GTA	originally CO44/31F
1 RDV	7ft 6in wide
CTT 513C	restored by the Oxford Bus Museum Trust

Dewsbury Bus Museum

Contact address: 5 Oakenshaw Street, Agbrigg, Wakefield WF1 5BT

Phone: 01924 258314

Website: www.dewsburybusmuseum.co.uk

Affiliation: NARTM

Brief description: The group was formed in the early 1970s and concentrated on ex-West Riding vehicles. By 1989 the collection had grown and, to provide covered accommodation, a new, 14-vehicle shed was erected. Vehicles can be seen at local events, or on site by appointment. Opening days/times: Open only on rally days and when work is being done on vehicles (please enquire before visiting).

Events planned:

8 March 2009 — Transport Collectors Fair

8 November 2009 — Transport Collectors Fair

Other information: Other events are being planned — please see enthusiast press for details.

Registration	Date	Chassis	Body	New to	Fleet No	Status
CCX 801	1945	Guy Arab II	Roe L27/26R	County Motors of Lepton	70	A
BHL 682	1948	Leyland Titan PD2/1	Leyland L27/26R	West Riding Automobile Co	640	RP
TWY 8	1950	Albion CX39N	Roe L27/26RD	South Yorkshire Motors of Pontefract	81	RP
EHL 344	1952	Leyland Tiger PS2/12A	Roe B39F	West Riding Automobile Co	733	R
JHL 708	1956	AEC Reliance MU3RV	Roe B44F	West Riding Automobile Co	808	RP
LEN 101	1960	Guy Wulfrunian	(chassis only)	Bury Corporation	101	A
UCX 275	1961	Guy Wulfrunian	Roe H43/32F	County Motors of Lepton	99	RP
PJX 35	1962	Leyland Leopard L1	Weymann B44F	Halifax Corporation	35	R
WHL 970	1963	Guy Wulfrunian	Roe H43/32F	West Riding Automobile Co	970	RP
CUV 208C	1965	AEC Routemaster R2RH	Park Royal H36/28R	London Transport	RM2208	R
JJD 524D	1966	AEC Routemaster R2RH/1	Park Royal H40/32R	London Transport	RML2524	RP
NWW 89E	1967	Leyland Leopard L1	Willowbrook B45F	Todmorden Joint Omnibus Committee	9	R
LHL 164F	1967	Leyland Panther PSUR1/1	Roe B51F	West Riding Automobile Co	164	R
MCK 229J	1971	Leyland Panther PSUR1B/1R	Pennine B47D	Preston Corporation	229	RP
WEX 685M	1973	AEC Swift 3MP2R	ECW B43D	Great Yarmouth Corporation	85	R
XUA 73X	1982	Leyland National 2 NL116AL11/1R	Leyland National B49F	West Riding Automobile Co	73	RP
D901 MWR	1987	Volkswagen LT55	Optare DP21F	Yorkshire Rider	1700	R

Notes:

CCX 801	rebodied 1953
TWY 8	originally registered JWT 112; rebodied and re-registered in 1958
XUA 73X	Gardner engine fitted c12/87

East Kent Road Car Heritage Trust

Contact address: 33 Alfred Road, Dover, Kent, CT16 2AD

Phone/Fax: 01304 204612

Brief Description: Between them the trust members have 18 former East Kent buses and coaches, based at various locations. A museum is planned, but in the meantime the vehicles can be seen by the public at rallies and on running days.

Registration	Date	Chassis	Body	New to	Fleet No	Status
CJG 959	1947	Leyland Titan PD1A	Leyland L27/26R	East Kent Road Car Co		A
EFN 592	1950	Dennis Lancet III	Park Royal C32F	East Kent Road Car Co		R
FFN 399	1951	Guy Arab III	Park Royal H32/26R	East Kent Road Car Co		R
MLL 570	1951	AEC Regal IV 9821LT	Metro-Cammell B39F	London Transport	RF183	RP
GFN 273	1952	Beadle-Leyland	Beadle C35F	East Kent Road Car Co		R
KFN 239	1955	AEC Reliance MU3RV	Weymann DP41F	East Kent Road Car Co		RP
MFN 898	1956	Guy Arab IV	Park Royal H33/28RD	East Kent Road Car Co		RP
PFN 867	1959	AEC Regent V 2LD3RA	Park Royal FH40/32F	East Kent Road Car Co		R
6801 FN	1961	AEC Regent V 2D3RA	Park Royal H40/32F	East Kent Road Car Co		R
YJG 807	1962	AEC Bridgemaster 2B3RA	Park Royal H43/29F	East Kent Road Car Co		R
AFN 780B	1963	AEC Regent V 2D3RA	Park Royal H40/30F	East Kent Road Car Co		R
AFN 488B	1964	AEC Reliance 2MU4RA	Duple C34F	East Kent Road Car Co		RP
DJG 619C	1965	AEC Reliance 2U3RA	Park Royal C49F	East Kent Road Car Co		A
OFN 721F	1968	AEC Reliance 6U3ZR	Marshall B53F	East Kent Road Car Co		RP
VJG 187J	1970	AEC Swift 5P2R	Marshall B51F	East Kent Road Car Co		R
EFN 178L	1973	Leyland National 1151/1R/2402	Leyland National B25DI	East Kent Road Car Co		R
NFN 84R	1977	Leyland National 11351A/1R	Leyland National DP48F	East Kent Road Car Co	1084	RP
RVB 977S	1978	Bristol VRTSL3/6LXB	Willowbrook O43/27F	East Kent Road Car Co	7977	R
TFN 980T	1978	Bristol VRTSL3/6LXB	Willowbrook H43/31F	East Kent Road Car Co	7980	R
SKL 681X	1981	Bristol VRTSL3/6LXB	ECW H43/31F	East Kent Road Car Co	7681	R

Notes:

GFN 273   running units ex Leyland TD5 AJG 30, new 1939

EFN 178L   originally B49F

RVB 977S   originally H43/31F, converted to open-top in 1981 following low-bridge accident and renumbered 0977

Eastern Transport Collection Society
Attleborough

Phone: 01603 891284

Affiliation: NARTM

Brief description: The collection includes a number of vehicles owned by the society and members, together with a range of bus memorabilia bequeathed by the late Tony Powell together with other items added by the society. Viewing is by appointment only.

Events planned: 6 September 2009 — Norwich Bus Rally.

Opening days/times: By appointment only.

Charges: Free admission but donations welcome.

Registration	Date	Chassis	Body	New to	Fleet No	Status
KNG 718	1950	Bristol LL5G	ECW B39F	Eastern Counties Omnibus Co	LL718	R
NAH 941	1952	Bristol KSW5G	ECW H32/28R	Eastern Counties Omnibus Co	LKH341	RP
MXX 481	1953	AEC Regal IV 9821LT	Metro-Cammell B41F	London Transport	RF504	R
OVF 229	1954	Bristol Lodekka LD5G	ECW H33/25RD	Eastern Counties Omnibus Co	LKD229	R
KDB 696	1957	Leyland Tiger Cub PSUC1/1	Weymann B44F	North Western Road Car Co	696	R

Registration	Date	Chassis	Body	New to	Fleet No	Status
5789 AH	1959	Bristol MW5G	ECW C39F	Eastern Counties Omnibus Co	LS789	R
675 OCV	1962	Bedford SB3	Duple C41F	Crimson Tours of St Ives		R
MOO 177	1962	Bristol MW6G	ECW B45F	Eastern National Omnibus Co	556	RP
KVF 658E	1967	Bristol RESL6G	ECW B46F	Eastern Counties Omnibus Co	RS658	R
PBJ 2F	1967	Leyland Titan PD2/47	Massey H34/28R	Lowestoft Corporation	12	RP
OCK 988K	1972	Bristol VRTSL6LX	ECW H39/31F	Ribble Motor Services	1988	RP
RRM 148M	1973	Leyland National 1151/1R/2308	Leyland National DP51F	Leyland Vehicles (demonstrator)		R
NAH 135P	1976	Bristol VRTSL3/501	ECW H43/31F	Eastern Counties Omnibus Co	VR172	RP
RGS 598R	1977	Bedford YMT	Duple C57F	Tricentrol Coaches of Dunstable		RP
CVF 31T	1979	Bristol VRTSL3/6LXB	ECW H43/31F	Great Yarmouth Borough Council	31	RP
H74 ANG	1990	Dennis Condor DDA1810	Duple Metsec H69/41D	China Motor Bus (Hong Kong)	DM17	R

Notes:

MOO 177	renumbered 1356 in 1964
OCK 988K	acquired by Eastern Counties Omnibus Co (VR378) in 1985
RRM 148M	Suburban Express demonstrator
H74 ANG	registered ES 997 in Hong Kong

Ensign Bus Museum

Contact address: Ensignbus, Jubilee Close, Purfleet, RM15 4YF

Telephone: 01708 865656

Affiliation: NARTM

Brief description: The collection is based on ex-London types, the emphasis being to keep vehicles to Class VI condition, enabling regular operation on heritage services. A number of buses have been successfully repatriated from overseas and Ensign continue to seek rare or unusual ex-London types.

Registration	Date	Chassis	Body	New to	Fleet No	Status
ED 6141	1930	Leyland Titan TD1	Massey H28/26R	Warrington Corporation	22	A
KR 1728	1930	Leyland Titan TD1	Short H48R	Maidstone & District Motor Services	321	A
KJ 2578	1931	Leyland Titan TD1	Weymann	Redcar Motor Services of Tunbridge Wells		A
KR 8385	1931	Leyland Tiger TS2	Burlingham B34F	Maidstone & District Motor Services	665	RP
BXD 628	1935	Leyland Cub KPO3	Short B20F	London Transport	C4	A
ELP 223	1938	AEC Regal O662	LPTB C33F	London Transport	T499	RP
FXT 183	1940	AEC Regent III O661	LPTB H30/26R	London Transport	RT8	RP
HLJ 44	1948	Bristol K6A	ECW L27/28R	Hants & Dorset Motor Services	TD895	R
JXC 432	1948	AEC Regent III O961	Weymann H30/26R	London Transport	RT624	R
JXC 194	1949	AEC Regent III O961	Cravens H30/26R	London Transport	RT1431	R
KGK 758	1949	AEC Regent III O961	Cravens H30/26R	London Transport	RT1499	R
KYY 961	1950	AEC Regent III O961	Weymann H30/26R	London Transport	RT3232	R
MXX 261	1952	AEC Regent III 9613E	Weymann L27/26R	London Transport	RLH61	R
MLL 735	1953	AEC Regal IV 9822E	Park Royal RC39C	British European Airways		A
NLE 603	1953	AEC Regal IV 9821LT	Metro-Cammell B39F	London Transport	RF603	A
NXP 775	1954	AEC Regent III O961	Weymann H30/26R	London Transport	RT4421	R
KGK 708	1954	AEC Regent III O961	Saunders H30/26R	London Transport	RT4686	A
5280 NW	1959	Leyland Titan PD3/5	Roe H38/32R	Leeds City Transport	280	R
VLT 25	1959	AEC Routemaster R2RH	Park Royal H36/28R	London Transport	RM25	R
LDS 279A	1959	AEC Routemaster R2RH	Park Royal H36/28R	London Transport	RM54	R
799 DYE	1963	AEC Routemaster R2RH	Park Royal H36/28R	London Transport	RM1799	R
BCJ 710B	1964	Leyland Tiger Cub PSUC1/12	Harrington C45F	Wye Valley of Hereford		R
CRU 184C	1965	Daimler Fleetline CRG6LX	Weymann O43/31F	Bournemouth Corporation	184	A
CUV 220C	1965	AEC Routemaster R2RH/1	Park Royal H36/29RD	London Transport	RCL2220	R
CUV 226C	1965	AEC Routemaster R2RH/1	Park Royal H36/29RD	London Transport	RCL2226	RP

Registration	Date	Chassis	Body	New to	Fleet No	Status
KTJ 204C	1965	Leyland Titan PD2/37	East Lancs H37/28F	Lancaster City Transport	204	R
JJD 405D	1966	AEC Routemaster R2RH/1	Park Royal H36/28R	London Transport	RML2405	R
NMY 655E	1967	AEC Routemaster R2RH/2	Park Royal H32/24F	British European Airways	RMA58	R
SMM 90F	1968	AEC Swift 3P2R	MCW B45D	London Transport	MB90	A
EGP 33J	1970	Daimler Fleetline CRG6LXB	Park Royal O45/23F	London Transport	DMS33	R
THX 646S	1978	Leyland Fleetline FE30ALRSp	Park Royal H44/27D	London Transport	DM2646	R
THX 101S	1978	MCW Metrobus DR101/3	MCW H43/28D	London Transport	M1	R
A249 SVW	1984	Leyland Tiger TRCTL11/3RP	Duple C57F	Southend Transport	249	A
B115 ORU	1984	MCW Metroliner DR130/3	MCW O—/—F	Shamrock & Rambler Coaches	3115	A
F292 NHJ	1988	MCW Metrobus DR102/71	MCW H46/31F	Ensignbus	292	A

Notes:

KJ 2578	originally H24/24R; converted to canteen by Liverpool Corporation (CL4)
KR 8385	fitted with utility body 1943
HLJ 44	loaned to London Transport when new
KGK 708	originally registered NXP 971; now fitted with 1950 body and to be restored as RT1239
LDS 279A	originally registered VLT 54
CRU 184C	originally CO43/31F; acquired by London Transport (DMO3) in 1977
NMY 655E	acquired by London Transport (RMA58) in 1979
EGP 33J	originally H44/24D
THX 646S	fitted with Iveco engine 1988-96
B115 ORU	originally CH55/27F
F292 NHJ	originally H46/27D; later renumbered 192

Friends of King Alfred Buses

Contact address: Dean Court, Hillside Close, Winchester SO22 5LW

E-mail: info@fokab.org.uk

Web site: www.fokab.org.uk

Affiliation: NARTM

Brief description: The collection includes 12 former King Alfred Motor Services vehicles that have been rescued from around the world and restored. A charitable trust, FoKAB aims eventually to establish a museum. In the meantime, the vehicles can be viewed at the annual running day and other events.

Events planned: 1 Jan 2010 — Annual running day in and around Winchester.

Registration	Date	Chassis	Body	New to	Fleet No	Status
OU 9286	1931	Dennis 30cwt	Short B18F	King Alfred Motor Services		R
JAA 708	1950	Leyland Olympic HR40	Weymann B40F	King Alfred Motor Services		RP
POU 494	1956	Leyland Titan PD2/24	East Lancs L27/28R	King Alfred Motor Services		R
WCG 104	1959	Leyland Tiger Cub PSUC1/1	Weymann B45F	King Alfred Motor Services		R
326 CAA	1961	Bedford SB3	Harrington C41F	King Alfred Motor Services		R
595 LCG	1964	AEC Renown 3B2RA	Park Royal H43/31F	King Alfred Motor Services		R
596 LCG	1964	AEC Renown 3B2RA	Park Royal H43/31F	King Alfred Motor Services		R
BHO 543C	1965	Bedford CAL230	Martin Walker B11	H. R. Richmond of Epsom		A
CCG 704C	1965	Bedford VAL14	Plaxton C49F	King Alfred Motor Services		R
HOR 590E	1967	Leyland Atlantean PDR1/2	Roe O43/31F	King Alfred Motor Services		R
HOR 592E	1967	Leyland Atlantean PDR1/2	Roe H43/33F	King Alfred Motor Services		R
UOU 417H	1970	Leyland Panther PSUR1A/1R	Plaxton B52F	King Alfred Motor Services		R
UOU 419H	1970	Leyland Panther PSUR1A/1R	Plaxton B52F	King Alfred Motor Services		R
NKJ 849P	1976	Commer Karrier KC6055	Rootes B22F	Enham Village Disabled Transport		R

Notes:

JAA 708	recovered from Republic of Ireland where registered BIC 670
POU 494	repatriated from USA 1993

596 LCG	repatriated from USA 1988	
BHO 543C	acquired by King Alfred in 1967; to be restored to King Alfred condition	
CCG 704C	body ex LAL 547E	
HOR 590E	originally H43/33F; acquired by Bristol Omnibus Co (8602) and converted to open-top in 1979	
HOR 592E	acquired by Bristol Omnibus Co (8600) and converted to open-top in 1979; restored using roof from sister vehicle HOR 591E	
NKJ 849P	mobile display vehicle	

Glasgow Vintage Vehicle Trust

Contact address: 76 Fordneuk Street, Glasgow G40 3AH

Museum address: Fordneuk Street, Glasgow G40 3AH

Phone: 0141 554 0544

E-mail: info@gvvt.org

Web site: www.gvvt.org

Affiliation: NARTM, Museums Galleries Scotland

Brief description: Established in a former Glasgow Corporation bus garage.

Opening days/times: Telephone for access information. Prior arrangement only.

Directions by car: From City centre follow London Road eastbound.

Directions by public transport: First Glasgow 43 or 64 from City centre. SPT rail network to Bridgeton station

Events planned: 28 June 2009 — West End Festival Vintage Bus Service
11 October 2009 — Open Day. Please see enthusiast press or web site for details for both

Facilities: B(e), D, T

Registration	Date	Chassis	Body	New to	Fleet No	Status
ES 5150	1922	Albion C20	Harvey B20F	Tighanloan Hotel at Fearnan		R
WG 2373	1934	Leyland Lion LT5B	Burlingham B35F	W. Alexander & Sons	P169	R
WG 4445	1937	Leyland Tiger TS7	Alexander C35F	W. Alexander & Sons	P331	A
BUS 181	1938	AEC Regent O661	Scottish Commercial	Glasgow Corporation	AR292	R
CRG 811	1947	Daimler CVD6	Alexander C35F	Aberdeen Corporation	11	A
CRS 834	1948	Daimler CVD6	Walker / Aberdeen CT C31F	Aberdeen Corporation	14	A
GUS 926	1949	Maudslay Marathon III	Park Royal C35F	MacBrayne	136	R
CHL 772	1950	Daimler CVD6	Willowbrook DP35F	Bullock of Featherstone		R
FVA 854	1950	Albion Valiant CX39N	Duple C33F	Hutchisons of Overtown		R
HGG 359	1950	Thornycroft HF/ER4	Croft B20F	MacBrayne	149	R
DBY 001	1953	Fordson ET7	Barbara B31F	(unknown) Malta		RP
6769	1955	Albion Victor FT39AN	Heaver B35F	Guernsey Railway Co	55	RP
NSF 757	1956	Leyland Titan PD2/20	Metro-Cammell H34/29R	Edinburgh Corporation	757	A
JPA 82V	1957	Albion Victor FT39KAN	Heaver B35F	Guernsey Motor Co	72	RP
KAG 856	1957	Leyland Titan PD2/20	Alexander L31/28R	Western SMT Co	D1375	A
YTS 916A	1957	AEC Reliance MU3RV	Alexander DP41F	W. Alexander & Sons	AC102	A
TVS 367	1958	Bristol Lodekka LD6G	ECW H33/27R	Central SMT Co	B87	R
FYS 999	1958	Daimler CVD6-30	Alexander H41/32R	Glasgow Corporation	D217	R
SGD 65	1958	Leyland Titan PD2/24	Alexander H33/28R	Glasgow Corporation	L163	R
FYS 8	1959	Leyland Titan PD2/24	Glasgow Corporation O29/28R	Glasgow Corporation	L108	R
MSD 407	1959	Leyland Titan PD3/3	Alexander L35/32RD	Western SMT Co	D1543	RP
MSD 408	1959	Leyland Titan PD3/3	Alexander L35/32RD	Western SMT Co	D1544	R
NMS 358	1960	AEC Reliance 2MU3RV	Alexander C41F	W. Alexander & Sons	AC147	R
YYS 174	1960	Bedford C5Z1	Duple C21FM	David MacBrayne of Glasgow	54	R
198 CUS	1961	AEC Reliance 2MU3RA	Duple (Midland) C41F	MacBrayne	63	R
RAG 400	1961	Bristol Lodekka LD6G	ECW H33/27RD	Western SMT Co	B1634	A
SGD 448	1961	Leyland Titan PD3/2	Alexander H41/31F	Glasgow Corporation	L446	R
SGD 500	1961	AEC Regent V 2D2RA	Alexander H41/31F	Glasgow Corporation	A350	RP
BJX 848C	1965	Bedford VAS1	Duple C29F	Abbeyways of Halifax		A
CUV 121C	1965	AEC Routemaster	Park Royal H36/28R	London Transport	RM2121	R

Registration	Date	Chassis	Body	New to	Fleet No	Status
DMS 348C	1965	Leyland Leopard PSU3/3R	Alexander	W. Alexander & Sons (Midland)	MPE62	R
GYS 896D	1966	Leyland Atlantean PDR1/1	Alexander H44/34F	Glasgow Corporation	LA320	R
HGA 983D	1966	Bedford VAS1	Willowbrook B24FM	David MacBrayne of Glasgow	210	R
GRS 334E	1967	Albion Viking VK43AL	Alexander DP40F	W. Alexander & Sons (Northern)	NNV34	A
HFR 501E	1967	Leyland Titan PD3A/1	MCW H41/30R	Blackpool Corporation	501	R
HGM 346E	1967	Bristol Lodekka FLF6G	ECW H44/34F	Central SMT Co	BL346	R
JMS 452E	1967	Albion Viking VK43AL	Alexander DP40F	W. Alexander & Sons (Midland)	MNV37	RP
MGB 286E	1967	Bedford SB5	Plaxton C41F	David MacBrayne of Glasgow	168	RP
NDL 375G	1969	Bedford VAM70	Duple C45F	Paul of Ryde	12	R
VMP 10G	1969	AEC Reliance 6U3ZR	Alexander DP57F	Road Transport Industry Training Board		R
NRG 26H	1969	AEC Swift 2MP2R	Alexander B43D	Aberdeen Corporation	26	A
XGA 15J	1970	Leyland Atlantean PDR1A/1	Alexander H45/29F	Glasgow Corporation	LA517	RP
WSD 756K	1972	Leyland Leopard PSU3/3R	Alexander -	Western SMT Co	L2366	R
XGM 450L	1972	Leyland Leopard PSU3/3R	Alexander B53F	Central SMT Co	T150	R
NMS 576M	1973	Leyland Leopard PSU3/3R	Alexander B53F	W. Alexander & Sons (Midland)	MPE176	A
SCS 335M	1974	Leyland Leopard PSU3/3R	Alexander C49F	Western SMT Co	L2466	R
VSB 164M	1974	Bedford YRT	Plaxton B60F	Craig ('West Coast Motors') of Campbeltown		RP
CST 703N	1974	Ford R1114	Alexander B53F	Highland Omnibuses	T93	RP
JGA 189N	1975	Leyland Atlantean AN68/1R	Alexander H45/31F	Greater Glasgow PTE	LA907	R
JUS 774N	1975	Leyland Atlantean AN68/1R	Alexander H45/31F	Greater Glasgow PTE	LA927	RP
MSF 122P	1975	Leyland Leopard PSU3C/4R	Alexander C49F	Lothian Region Transport	122	A
MSJ 385P	1976	Seddon Pennine VII	Alexander C24FI	Western SMT Co	S2579	RP
OJD 903R	1977	Leyland National 10351A/2R	Leyland National B36D	London Transport	LS103	R
RSD 973R	1977	Seddon Pennine VII	Alexander C49F	Western SMT Co	S2670	RP
SSN 248S	1977	Volvo Ailsa B55-10	Alexander H44/35F	Tayside Regional Council	248	RP
XUS 575S	1977	Leyland Atlantean AN68A/1R	Alexander H—/—F	Greater Glasgow PTE	LA1204	RP
EFS 229S	1978	Leyland Leopard PSU3E/4R	Alexander C49F	Lothian Region Transport	229	R
TSJ 47S	1978	Leyland Leopard PSU3D/4R	Alexander B53F	Western SMT Co	L2747	RP
VHB 678S	1978	Bristol VRTSL3/501	ECW O43/31F	National Welsh Omnibus Services	HR4378	A
SAS 859T	1978	Leyland Fleetline FE30AGR	ECW H43/32F	Highland Omnibuses	D17	RP
WTS 270T	1979	Volvo Ailsa B55-10	Alexander H44/31D	Tayside Regional Council	270	A
EMS 362V	1980	Leyland Leopard PSU3E/4R	Alexander C49F	W. Alexander & Sons (Midland)	MPE362	R
GSO 80V	1980	Leyland Leopard PSU3E/4R	Alexander B53F	W. Alexander & Sons (Northern)	NPE80	R
HSD 86V	1980	Leyland Fleetline FE30AGR	Alexander H44/31F	Western SMT Co	R86	R
UHG 141V	1980	Leyland Atlantean AN68A/2R	Alexander H49/36F	Preston Borough Transport	141	R
FSL 615W	1980	Bedford YMQ	Plaxton C45F	Henderson Coaltown of Markinch		R
LMS 168W	1980	Leyland Fleetline FE30AGR	Alexander H44/31F	W. Alexander & Sons (Midland)	MRF168	R
RMS 400W	1981	Leyland Leopard PSU3F/4R	Alexander C49F	W. Alexander & Sons (Midland)	MPE400	R
UGB 196W	1981	Leyland Atlantean AN68A/1R	Alexander H45/33F	Strathclyde PTE	LA1443	RP
SSA 5X	1981	Leyland Olympian ONLXB/1R	Alexander H45/32F	W. Alexander & Sons (Northern)	NLO5	R
FGE 423X	1982	Dennis Dominator DD137B	Alexander H45/34F	Central SMT Co	D23	RP
KYV 781X	1982	MCW Metrobus DR101/14	MCW H43/28D	London Transport	M781	R
TSO 16X	1982	Leyland Olympian ONLXB/1R	ECW H45/32F	W. Alexander & Sons (Northern)	NLO16	R
FLD 447Y	1982	Bedford YMP	Plaxton C35F	Bonas of Coventry		RP
RSC 194Y	1982	Leyland Leopard PSU3G/4R	Alexander C49F	W. Alexander & Sons (Fife)	FPE194	R
ALS 102Y	1983	Leyland Tiger TRBTL11/2R	Alexander C49F	W. Alexander & Sons (Midland)	MPT102	RP
MNS 10Y	1983	Leyland Tiger TRBTL11/2R	Alexander C49F	Central SMT Co	LT10	RP
A735 PSU	1983	Volvo Ailsa B55-10 Mk III	Alexander H44/35F	Strathclyde PTE	A109	RP
47638	1984	Ford R1015	Wadham Stringer B45F	Jersey Motor Transport Co	23	RP
B177 FFS	1985	Volvo Citybus B10M-50	Alexander H47/37F	W. Alexander & Sons (Fife)	FRA77	A
B100 PKS	1985	MCW Metrobus DR132/6	Alexander H45/33F	W. Alexander & Sons (Midland)	MRM100	R
D902 CSH	1987	Leyland Olympian ONTL11/1RH	Alexander DPH43/27F	Lowland Scottish Omnibuses	902	R
E186 BNS	1988	MCW Metrorider MF154/12	MCW B33F	Strathclyde Buses	M89	R
G545 RDS	1990	Volvo Citybus B10M-50	Alexander H47/37F	Strathclyde Buses	AH101	A
G571 PNS	1990	Leyland Roadrunner	Wright B28FI	Strathclyde Regional Council	23189	RP

Golcar Transport Collection

Contact address: 45 Cowlersley Lane, Cowlersley, Huddersfield HD4 5TZ

Affiliation: NARTM

Brief description: A unique collection of Karrier vehicles, most of which are long-term restoration projects. The collection includes a WL6 six-wheeled saloon with clerestory-roofed body built by English Electric.

Opening days/times: Collection opens to coincide with craft weekends at the Colne Valley Museum; can be opened at other times by prior arrangement.

Registration	Date	Chassis	Body	New to	Fleet No	Status
note v	1922	Karrier	(unknown) B20F	(unknown)		A
WT 9156	1925	Karrier JH	Strachan & Brown B26F	Premier Transport of Keighley		RP
DY 5029	1928	Karrier JKL	London Lorries C26D	A. Timpson & Son of Catford	117	A
TE 5780	1928	Karrier WL6	English Electric B32F	Ashton-under-Lyne Corporation	8	RP
VH 2088	1929	Karrier ZA	(unknown) B14F			RP
RB 4757	1932	Commer Centaur	Reeve & Kenning B14D	H. G. Fox of Alfreton		R
JC 5313	1938	Guy Wolf	Waveney C20F	Llandudno UDC		R
14 PKR	1961	Karrier BFD	Plaxton C14F	W. Davis & Sons of Sevenoaks		A

Notes:

note v	unregistered solid-tyred disc-wheeled chassis
WT 9156	body originally on EH 4960
VH 2088	period body acquired from Anglesey
RB 4757	carries 1929 body from Ford AA chassis

Irish Transport Trust

Contact address: 14 Mayfields, Lisburn, Co Antrim, Northern Ireland BT28 3RP

Affiliation: NARTM

Website: www.ith.org.uk

Brief description: Formed in 1969, the Trust provides for the preservation, recording and information exchange on all aspects pertaining to road transport history, current and future matters. A number of vehicles both pre- and postwar have been restored by Trust members and the Trust itself has eight vehicles from more recent times which are typical of those operated by Ulsterbus and Citybus over most of their existance. After a number of false starts the trust is currently in the process of obtaining Limited Company and charitable status lading to the ultimate ambition of establishing a museum dedicated to road passenger transport in Northern Ireland.

Events planned: Annual bus and coach rally at Cultra, Co Down, at the site of the Ulster Folk & Transport Museum. For other events please refer to the enthusiast press and web site.

Registration	Date	Chassis	Body	New to	Fleet No	Status
FOI 1629	1973	Bristol LH6L	Alexander (Belfast) B45F	Ulsterbus	1629	R
OSJ 620R	1977	Leyland Leopard PSU3C/3R	Alexander B53F	Western SMT Co	L2620	R
SOI 3591	1978	Leyland Leopard PSU3A/4R	Alexander (Belfast) B53F	Ulsterbus	1591	R
VOI 8415	1980	Bristol RELL6G	Alexander (Belfast) B43D	Citybus	2415	R
AXI 2259	1982	Leyland Leopard PSU3E/4R	Wright C49F	Ulsterbus	259	R
BXI 2583	1982	Bristol RELL6G	Alexander (Belfast) B51F	Ulsterbus	2583	R
BXI 339	1982	Leyland Leopard PSU3F/4R	Alexander (Belfast) DP49F	Ulsterbus	339	R
DXI 3343	1984	Leyland Tiger TRBTL11/2RP	Alexander (Belfast) DP53F	Ulsterbus	343	R

Notes:

OSJ 620R	acquired by Ulsterbus (1886)
SOI 3591	chassis originally AOI 1347 of 1969; rebuilt 1974-8
VOI 8415	B32D+47 standing when new
AXI 2259	Wright Royale body

John Shearman Collection

Phone: 01892 534067

E-mail: johnshearmanbuses@hotmail.com

Brief description: A private collection which includes vehicles representing traditional British double-deckers designed for export markets.

Opening days/times: Vehicles attend rallies every summer.

Registration	Date	Chassis	Body	New to	Fleet No	Status
LEV 917	1946	Leyland Titan PD1/1	Alexander O33/26R	City Coach Co of Brentwood	LD1	R
KSV 102	1954	AEC Regent III 9631E	Weymann H37/28R	CARRIS (Lisbon)	255	R
ABW 225D	1966	AEC Regent V 2D2RA	Metal Sections H51/39D	Kowloon Motor Bus (Hong Kong)	A165	R

Notes:

LEV 917	originally H30/26R, converted to open-top in 1958; restored as Eastern National 2102 with support of the Springhill Vehicle Preservation Group
KSV 102	originally H32/26R, with Portuguese registration GB-21-07; restored with support of CARRIS AEC Preservation Group
ABW 225D	originally H50/28D, with Hong Kong registration AD 7156; restored with support of KMB and on display at the Oxford Bus Museum

Kelvin Amos Collection

Contact address: 30 Blandford Close, Nailsea, Bristol BS48 2QQ

Brief description: The vehicles in the collection are regularly shown and run on free bus services.

Registration	Date	Chassis	Body	New to	Fleet No	Status
LHT 911	1948	Bristol L5G	BBW B35R	Bristol Tramways & Carriage Co	2388	R
KED 546F	1968	Leyland Panther Cub PSURC1	East Lancs B41D	Warrington Corporation	92	R
PWS 492S	1977	Leyland Leopard PSU3E/4R	Plaxton C49F	Bristol Omnibus Co	2098	R

Notes:

LHT 911	rebodied 1958 with 1950 body
PWS 492S	rebodied 1983 with Paramount body after fire

Kent Heritage Bus Collection

Contact: 6 Chelsfield House, Queen's Avenue, Maidstone, ME16 0EP

Brief description: From its beginnings in 1967 the main emphasis has been to secure for preservation a good cross-section of the important passenger models constructed by Tilling-Stevens of Maidstone backed by a general archive of their activities. Local body builders, Short Bros of Rochester and Beadle of Dartford are also represented. The early years of Maidstone & District Motor Services are another special interest. To this end, rare examples operated by the company during its first 50 years (1911-61) have been secured.

Opening days/times: Viewing by prior arrangements only.

Registration	Date	Chassis	Body	New to	Fleet No	Status
KL 7796	1925	Tilling-Stevens TS6 Petrol-Electric	Short O51RO	Maidstone & District Motor Services	73	RP
KO 117	1927	Tilling-Stevens B9A Express	(chassis only)	Maidstone & District Motor Services	425	A
KO 54	1927	Albion PM28	Beadle B—R	Redcar Services of Tunbridge Wells	A54	A
DX 7657	1928	Tilling-Stevens B10B2 Express	(chassis only)	Eastern Counties Roadcar Co	P113	R
KO 7311	1928	Tilling-Stevens B9A Express	Short B31R	Maidstone & District Motor Services	461	RP
JG 669	1930	Tilling-Stevens B10C2 Express	Brush B37R	East Kent Road Car Co		R
JG 691	1930	Tilling-Stevens B10C2 Express	Brush B37R	East Kent Road Car Co		A
OU 7951	1931	Tilling-Stevens B10A2 Express	(chassis only)	Aldershot & District Traction Co	TS15	A
LKT 991	1950	Bristol L6A	ECW B35R	Maidstone & District Motor Services	SO43	R

Notes:
KO 54   originally B30R; exhibited at Amberley Working Museum as example of prewar holiday home
KO 7311   body reconstructed from original using original parts

Lancashire United Transport Society

Contact address: Secretary, 45 Tarn Drive, Bury, Lancashire, BL9 9QB

E-mail: secretary@lancashireunited.org.uk

Web: www.lancashireunited.org.uk

Affiliation: NARTM

Brief dscription: Representing the history of former Lancashire United Transport, the largest independent operator in the country.

Events planned: Please refer to web site for details.

Registration	Date	Chassis	Body	New to	Fleet No	Status
6219 TF	1963	Guy Arab IV	Northern Counties H41/32R	Lancashire United Transport	135	RP
HTJ 522B	1964	Guy Arab V	Northern Counties H41/32F	Lancashire United Transport	167	R
EIB 8234	1970	Bristol LH6L	Northern Counties B39D	Lancashire United Transport	335	A
LTE 491P	1976	Leyland Leopard PSU3C/4R	Plaxton B48F	Lancashire United Transport	440	R
PTD 655S	1978	Leyland Fleetline FE30AGR	Northern Counties H43/32F	Lancashire United Transport	511	R
TWH 689T	1978	Leyland Leopard PSU3E/4R	Plaxton C51F	Lancashire United Transport	541	A
124 YTW	1980	Volvo B58-61	Plaxton C53F	Lancashire United Transport	616	A

Notes:
EIB 8234   originally registered UTD 298H
124 YTW   originally registered DEN 245W

Lancastrian Transport Trust

Contact address: Apt. 11, Admiral Heights, 164 Queens Promenade, Blackpool FY2 9GJ

E-mail: philip@ltt.org.uk

Web site: www.ltt.org.uk

Brief description: The Trust is dedicated to preserving historic buses from Fylde Coast. Vehicles can often be seen at local rallies and other events. Open days held at Blackpool based vehicle restoration workshops. The Lancashire Transport trust also has a growing tramcar collection

Membership details: Support organisation is TransSupport with a £12 annual membership fee. Quarterly magazine published *In Trust*.

Registration	Date	Chassis	Body	New to	Fleet No	Status
GTB 903	1946	Leyland Titan PD1	Leyland H30/26R	Lytham St Annes Corporation	19	R
CCK 663	1949	Leyland Titan PD2/3	Brush L27/26R	Ribble Motor Services	2687	A
DFV 146	1949	Leyland Titan PD2/5	Burlingham FH31/23C	Blackpool Corporation	246	A
JCK 530	1956	Leyland Titan PD2/12	Burlingham H33/28RD	Ribble Motor Services	1455	RP
760 CTD	1957	Leyland Titan PD2/20	Northern Counties H30/28R	Lytham St Annes Corporation	61	A
PFR 346	1959	Leyland Titan PD2/27	Metro-Cammell FH35/28RD	Blackpool Corporation	346	A
534 RTB	1961	Guy Arab IV	Metro-Cammell H41/32R	Lancashire United Transport	43	R
561 TD	1962	Daimler Fleetline CRG6LX	Northern Counties H43/33F	Lancashire United Transport	97	R
583 CLT	1962	AEC Routemaster 2R2RH	Park Royal H36/28R	London Transport	RM1583	R
RRN 405	1962	Leyland Atlantean PDR1/1	Metro-Cammell L38/33F	Ribble Motor Services	1805	RP
YFR 351	1962	Leyland Titan PD3/1	Metro Cammell FH41/32R	Blackpool Corporation	351	A
CTF 627B	1964	Leyland Titan PD2A/27	Massey H37/27F	Lytham St Annes Corporation	70	R
CUV 290C	1965	AEC Routemaster R2RH/1	Park Royal H40/32R	London Transport	RML2290	R
HFR 512E	1967	Leyland Titan PD3A/1	MCW H41/30R	Blackpool Corporation	512	R
HFR 516E	1967	Leyland Titan PD3A/1	MCW H41/30R	Blackpool Corporation	516	R
SMK 734F	1967	AEC Routemaster R2RH/1	Park Royal H40/32R	London Transport	RML2734	R
LFR 529F	1968	Leyland Titan PD3/11	MCW H41/30R	Blackpool Corporation	529	R
LFR 540G	1968	Leyland Titan PD3/11	MCW H41/30R	Blackpool Corporation	540	A
PFR 554H	1970	AEC Swift MP2R	Marshall B47D	Blackpool Corporation	554	R
ATD 281J	1971	Leyland Atlantean PDR1A/1	Northern Counties H44/33F	Lytham St Annes Corporation	77	R
OCK 995K	1972	Bristol VRTSL6LX	ECW O39/31F	Ribble Motor Services	1995	RP
OCK 997K	1972	Bristol VRTSL6LX	ECW H39/31F	Ribble Motor Services	1997	RP
STJ 847L	1972	Seddon RU	Pennine B51F	Lytham St Annes Corporation	47	A
OFR 970M	1974	AEC Swift 3MP2R	Marshall B47D	Blackpool Corporation	570	R
HRN 99N	1975	Leyland Atlantean AN68/1R	Willowbrook H43/31F	Fylde Borough Transport	79	RP
NRN 397P	1976	Leyland Atlantean AN68/1R	Park Royal H43/30F	Ribble Motor Services	1397	RP
OJI 4371	1977	Leyland Atlantean AN68A/1R	Northern Counties H43/31F	Fylde Borough Transport	85	R
AHG 334V	1980	Leyland Atlantean AN68A/2R	East Lancs H50/36F	Blackpool Transport	334	RP
NKU 214X	1982	Dennis Dominator DDA133	Alexander H47/33F	South Yorkshire PTE	2214	R
F575 RCW	1988	Volkswagen LT55	Optare B21F	Blackpool Transport	575	R

Notes:

583 CLT	acquired by Blackpool Transport (521) in 1986; preserved in Blackpool livery
CTF 627B	on loan from North West Museum of Road Transport
HFR 516E	preserved as driver-training bus
OCK 995K	originally H39/31F; converted to open-top in 1985
HRN 99N	body built on Northern Counties frames
OJI 4371	originally registered EBV 85S; renumbered 71 upon re-registration
NKU 214X	restored in traditional Doncaster Tramways livery, as applied when new

Legionnaire Group

Contact address: 66 Montfort Road, Strood, Rochester, Kent ME2 3EX

E-mail: bob.wingrove@btinternet.com

Brief description: The group aims to restore at least one of each combination of chassis/Legionnaire so that Harrington's last body style is represented in preservation.

Registration	Date	Chassis	Body	New to	Fleet No	Status
SPU 985	1951	Leyland Olympic HR44	Weymann DP44F	Jennings Coaches of Ashen		RP
72 MMJ	1964	Bedford VAL14	Harrington C52F	Reliance Coaches of Meppershall	72	RP
CDK 409C	1965	Bedford VAL14	Harrington C52F	Yelloway Motor Services of Rochdale		A
JNK 681C	1965	Ford Thames 36 676E	Harrington C52F	Capital Coaches of London		RP

Notes:
JNK 681C   used as Harrington demonstrator when new

Leicester Transport Heritage trust

Contact address: 13 Warren Road, Enderby, Leicester LE19 2DR

Phone: 0116 2751642 or 07891 071908

Affiliation: NARTM

Brief description: The LTHT caters for people interested in recording, preserving and promoting Leicester's transport heritage, a number of vehicles from the area being in the collection.

Registration	Date	Chassis	Body	New to	Fleet No	Status
FJF 193	1950	Leyland Titan PD2/1	Leyland H30/26R	Leicester City Transport	154	R
GAY 171	1950	Leyland Tiger PS1/1	Willowbrook DP35F	Allen of Mountsorrel	43	RP
OJF 191	1956	Leyland Tiger Cub PSUC1/1	Weymann B44F	Leicester City Transport	191	A
217 AJF	1961	AEC Bridgemaster B3RA	Park Royal H76R	Leicester City Transport	217	RP
90 HBC	1964	Leyland Titan PD3A/1	East Lancs H41/33R	Leicester City Transport	90	RP
DBC 190C	1965	AEC Renown 3B3RA	East Lancs H44/31F	Leicester City Transport	190	R
FJF 40D	1966	AEC Renown 3B3RA	East Lancs H43/31R	Leicester City Transport	40	RP
GRY 48D	1966	Leyland Titan PD3A/1	Metro-Cammell H41/33R	Leicester City Transport	48	RP
PBC 98G	1968	Leyland Atlantean PDR1A/1	ECW H43/31F	Leicester City Transport	98	A
PBC 113G	1969	Leyland Atlantean PDR1A/1	Park Royal H43/31F	Leicester City Transport	113	A
TRY 122H	1969	Bristol RELL6L	ECW B47D	Leicester City Transport	122	RP
ARY 225K	1972	Scania BR111MH	MCW B46D	Leicester City Transport	225	R
GJF 301N	1975	Scania BR111DH	MCW H45/28D	Leicester City Transport	301	R
UFP 175S	1977	Scania BR111DH	MCW H44/31F	Leicester City Transport	175	A
UFP 233S	1977	Dennis Dominator DD101	East Lancs H43/33F	Leicester City Transport	233	A
FUT 240V	1979	Dennis Dominator DD120	East Lancs H43/33F	Leicester City Transport	240	RP
TBC 50X	1981	Dennis Dominator DDA141	East Lancs H43/33F	Leicester City Transport	50	RP

Notes:
ARY 225K   exhibited at Earl's Court in 1972

London Transport Museum Depot
Acton

Contact address: London Transport Museum, 39 Wellington Street, London WC2E 7BB.

Depot address: 2 Museum Way, 118-120 Gunnersbury Lane, Acton, London W3 8BQ.

Phone: 020 7565 7299 — 24hr recorded information; 020 7379 6344 — Admin etc

Fax: 020 7565 7250

E-mail: enquiry@ltmuseum.co.uk

Web site: www.ltmuseum.co.uk

Affiliation: HRA, NARTM, TT

Brief description:
The Depot is a working museum store and treasure trove of over 370,000 objects. Attractions include rare road and rail vehicles, station models, signs, ticket machines, posters and original artwork.

Depot location: 2 Museum Way, 118-120 Gunnersbury Lane, Acton, London W3 8BQ

Opening days/times: Please contact for details.

Access by public transport: Tube: Acton Town
Bus: to Acton Town

Car parking: On site parking is reserved for Blue Badge holders and must be requested in advance. Parking available for groups booking a private view.

Facilities for the disabled: Full disabled access including toilets

Charges: Guided Tours — Adult £10, Concession £8.50

Facilities: L S (weekends only)

Registration	Date	Chassis	Body	New to	Fleet No	Status
note p	1888	Horse bus	LGOC -26-	London General Omnibus Co		R
LC 3701	1906	De Dion	(chassis only)	London General Omnibus Co	L7	R
XC 8059	1921	AEC K	LGOC O24/22RO	London General Omnibus Co	K424	R
MN 2615	1923	Tilling-Stevens TS3A Petrol-Electric	(chassis only)	Douglas Corporation	10	R
XM 7399	1923	AEC S	LGOC O28/26RO	London General Omnibus Co	S742	R
YR 3844	1926	AEC NS	LGOC H28/24RO	London General Omnibus Co	NS1995	R
GK 3192	1931	AEC Regent 661	LGOC H28/20R	London General Omnibus Co	ST821	R
GK 5323	1931	AEC Renown 663	LGOC H33/23R	London General Omnibus Co	LT165	R
GK 5486	1931	AEC Regal 662	Duple C30F	London General Omnibus Co	T219	R
GO 5198	1931	AEC Renown 664	LGOC B35F	London General Omnibus Co	LT1076	R
HX 2756+	1931	AEC 663T	UCC H32/24R	London United Tramways	1	R
AXM 649	1934	AEC Regent 661	Chalmers -	London Transport	830J	R
AYV 651	1934	AEC Regent 661	LPTB H30/26R	London Transport	STL469	R
BXD 576	1935	AEC Q O762	Birmingham RC&W B35C	London Transport	Q55	R
CLE 122	1936	Leyland Cub KP03	Weymann B20F	London Transport	C94	R
HYM 768+	1948	BUT 9641T	Metro-Cammell H40/30R	London Transport	1768	R
MXX 364	1953	Guy Special NLLVP	ECW B26F	London Transport	GS64	R
NLE 537	1953	AEC Regal IV 9821LT	Metro-Cammell B39F	London Transport	RF537	R
NXP 997	1954	AEC Regent III O961	Park Royal H30/26R	London Transport	RT4712	R
OLD 589	1954	AEC Regent III O961	Park Royal H30/26R	London Transport	RT4825	R
SLT 56	1954	AEC Routemaster	Park Royal/LTE H36/28R	London Transport	RM1	R
SLT 57	1955	AEC Routemaster	Park Royal/LTE H36/28R	London Transport	RM2	RP
CUV 229C	1965	AEC Routemaster R2RH/1	Park Royal H36/29RD	London Transport	RCL2229	R
KGY 4D	1966	AEC Routemaster FR2R	Park Royal H41/31F	London Transport	FRM1	R
AML 582H	1969	AEC Swift 4P2R	MCW B25D	London Transport	MBA582	R
KJD 401P	1976	Bristol LH6L	ECW B39F	London Transport	BL1	A
TPJ 61S	1977	Bristol LHS6L	ECW B35F	London Country Bus Services	BN61	R
NUW 567Y	1982	Leyland Titan TNLXB/2RR	Leyland H44/24D	London Transport	T567	R
C526 DYT	1986	Volkswagen LT55	Optare B25F	London Buses	OV2	R
F115 PHM	1988	Volvo B10M-50	Alexander H46/29D	Grey-Green, London	115	R
note r	1993	Optare MetroRider	Optare B26F	London Transport Museum	MRL242	R

+ trolleybus

Notes:

note p	unregistered; 'garden seat' type
AXM 649	rebuilt with breakdown-vehicle body in 1950
SLT 56	prototype; first registered 1956
SLT 57	prototype; first registered 1957
TPJ 61S	support vehicle
note r	unregistered sectioned exhibit built especially for LT Museum

Medstead Depot Omnibus Group

Contact address: Hon Secretary, Medstead Depot Omnibus Group, c/o InterPower House, Windsor Way, Aldershot, Hants GU11 1JG.

Affiliation: NARTM, WOMP, Aldershot & District Bus Interest Group, Aldershot & District Omnibuses Rescue & Restoration Society, Southampton & District Transport Heritage Trust. MDOG is a part of the Working Omnibus Museum Project (WOMP), which is a registered charity.

Brief description: Vehicles from the Medstead Depot Omnibus Group are regularly to be seen at shows and rallies throughout the season. In addition to the vehicles listed, others belonging to members of the Aldershot & District Bus Interest Groups and the Southampton & District Transport Heritage Trust are associated with the Group and stored on site from time to time. There is an open day once per year, associated with the Mid-Hants Railway and Alton Bus Rally. This year's rally will be held on Sunday 19 July.

Events planned: Free bus services between Alton station and Chawton. Services will operate on the following dates in 2009: Sundays 3 May, 7 June, 5 July, 2 August and 6 September. Seats may be limited on busy days

Registration	Date	Chassis	Body	New to	Fleet No	Status
JRX 823	1955	Bristol KSW6B	ECW L27/28R	Thames Valley Traction Co	748	R
TDL 998	1960	Bristol Lodekka FS6G	ECW H33/27R	Southern Vectis Omnibus Co	565	R
RCP 237	1962	AEC Regent V 2D3RA	Northern Counties H39/32F	Hebble Motor Services	619	A
YDL 315	1962	Bristol Lodekka FS6G	ECW H33/27RD	Southern Vectis Omnibus Co	570	R
KHC 367	1963	AEC Regent V 2D3RV	East Lancs H32/28R	Eastbourne Corporation	67	R

Merseyside Transport Trust

Contact address: The Secretary, Merseyside Transport Trust, Carlton House, 17-19 Carlton Street, Liverpool L3 7ED

E-mail: info@mttrust,co,uk

Web site: www.mttrust.co.uk

Affiliation: NARTM

Brief description: The MTT's collection of former Liverpool Corporation buses, ranging from one of the first postwar AECs right through to the last bus delivered to the Corporation in 1969, is probably the country's most representative preserved collection from a municipal bus fleet. The collection also includes a growing number of buses from the Merseyside Passenger Transport Executive (MPTE) fleet which operated most of the bus services on Merseyside between December 1969 and October 1986 and the MPTE's successors Merseybus. In addition to these, there is a small number of former Crosville Motor Services buses, Crosville being at one time one of the largest operators on Merseyside.

Registration	Date	Chassis	Body	New to	Fleet No	Status
GKD 434	1946	AEC Regent II O661	Weymann/LCPT H30/26R	Liverpool Corporation	A233	A
JKC 178	1949	Daimler CVA6	Northern Counties H30/26R	Liverpool Corporation	D553	A
KMN 501	1949	Leyland Titan PD2/1	Leyland H30/26R	Isle of Man Road Services	71	A
KMN 519	1950	Leyland Comet CPO1	Park Royal B30F	Douglas Corporation	21	R
MKB 994	1952	AEC Regent III 9613A	Crossley H30/26R	Liverpool Corporation	A801	A
NKD 536	1953	AEC Regent III 9613S	Crossley H30/26R	Liverpool Corporation	A36	RP
NKD 540	1954	AEC Regent III 9613S	Saunders-Roe H32/26R	Liverpool Corporation	A40	RP

Registration	Date	Chassis	Body	New to	Fleet No	Status
RKC 262	1955	Leyland Titan PD2/20	Alexander H32/26R	Liverpool Corporation	L161	RP
SKB 168	1956	Leyland Royal Tiger PSU1/13	Crossley/MCW RC23/21F	Liverpool Corporation	XL171	RP
SKB 224	1956	Leyland Titan PD2/20	Crossley/LCPT H32/26R	Liverpool Corporation	L227	RP
VKB 711	1956	Leyland Titan PD2/20	Crossley H33/29R	Liverpool Corporation	L255	R
VKB 841	1957	Leyland Titan PD2/20	Crossley H33/29R	Liverpool Corporation	L320	A
VKB 900	1957	AEC Regent V D3RV	Metro-Cammell H33/29R	Liverpool Corporation	A267	R
116 TMD	1958	AEC Bridgemaster B3RA	Park Royal H43/33R	AEC (demonstrator)		A
371 BKA	1959	AEC Regent V LD3RA	Park Royal FH40/32F	Liverpool Corporation	E1	R
372 BKA	1959	Leyland Atlantean PDR1/1	Metro-Cammell H43/35F	Liverpool Corporation	E2	A
BHT 677A	1960	Leyland Atlantean PDR1/1	Metro-Cammell H44/339R	Wallasey Corporation	15	RP
256 SFM	1961	Bristol Lodekka FLF6B	ECW H38/22F	Crosville Motor Services	DFB43	A
875 VFM	1961	Bristol Lodekka FSF6G	ECW H34/26F	Crosville Motor Services	DFG65	A
501 KD	1962	Leyland Atlantean PDR1/1	Metro-Cammell H43/35F	Liverpool Corporation	L501	R
FKF 801D	1966	Leyland Atlantean PDR1/1	MCW H43/35F	Liverpool City Transport	L801	A
FKF 835E	1967	Leyland Atlantean PDR1/1	MCW H43/28D	Liverpool City Transport	L835	R
FKF 933G	1968	Leyland Panther PSUR1A/1R	MCW B47D	Liverpool City Transport	1054	R
SKB 695G	1969	Bristol RELL6G	Park Royal B45D	Liverpool City Transport	2025	R
UKA 562H	1969	Leyland Atlantean PDR2/1	Alexander H47/32D	Liverpool City Transport	1111	R
BKC 236K	1972	Leyland Atlantean PDR1A/1Sp	Alexander H43/32F	Merseyside PTE	1236	R
BKC 276K	1972	Leyland Atlantean PDR1A/1Sp	Alexander H43/32F	Merseyside PTE	1276	RP
CKC 308L	1972	Daimler Fleetline CRG6LXB	MCW H43/32F	Merseyside PTE	3008	A
DKC 330L	1972	Leyland Atlantean AN68/1R	Alexander H43/32F	Merseyside PTE	1330	A
VWM 83L	1973	Leyland Atlantean AN68/1R	Alexander H45/29D	Southport Corporation	83	R
OLV 551M	1974	Leyland Atlantean AN68/1R	Alexander O43/32F	Merseyside PTE	1551	A
GKA 74N	1975	Bristol VRTSL6LX	East Lancs H43/32F	Merseyside PTE	2122	A
MTJ 771S	1977	Leyland National 11351A/1R	Leyland National B49F	Merseyside PTE	1771	A
OEM 788S	1978	Leyland Atlantean AN68A/1R	MCW H43/32F	Merseyside PTE	1788	A
TWM 220V	1979	Leyland Atlantean AN68A/1R	East Lancs H45/33F	Merseyside PTE	1836	R
UKA 23V	1980	MCW Metrobus DR103/2	MCW H43/30F	Merseyside PTE	0023	A
VHF 57V	1980	Bedford YMT	Plaxton C49F	Toppings Coaches of Liverpool		A
WWM 904W	1980	Dennis Dominator DD120B	Willowbrook H45/33F	Merseyside PTE	0027	A
XLV 156W	1981	Leyland National 2 NL116L11/1R	Leyland National B49F	Merseyside PTE	6156	R
EKA 220Y	1982	Leyland Tiger TRCTL11/2R	Duple C49F	Merseyside PTE	7020	RP
A135 HLV	1984	Leyland Atlantean AN68D/1R	Alexander H43/32F	Merseyside PTE	1055	R
D685 SEM	1986	Dodge S56	Alexander B23F	Merseyside Transport	7685	RP
F261 YTJ	1989	Leyland Olympian ONCL10/1RZ	Northern Counties H47/30F	Merseyside Transport	261	RP

Notes

SKB 168	originally B40D, numbered SL171; rebuilt by Metro-Cammell in 1961
116 TMD	acquired by Liverpool Corporation (E3) in 1959
BHT 677A	originally registered HHF 15
FKF 835E	originally H43/35F; rebuilt by Pennine Coachcraft in 1969
OLV 551M	originally H43/32F
OEM 788S	privately owned; on loan to MTT

The Mike Sutcliffe Collection

Phone: 01525 221676

E-mail: sutcliffes@leylandman.co.uk

Web site: www.mikesutcliffe.com

Affiliation: NARTM; Leyland Society member; HCVS member

Brief description: A collection of 15 vehicles, mainly buses of Leyland manufacture from the period 1908 to 1934, this is the most significant collection of early motorbuses in the world, and includes the oldest British-built motorbus. Mike Sutcliffe was awarded the MBE in 2004 'for services to Motor Heritage'

Opening days/times: Viewing can be arranged by prior appointment only. There is no charge, but donations are welcome.

Registration	Date	Chassis	Body	New to	Fleet No	Status
LN 7270	1908	Leyland X2	Thomas Tilling O18/16RO	London Central Motor Omnibus Co	14	R
HE 12	1913	Leyland S3.30.T	Brush B27F	Barnsley & District Electric Traction Co	5	R
LF 9967	1913	Leyland S3.30.T	Birch O20/16RO	Wellingborough Motor Omnibus Co	H	R
CC 1087	1914	Leyland S4.36.T3	Leyland Ch32	London & North Western Railway	59	R
BD 209	1921	Leyland G7	Dodson Ch/B32D	United Counties Omnibus Co	B15	R
C 2367	1921	Leyland G	Phoenix O23/20RO	Todmorden Corporation	14	R
DM 2583	1923	Leyland SG7	Leyland FB40D	Brookes Bros ('White Rose') of Rhyl	27	R
XU 7498	1924	Leyland LB5	Dodson O26/22RO	Chocolate Express Omnibus Co	B6	R
PW 8605	1926	ADC 415	United B35F	United Automobile Services	E61	A
YG 7831	1934	Leyland Tiger TS6	Northern Counties	Todmorden Joint Omnibus Committee	15	RP

Notes:

LN 7270	body new 1906 on Milnes-Daimler chassis of Thomas Tilling; bought by London Central in 1908
LF 9967	on loan to British Commercial Vehicle Museum at Leyland
CC 1087	registered LP 8597 by War Office in 1915; re-registered XA 8086 in 1921, reverting to CC1087 in 1980
C 2367	on loan to Manchester Museum of Transport
BD 209	formerly a Dodson demonstrator; exhibited at Olympia Commercial Motor Show in 1921
YG 7831	originally B36R but later rebuilt as recovery vehicle; being restored as a bus

National Museum of Science and Industry
Science Museum, Swindon

Contact address: Science Museum Swindon, Wroughton, Swindon SW4 9LT

Phone: 01793 846200

E-mail: wroughton.enquiries@nmsi.ac.uk

Website: www.sciencemuseum.org.uk

Brief description: The bus collection is located at Science Museum Swindon, Wroughton, near Swindon, Wiltshire.

Opening days/times: By appointment only.

Directions by car: On A4361 approx 4 miles south of Swindon.

Directions by public transport: Publicised for Open Days

Charges: Published for each event.

Registration	Date	Chassis	Body	New to	Fleet No	Status
LMJ 653G	1913	FIAT 52B		(operator unknown)		RP
JCP 60F	1928	Leyland Lion PLSC1	Leyland B31F	Jersey Railways & Tramways		A
DR 4902	1929	Leyland Titan TD1	Leyland L51RO	National Omnibus & Transport Co	2849	A
DX 8871+	1930	Ransomes Sims & Jefferies D	Ransomes Sims & Jefferies B31D	Ipswich Corporation	44	A
GW 713	1931	Gilford 168OT	Weymann C30D	Valliant of Ealing		A
VO 6806	1931	AEC Regal 662	Cravens B32F	Red Bus of Mansfield		A
JN 5783	1935	AEC Q 762	(chassis only)	Westcliff-on-Sea Motor Services		A
CPM 61+	1939	AEC 661T	Weymann H28/26R	Brighton Hove & District	6340	A
HVF 455L	1940	Saurer CRD		GFM (Switzerland)	52	A
DHR 192	1943	Guy Arab II	Weymann UH30/26R	Swindon Corporation	51	A
KPT 909	1949	Leyland Titan PD2/1	Leyland L27/26R	Weardale Motor Services of Frosterley		R
HET 513	1953	Crossley DD42/7	Crossley H30/26R	Rotherham Corporation	213	A
NLP 645	1953	AEC Regal IV 9822E	Park Royal RDP37C	British European Airways	1035	A
OTT 55	1953	Bristol LS5G	ECW B41F	Southern National Omnibus Co	1701	A
OLJ 291	1954	Bedford CAV	Bedford B12	(non-PSV owner)		A
504 EBL	1963	Bedford VAL14	Duple C52F	Reliance Motor Services of Newbury	87	A
note u	1970	Moulton MD	Moulton C23F	Moulton (development vehicle)		A

Registration	Date	Chassis	Body	New to	Fleet No	Status
BCD 820L	1973	Leyland National 1151/1R/0102	Leyland National B49F	Southdown Motor Services	20	A
+ trolleybus						

Notes:

LMJ 653G	of Yugoslavian origin
JCP 60F	originally registered J 4601
HVF 455L	displays original Swiss registration FR1347
note u	eight-wheeled integral (unregistered)

North East Bus Preservation Trust Ltd

Contact address: The Secretary, 8 Seaburn Hill, Sunderland SR6 8BS

Phone: 0191 548 7367

E-mail: hines.a@sky.com

Affiliation: NARTM

Brief description: The collection is displayed at an 1826 former locomotive shed on the Bowes Railway, Gateshead. This accommodates up to 10 vehicles, and so vehicles rotate between this and other locations. If you wish to view a particular vehicle, you will need to mention this when making arrangements to view.

Opening days/times: Viewing by prior arrangement only.

Registration	Date	Chassis	Body	New to	Fleet No	Status
EX 1128	1924	Guy BB	United B26D	Great Yarmouth Corporation	30	A
KO 63	1927	Albion PM28	Vickers B—R	Redcar	A63	A
EE 8128	1928	Albion PM28	Tower Wagon	Grimsby Corporation	32	A
CN 4740	1931	SOS IM4	Short B34F	Northern General Transport Co	540	A
MV 8996	1931	Bedford WLB	Duple B20F	Howards of West Byfleet		R
CN 6100	1934	NGT SE6 (LSE4)	Short B44F	Northern General Transport Co	604	RP
DPT 848	1939	Leyland Tiger TS8	Roe B32F	Sunderland District Omnibus Co	159	R
EF 7380	1942	Leyland Titan TD7	Roe H26/22C	West Hartlepool Corporation	36	R
GSR 244	1943	Commer Q4	Scottish Aviation C29F	Meffan of Kirriemiur		RP
KTJ 502	1947	Leyland Tiger PS1	Burlingham B35F	Haslingden Corporation	2	RP
ABR 433	1949	Crossley DD42/7C	Crossley H30/26R	Sunderland Corporation	100	RP
CFK 340	1949	AEC Regal III 6821A	Burlingham C33F	H. & E. Burnham of Worcester		R
LYM 729	1951	AEC Regal IV 9621E	ECW C—F	Tillings Transport		RP
CBR 539	1952	Guy Arab III	Roe H33/25R	Sunderland Corporation	139	RP
PHN 831	1952	Bristol LS5G	ECW B45F	United Automobile Services	BU2	A
SHN 301	1952	AEC Regal IV 9821E	Burlingham C41C	Scotts Greys of Darlington	5	R
DCN 83	1953	Beadle-AEC	Beadle C35F	Northern General Transport Co	1483	RP
MWD 908	1953	Bedford SB	Duple C35F	Hill of Stockingford		RP
SPT 65	1955	Guy Arab LUF	Weymann B44F	Northern General Transport Co	1665	RP
UUA 212	1955	Leyland Titan PD2/11	Roe H33/25R	Leeds City Transport	212	R
JHL 701	1956	Bedford SBG	Plaxton C41F	Swan of Berwick		R
UFJ 292	1957	Guy Arab IV	Massey H30/26R	Exeter Corporation	52	R
WTS 708A	1957	Bristol LS5G	ECW B45F	United Automobile Services	BU250	A
AFT 930	1958	Leyland Titan PD3/4	Metro-Cammell H41/32R	Tynemouth & District Omnibus Co	230	RP
TCO 537	1960	Leyland Atlantean PDR1/1	Metro-Cammell H44/33F	Plymouth Corporation	137	R
204 UXJ	1961	AEC Routemaster 2R2RH	Park Royal H36/28R	London Transport	RM1058	R
8124 WX	1961	Bristol MW6G	ECW C39F	West Yorkshire Road Car Co	CUG27	R
6249 UP	1963	Leyland Leopard PSU3/3RT	Alexander DP51F	Venture Transport Co of Consett	249	RP
ACU 304B	1963	Leyland Leopard PSU3/3R	Plaxton B55F	Stanhope Motor Services		R
PCN 762	1964	AEC Routemaster 3R2RH	Park Royal H41/31F	Northern General Transport Co	2099	R
WBR 248	1964	Atkinson Alpha PM746HL	Marshall B45D	Sunderland Corporation	48	R
CUV 186C	1965	AEC Routemaster R2RH	Park Royal H36/28R	London Transport	RM2186	R
JJD 551D	1966	AEC Routemaster R2RH/1	Park Royal H40/32R	London Transport	RML2551	R

Registration	Date	Chassis	Body	New to	Fleet No	Status
ZV 1510	1966	Leyland Atlantean PDR1/1	Metro-Cammell O44/34F	Newcastle Corporation	118	A
ECU 201E	1967	Bristol RESL6L	ECW B45D	South Shields Corporation	1	R
SMK 686F	1967	AEC Routemaster R2RH/1	Park Royal H40/32R	London Transport	RML2686	R
SMK 732F	1967	AEC Routemaster R2RH/1	Park Royal H40/32R	London Transport	RML2732	R
VVK 149G	1969	Bedford J6	Nicolou B33D	(unknown) Cyprus		R
WHN 411G	1969	Bristol VRTSL6LX	ECW H39/31F	United Automobile Services	601	RP
WHA 237H	1970	Leyland Leopard PSU3A/4R	Plaxton	BMMO ('Midland Red')	6237	RP
GAN 744J	1971	Leyland Leopard PSU5/4RT	Plaxton C57F	Banfield Coaches of London		RP
GAN 745J	1971	Leyland Leopard PSU5/4RT	Plaxton C57F	Banfield Coaches of London		RP
PCW 203J	1971	Bristol RESL6L	Pennine B45F	Burnley, Colne & Nelson Joint Transport Committee	103	R
SWV 155J	1971	Daimler Fleetline CRG6LX	Northern Counties H—/—D	Swindon Corporation		RP
JPF 113K	1972	AEC Swift 3MP2R	Alexander DP45F	London Country Bus Services	SMA13	A
MCN 30K	1972	Leyland/NGT Tynesider	Metro-Cammell/NGT H39/29F	Northern General Transport Co	3000	R
NHN 250K	1972	Daimler Fleetline SRG6LX-36	Roe B48D	Darlington Corporation	50	R
BUP 736L	1973	Leyland Leopard PSU5/4R	Plaxton DP57F	Weardale Motor Services of Stanhope		RP
E901 DRG	1973	Bedford YRQ	Plaxton C45F	Smith of Langley Park		RP
TME 134M	1974	AEC Reliance 6MU4R	Plaxton C38C	Glenton Tours of London		A
JFT 228N	1974	Leyland Atlantean AN68/1R	Park Royal O43/34F	Gateshead & District Omnibus Co	211N	R
GUP 907N	1975	Bristol LH6L	ECW B43F	United Automobile Services	1623	R
E903 DRG	1975	Ford R1114	Plaxton C53F	Smith of Langley Park		RP
PPT 446P	1976	Leyland Leopard PSU3C/4R	Plaxton B55F	The Eden of West Auckland	43	RP
RFR 424P	1976	Leyland Atlantean AN68/1R	ECW H43/31F	Ribble Motor Services	1424	A
OCU 769R	1977	Scania BR111DH	MCW H45/29D	Tyne & Wear PTE	769	RP
OCU 807R	1977	Leyland Fleetline FE30AGR	Alexander H44/30F	Tyne & Wear PTE	807	RP
RCU 838S	1977	Leyland Fleetline FE30AGR	Alexander H44/30F	Tyne & Wear PTE	838	R
RCU 588S	1978	Leyland Atlantean AN68A/2R	Willowbrook H48/34F	Tyne & Wear PTE	588	RP
SCN 268S	1978	Leyland Atlantean AN68A/2R	Alexander H49/37F	Tyne & Wear PTE	268	R
JPT 901T	1978	Bristol VRTSL3/501	ECW H43/31F	Northern General Transport Co	3401	R
UVK 290T	1978	Leyland Atlantean AN68A/2R	Alexander H49/37F	Tyne & Wear PTE	290	R
UPT 681V	1980	Leyland National 2 NL116L11/1R	Leyland National B49F	Northern General Transport Co	4681	RP
EJR 110W	1980	Leyland Atlantean AN68A/2R	Alexander H49/37F	Tyne & Wear PTE	110	R
EJR 111W	1980	Leyland Atlantean AN68A/2R	Alexander H49/37F	Tyne & Wear PTE	111	R
FTN 710W	1981	Leyland National 2 NL116AL11/1R	Leyland National B49F	Northern General Transport Co	4710	R
PAJ 829X	1981	Bristol VRTSL3/6LXB	ECW H43/31F	United Automobile Services	829	RP
JFT 413X	1982	Scania BR112DH	Alexander H47/31F	Tyne & Wear PTE	413	R
C655 LFT	1986	Leyland Olympian ONLXB/1R	Alexander H45/31F	Tyne & Wear PTE	655	RP

Notes:

GSR 244	lengthened 1943 military chassis, bodied 1950
ABR 433	fitted with Gardner 5LW engine
WTS 708A	originally registered 650 CHN
OSK 831	originally registered 6666 U
ACU 304B	originally registered 6 MPT
PCN 762	originally registered RCN 699
ZV 1510	originally H44/34F, registered KBB 118D
VVK 149G	Cyprus registration TEC 598; fitted with replica body constructed 2003
WHA 237H	originally C49F; rebuilt as towing vehicle
SWV 155J	originally H44/27D
MCN 30K	rebuild of 1958 Leyland Titan PD3/4 new to Tyneside Tramways & Tramroads Co (49) registered NNL 49
E901 DRG	built 1973, stored until 1988
JFT 228N	originally H43/28D, registered RCN 111N; passed to Northern General Transport Co (3285) in 1976 and converted to open-top in 1986
E903 DRG	built 1975, stored until 1988
OCU 807R	originally H44/27D
RCU 838S	originally H44/27D

Peter Stanier Collection

Phone: 01474 814476

Brief description: A collection of preserved Leyland petrol-engined vehicles with their origins in the island of Jersey

Opening days/times: Not normally open for viewing. Arrangements to visit can be made, strictly by appointment, telephoning first for details

Registration	Date	Chassis	Body	New to	Fleet No	Status
DM 6228	1929	Leyland Lioness LTB1	Burlingham C26D	Brookes Bros of Rhyl	7	
SV 6107	1929	Leyland Titan TD1	Leyland L24/24R (1931)	Jersey Motor Transport Co	24	

Notes:

SV 6107   rebodied in 1934; originally registered J 1199

Ribble Vehicle Preservation Trust

Contact address: 37 Hall Park, Lancaster LA1 4SH

Affiliation: NARTM

Brief description: The Trust promotes the preservation and restoration of vehicles from Ribble and associated companies.

Registration	Date	Chassis	Body	New to	Fleet No	Status
CK 4474	1931	Leyland Tiger TS3	Leyland C26F	Ribble Motor Services	1117	A
RN 7588	1935	Leyland Tiger TS7	Burlingham B35F	Ribble Motor Services	209	RP
TJ 6760	1935	Leyland Lion LT5A	Leyland B32R	Lytham St Annes Corporation	24	RP
BTF 25	1937	Leyland Titan TD4c	Leyland FH30/24R	Lytham St Annes Corporation	45	A
RN 8622	1939	Leyland Titan TD5	Alexander L27/26R	Ribble Motor Services	2057	R
ACK 796	1944	Guy Arab II	Northern Counties / Bond L27/26R	Ribble Motor Services	2413	A
DRN 289	1950	Leyland Titan PD2/3	Leyland L27/26RD	Ribble Motor Services	1349	A
MTC 540	1950	AEC Regent III 9613E	Park Royal H30/26R	Morecambe & Heysham	72	RP
ERN 700	1952	Leyland Royal Tiger PSU1/13	Leyland B44F	Ribble Motor Services	377	RP
FCK 884	1954	Leyland Tiger Cub PSUC1/1T	Saunders Roe B44F	Ribble Motor Services	452	R
HRN 31	1955	Leyland Titan PD2/13	Metro-Cammell H33/28RD	Ribble Motor Services	1391	A
JFV 527	1955	Commer TS3	Harrington C41C	Abbott of Blackpool		A
JCK 542	1956	Leyland Titan PD2/12	Burlingham H33/28RD	Ribble Motor Services	1467	RP
528 CTF	1957	Leyland Titan PD2/40	Weymann L29/28RD	J. Fishwick & Sons of Leyland	5	R
881 BTF	1958	Leyland Titan PD2/41	East Lancs H35/28R	Lancaster City Transport	881	A
KCK 869	1958	Leyland Titan PD3/4	Burlingham FH41/31F	Ribble Motor Services	1523	A
MBN 177	1958	Leyland Titan PD3/5	East Lancs H41/33R	Bolton Corporation	122	RP
NRN 586	1960	Leyland Atlantean PDR1/1	Metro-Cammell H44/33F	Ribble Motor Services	1686	R
SFV 421	1960	Leyland Atlantean PDR1/1	Weymann CH34/16Ft	W. C. Standerwick	25	A
PCK 618	1961	Leyland Leopard L2	Harrington C32F	Ribble Motor Services	1036	R
PRN 145	1961	Leyland Atlantean PDR1/1	Metro-Cammell H44/33F	Scout Motor Services of Preston	5	A
PRN 906	1961	Leyland Titan PD3/4	Metro-Cammell H39/31F	Preston Corporation	14	A
RRN 428	1962	Leyland Atlantean PDR1/1	Weymann CH39/20F	Ribble Motor Services	1279	R
TCK 465	1963	Leyland Leopard PSU3/1R	Marshall B53F	Ribble Motor Services	465	A
TCK 726	1963	Leyland Leopard PSU3/3RT	Harrington C49F	Ribble Motor Services	726	A
TRN 731	1964	Leyland Leopard PSU3/3R	Plaxton C49F	W. C. Standerwick	731S	R
ARN 811C	1965	Leyland Leopard PSU3/3RT	Weymann DP49F	Ribble Motor Services	811	R
FPT 6G	1969	Leyland Leopard PSU3/3RT	Plaxton C51F	Stanhope Motor Services		A
LRN 321J	1970	Bristol RESL6L	Marshall B47F	Ribble Motor Services	321	A
NCK 106J	1971	Leyland Leopard PSU4B/4R	Plaxton C43F	Ribble Motor Services	1006	RP

Registration	Date	Chassis	Body	New to	Fleet No	Status
NCK 338J	1971	Bristol RESL6L	ECW B47F	Ribble Motor Services	338	R
PRN 79K	1972	Bristol VRLLH6L	ECW CH42/18Ct	W. C. Standerwick	79	A
PTF 714L	1972	Bristol RELH6L	ECW C49F	Ribble Motor Services	1019	A
PTF 718L	1972	Leyland National 1151/2R/0401	Leyland National B48D	Ribble Motor Services	372	A
PTF 727L	1972	Leyland National 1151/2R/0401	Leyland National B48D	Ribble Motor Services	386	R
UTF 732M	1974	Leyland Leopard PSU3B/4R	Duple C49F	Ribble Motor Services	1052	RP
MFR 306P	1976	Leyland Leopard PSU3C/2R	Alexander B53F	Lancaster City Council	306	R
XCW 955R	1978	Leyland National 11351A/1R	Leyland National B49F	J. Fishwick & Sons of Leyland	24	R
TRN 481V	1979	Leyland Atlantean AN68A/1R	ECW H43/31F	Ribble Motor Services	1481	R
DBV 100W	1980	Leyland Olympian ONLXB/1R	ECW H45/33F	Ribble Motor Services	2100	RP
DBV 831W	1980	Leyland National 2 NL106L11/1R	Leyland National B44F	Ribble Motor Services	831	R
B900 WRN	1984	Leyland Tiger TRCTL11/2RH	Duple B49F	Ribble Motor Services	900	RP

Notes:

RN 7588	rebodied 1949
RN 8622	chassis refurbished and rebodied in 1949
ERN 700	originally B44F
SFV 421	'Gay Hostess' double-deck motorway coach
NCK 106J	in Ireland 1982-2005 registered 411 LIP
PTF 727L	used as exhibition bus
TRN 481V	on display at North West Museum of Road Transport

The Roger Burdett Collection

Contact address: Fir Tree Farm, off Common Lane, Corley Moor, Coventry CV7 8AR

E-mail: rogerrbctc@aol.com

Affiliation: NARTM

Brief description: A collection of distinctive coaches supplemented by four double deckers of interest to the collection owner. All vehicles with the exception of the Bristol RE are either unique or one of a small number of survivors.

Opening days/times: Vehicles regularly attend rallies and events and the collection can be viewed by appointment. Please write to the address given.

Registration	Date	Chassis	Body	New to	Fleet No	Status
VG 5541	1933	Bristol GJW	Weymann O28/26R	Norwich Electric Tramways		RP
JYC 855	1948	Leyland Tiger PS1	Harrington C33F	Scarlet Motors of Minehead		R
GOU 732	1949	Tilling Stevens K6LA7	Scottish Aviation C33F	Altonian Coaches of Alton		R
FNV 557	1950	Leyland Tiger PS2/3	Whitson FC33F	Church ('Royal Blue') of Pytchley		R
GKV 94	1950	Daimler CVA6	Metro-Cammell H31/29R	Coventry City Transport	94	RP
LTA 813	1950	Bristol KS5G	ECW L27/28R	Western National Omnibus Co	994	R
NTU 125	1951	Foden PVRF6	Metalcraft C41C	Hollinshead of Biddulph		R
EHL 336	1952	Leyland Tiger PS2/13A	Roe C35F	West Riding Automobile Co	725	R
NXL 847	1953	AEC Regal III 6821A	Duple C39F	Eastern Belle of Bow, London		R
OTT 43	1953	Bristol LS6G	ECW C39F	Western National Omnibus Co (Royal Blue)	2200	R
WKJ 787	1956	Beadle-Commer	Beadle C41C	Beadle demonstrator		R
780 GHA	1959	BMMO C5	BMMO C41F	BMMO ('Midland Red')	4780	R
56 GUO	1961	Bristol MW6G	ECW C39F	Western National Omnibus Co (Royal Blue)	2267	RP
5056 HA	1962	BMMO S15	BMMO B40F	BMMO ('Midland Red')	5056	R
EHA 424D	1966	BMMO D9	BMMO/Willowbrook H40/32RD	BMMO ('Midland Red')	5424	R
OTA 640G	1969	Bristol RELH6G	ECW C45F	Southern National Omnibus Co (Royal Blue)	2380	R

Notes:

VG 5541	converted to diesel 1938 and open-top 1950

Rotherham Trolleybus Group

Contact address: 113 Tinker Lane, Walkley, Sheffield S6 5EA

Phone: 0114 266 3173

Affiliation: Trolleybus Museum at Sandtoft

Brief description: This group is open to all with an interest in Rotherham area trolleys, the vehicles and the system. Active restoration of the vehicles takes place and the group works closely with the Trolleybus Museum at Sandtoft. A video *Remember the Trackless* is sold to raise funds for restoration. Vehicles can be viewed by contacting the group.

Registration	Date	Chassis	Body	New to	Fleet No	Status
CET 613+	1943	Sunbeam MS2c	East Lancs B39C	Rotherham Corporation	88	RP
FET 617+	1950	Daimler CTE6	Roe H40/30R	Rotherham Corporation	37	R
+ trolleybus						

Notes:

FET 617   rebodied 1956 (formerly single-decker); on display at the Trolleybus Museum at Sandtoft

RTW Bus Group

Contact address: 7 Oldbury Close, St Mary Cray, BR5 3TH

Affiliation: RT/RF Register, Cobham Bus Museum, HCVS

Brief description: The group was formed in 1999 and comprises the owners of the preserved RTW vehicles and those interested in the type. The vehicles appear at rallies from time to time. A DVD on the history of the RTW is available from the group.

Registration	Date	Chassis	Body	New to	Fleet No	Status
KGK 529	1949	Leyland Titan 6RT	Leyland H30/26R	London Transport	RTW29	R
KGK 575	1949	Leyland Titan 6RT	Leyland H30/26R	London Transport	RTW75	R
KLB 881	1949	Leyland Titan 6RT	Leyland H30/26R	London Transport	RTW151	A
KLB 908	1949	Leyland Titan 6RT	Leyland H30/26RD	London Transport	RTW178	R
KLB 915	1949	Leyland Titan 6RT	Leyland H30/26R	London Transport	RTW185	R
KXW 435	1949	Leyland Titan 6RT	Leyland H30/26RD	London Transport	RTW335	RP
LLU 957	1950	Leyland Titan 6RT	Leyland H30/26R	London Transport	RTW467	R
LLU 987	1950	Leyland Titan 6RT	Leyland H30/26R	London Transport	RTW497	R

Notes:

KGK 529   on loan to Bristol Vintage Bus Group

KGK 575   owned by London Bus Co and operated as a PSV

KLB 908   originally H30/26R; acquired by Stevensons of Spath in 1966 and fitted with platform doors and saloon heaters

SELNEC Preservation Society

Contact address: 267 Rivington Crescent, Pendlebury, Swinton, Manchester M27 8TQ

Affiliation: NARTM

Brief description: A collection of buses from the SELNEC era including SELNEC Standards, the trail-blazing 'Mancunian' and other vehicles from the Greater Manchester area.

Events planned: The operational vehicles will appear at a range of local rallies and shows.

Registration	Date	Chassis	Body	New to	Fleet No	Status
EN 9965	1950	Leyland Titan PD2/4	Weymann	Bury Corporation	165	RP
DNF 708C	1965	Daimler Fleetline CRG6LX	Metro-Cammell O43/29C	Manchester Corporation	4708	A
END 832D	1966	Leyland Atlantean PDR1/2	Metro-Cammell H43/32F	Manchester Corporation	3832	RP
GNB 518D	1966	Bedford VAL14	Plaxton C47F	Manchester Corporation	205	A
LNA 166G	1968	Leyland Atlantean PDR2/1	Park Royal H26/7D	Manchester City Transport	1066	R
NNB 547H	1969	Leyland Atlantean PDR2/1	East Lancs H47/32F	Manchester City Transport	1142	A
NNB 589H	1970	Daimler Fleetline CRG6LXB	Park Royal H47/28D	SELNEC PTE	2130	A
ONF 865H	1970	Leyland Atlantean PDR2/1	Park Royal H47/28D	SELNEC PTE	1177	A
PNF 941J	1971	Leyland Atlantean PDR1A/1	Northern Counties H43/32F	SELNEC PTE	EX1	R
RNA 220J	1971	Daimler Fleetline CRG6LXB	Park Royal H47/29D	SELNEC PTE	2220	A
TNB 759K	1972	Daimler Fleetline CRG6LXB	Northern Counties H45/27D	SELNEC PTE	EX19	R
VNB 132L	1972	Leyland Atlantean AN68/1R	Park Royal O43/32F	SELNEC PTE	7032	R
VNB 173L	1972	Leyland Atlantean AN68/1R	Northern Counties H43/32F	SELNEC PTE	7147	A
VNB 177L	1972	Daimler Fleetline CRG6LXB	Northern Counties H45/27D	SELNEC PTE	7206	R
VNB 203L	1972	Daimler Fleetline CRG6LXB	Northern Counties H31/4D	SELNEC PTE	7232	R
WBN 955L	1972	Leyland Atlantean AN68/1R	Park Royal O43/32F	SELNEC PTE	7077	R
YDB 453L	1972	Seddon Pennine IV-236	Seddon DP25F	SELNEC PTE	1700	R
AJA 408L	1973	Bristol VRTSL6LX	ECW H43/32F	SELNEC Cheshire Bus Co	408	RP
WWH 43L	1973	Daimler Fleetline CRG6LXB	Park Royal H43/32F	SELNEC PTE	7185	R
XJA 534L	1973	Leyland Atlantean AN68/1R	Park Royal H43/32F	SELNEC PTE	7143	A
XVU 341M	1973	Seddon Pennine IV-236	Seddon B23F	SELNEC PTE	1711	A
YNA 321M	1973	Daimler Fleetline CRG6LXB	Northern Counties H43/32F	SELNEC PTE	7366	A
XVU 363M	1974	Seddon Pennine IV-236	Seddon B19F	Greater Manchester PTE	1733	A
BNE 729N	1974	Seddon Pennine IV-236	Seddon B19F	Greater Manchester PTE	1735	A
BNE 751N	1974	Leyland Atlantean AN68/1R	Northern Counties H43/32F	Greater Manchester PTE	7501	A
BNE 764N	1974	Bristol LH6L	ECW B43F	Greater Manchester PTE	1321	A
HNB 24N	1975	Leyland National 10351/1R	Leyland National B41F	Greater Manchester PTE	105	R
OBN 502R	1977	Leyland Fleetline FE30AGR	Northern Counties H43/32F	Lancashire United Transport	485	A
PTD 640S	1977	Leyland Fleetline FE30AGR	Northern Counties H43/32F	Lancashire United Transport	496	A
XBU 1S	1978	Leyland Fleetline FE30AGR	Northern Counties H43/32F	Greater Manchester PTE	8001	R
ANE 2T	1979	Leyland Titan TNLXB1RF	Park Royal H47/26F	Greater Manchester PTE	4002	RP
BNC 960T	1979	Leyland Atlantean AN68A/1R	Park Royal H43/32F	Greater Manchester PTE	7960	R
GBU 1V	1979	MCW Metrobus DR101/6	MCW H43/30F	Greater Manchester PTE	5001	R
GNF 15V	1980	Leyland Titan TNTL11/1RF	Park Royal H47/26F	Greater Manchester PTE	4015	A
GNF 16V	1980	Leyland Fleetline FE30AGR	Northern Counties H43/32F	Greater Manchester PTE	8141	RP
HDB 116V	1980	Leyland Fleetline FE30AGR	Northern Counties H43/32F	Greater Manchester PTE	8116	R
MNC 525W	1980	Leyland Atlantean AN68A/1R	Northern Counties H43/32F	Greater Manchester PTE	8325	A
NJA 568W	1980	Leyland Olympian B45/TL11/1R	Northern Counties H43/30F	Greater Manchester PTE	1451	R
DWH 706W	1981	Leyland Fleetline FE30AGR	Northern Counties H43/32F	Lancashire United Transport	613	R
SND 455X	1981	Leyland Atlantean AN68B/1R	Northern Counties H43/32F	Greater Manchester PTE	8455	A
SND 460X	1981	Leyland Atlantean AN68B/1R	Northern Counties H43/32F	Greater Manchester PTE	8460	R
SND 501X	1982	Leyland Atlantean AN68B/1R	Northern Counties H43/32F	Greater Manchester PTE	8501	A
WRJ 448X	1982	Volvo Ailsa B55-10	Northern Counties H44/35F	Greater Manchester PTE	1448	A
ANA 1Y	1982	Leyland Olympian ONTL11/1R	Northern Counties H43/30F	Greater Manchester PTE	3001	R
ANA 10Y	1983	Leyland Olympian ONTL11/1R	Northern Counties H43/30F	Greater Manchester PTE	3010	A
ANA 601Y	1983	Leyland Atlantean AN68D/1R	Northern Counties H43/32F	Greater Manchester PTE	8601	A
ANA 645Y	1983	Leyland Atlantean AN68D/1R	Northern Counties H43/32F	Greater Manchester PTE	8645	R
FWH 461Y	1983	Scania BR112DH	Northern Counties H43/32F	Greater Manchester PTE	1461	A
A472 HNC	1984	Dennis Falcon V DD405	Northern Counties H43/37F	Greater Manchester PTE	1472	A
A700 HNB	1984	Leyland Atlantean AN68D/1R	Northern Counties H43/32F	Greater Manchester PTE	8700	RP
A701 LNC	1984	Leyland Atlantean AN68D/1R	Northern Counties H43/32F	Greater Manchester PTE	8701	A
A765 NNA	1984	Leyland Atlantean AN68D/1R	Northern Counties H43/32F	Greater Manchester PTE	8765	RP
A30 ORJ	1984	Leyland Olympian ONLXB/1R	Northern Counties H43/30F	Greater Manchester PTE	3030	RP
B101 SJA	1985	Leyland Olympian ONLXB/1R	Northern Counties H44/30F	Greater Manchester PTE	3101	A
B901 TVR	1985	Dennis Dominator DDA1003	Northern Counties H43/32F	Greater Manchester PTE	2001	A
C751 YBA	1985	Dennis Domino SDA1201	Northern Counties B24F	Greater Manchester PTE	1751	R
C201 CBU	1986	Leyland Olympian ONLXB/1R	Northern Counties H43/30F	Greater Manchester PTE	3201	A
C225 CBU	1986	Leyland Olympian ONLXB/1R	Northern Counties H43/30F	Greater Manchester PTE	3225	A
C481 CBU	1986	Volvo Citybus B10M-50	Northern Counties H46/33F	Greater Manchester PTE	1481	A
C823 CBU	1986	Dodge S56	Northern Counties B18F	Greater Manchester PTE	1823	RP

Registration	Date	Chassis	Body	New to	Fleet No	Status
D302 JVR	1986	MCW Metrobus DR102/51	Northern Counties DPH43/29F	Greater Manchester PTE	5302	A
D501 LNA	1986	Leyland Lynx LX563LXCTZR1	Leyland B48F	Greater Manchester Buses	501	A
D277 JVR	1987	Leyland Olympian ONLXB/1R	Northern Counties DPH43/26F	Greater Manchester Buses	3277	A
D320 LNB	1987	MCW Metrobus DR102/51	Northern Counties DPH43/29F	Greater Manchester Buses	5320	R
D509 MJA	1987	Iveco 49-10	Robin Hood B21F	Greater Manchester Buses	1509	A
F301 DRJ	1989	Leyland Olympian ONLXB/1RZ	Northern Counties H43/30F	Greater Manchester Buses	3301	A
F305 DRJ	1989	Leyland Olympian ONLXB/1RZ	Northern Counties H43/30F	Greater Manchester Buses	3305	A
H140 GVM	1991	Dennis Dominator DDA2033	Northern Counties H43/29F	Greater Manchester Buses	2040	A

Notes:

EN 9965	converted to breakdown vehicle
DNF 708C	originally H43/32F
LNA 166G	originally H47/29D; converted by GMPTE for use as 'Exhibus' exhibition vehicle and restored in this condition
PNF 941J	exhibited at 1970 Commercial Motor Show as prototype SELNEC Standard
VNB 132L	originally H43/32F
VNB 177L	exhibited at 1972 Commercial Motor Show
VNB 203L	originally H45/27D; used as exhibition vehicle
WBN 955L	originally H43/32F
OBN 502R	passed to Greater Manchester PTE (6901) in 1981
PTD 640S	passed to GMPTE (6912) in 1981; rebodied 1983
HDB 116V	preserved in Birkenhead & District livery
NJA 568W	exhibited at 1980 Commercial Motor Show
DWH 706W	passed to Greater Manchester PTE (6990) in 1981
SND 455X	seating reduced — converted to driver-training vehicle
ANA 1Y	exhibited at 1982 Commercial Motor Show
C751 YBA	exhibited at 1984 Commercial Motor Show

South Yorkshire Transport Museum
Aldwarke

Contact address: 206 London Road, Sheffield S2 4LW

Phone: 0114 255 3010

Website: www.sheffieldbusmuseum.com / www.sytm.co.uk

Brief description: A collection of over 25 vehicles and many artifacts

Events planned: Please see enthusiast press and website for details.

Directions by car: From A1(M) Jct 36 follow Sheffield Road (A630) to Rotherham, then follow the A6123 (Aldwarke Lane) for about 1 mile, then turn left onto Waddington Way (just before the railway bridge) and the museum is on the left.

Registration	Date	Chassis	Body	New to	Fleet No	Status
GWJ 724	1941	AEC Regent O661	Sheffield Transport Department -	Sheffield Corporation	G54	A
JWB 416	1947	Leyland Tiger PS1	Weymann B34R	Sheffield Corporation	216	A
HD 7905	1948	Leyland Tiger PS1	Brush B34F	Yorkshire Woollen District Transport Co	622	R
KWE 255	1948	AEC Regent III 9612E	Weymann -	Sheffield Corporation	G55	R
MHY 765	1950	Leyland Comet ECPO/1R	Duple C32F	Orient Coaches of Bristol		RP
OWE 116	1952	AEC Regent III 9613A	Roe H33/25R	Sheffield Joint Omnibus Committee	116	RP
KET 220	1954	Daimler CVG6	Weymann H30/26R	Rotherham Corporation	220	R
RWB 87	1954	Leyland Titan PD2/12	Weymann H32/26R	Sheffield Corporation	687	R
WRA 12	1955	AEC Monocoach MC3RV	Park Royal B45F	Booth & Fisher of Halfway		R
VDV 760	1958	Bristol Lodekka LD6G	ECW H33/27RD	Western National Omnibus Co	1943	R
TDK 322	1959	AEC Regent V D2RA	Weymann H33/28RD	Rochdale Corporation	322	R
TET 135	1959	Daimler CVG6-30	Roe -	Rotherham Corporation	135	RP
6330 WJ	1960	AEC Regent V 2D3RA	Roe H39/30RD	Sheffield Joint Omnibus Committee	1330	A
1322 WA	1961	AEC Reliance 2MU3RA	Plaxton C36F	Sheffield United Tours	322	RP
388 KDT	1963	Leyland Titan PD2/40	Roe H34/28R	Doncaster Corporation	188	R

Registration	Date	Chassis	Body	New to	Fleet No	Status
LJF 30F	1967	Leyland PD3A/12	Metro-Cammell H41/33R	Leicester City Transport	30	RP
BWB 148H	1969	Leyland Atlantean PDR2/1	Park Royal H—/—/D	Sheffield Joint Omnibus Committee	1148	R
DWB 54H	1970	AEC Swift 5P2R	Park Royal B50F	Sheffield Transport	54	RP
CWG 756V	1979	Leyland Atlantean AN68A/1R	Roe H45/29D	South Yorkshire PTE	1756	R
C53 HDT	1985	Dennis Domino SDA1202	Optare B33F	South Yorkshire PTE	53	RP

Notes:

GWJ 724	originally bus 462; converted to grit wagon
KWE 255	originally bus 255; converted to grit wagon
TET 135	originally H39/31F; converted to breakdown vehicle
388 KDT	fitted from new with 1955 trolleybus body
BWB 148H	renumbered 748 upon dissolution of JOC; originally H47/32D but rebuilt as exhibition vehicle and restored in this condition

Southampton & District Transport Trust

Contact address: 104 Oak Tree Road, Southampton SO18 1PH

Affiliation: NARTM; WOMP

Brief description: The collection includes a selection of Southampton's fleet from the early 1970s. The small membership carries out restoration work. Several of the vehicles are privately owned by Trust members.

Registration	Date	Chassis	Body	New to	Fleet No	Status
FTR 511	1949	Guy Arab III	Park Royal O30/26R	Southampton Corporation	64	R
LOW 217	1954	Guy Arab III	Park Royal H30/26R	Southampton Corporation	71	R
JOW 928	1955	Guy Arab UF	Park Royal B39F	Southampton Corporation	255	RP
318 AOW	1962	AEC Regent V 2D3RA	Park Royal H37/29R	Southampton Corporation	318	RP
335 AOW	1963	Leyland Titan PD2A/27	Park Royal H37/29R	Southampton Corporation	335	RP
370 FCR	1963	AEC Regent V 2D3RA	East Lancs H37/29R	Southampton Corporation	350	R
JOW 499E	1967	AEC Swift MP2R	Strachans B47D	Southampton Corporation	1	RP
KOW 901F	1967	AEC Regent V 3D2RA	Neepsend H40/30R	Southampton Corporation	393	RP
KOW 910F	1967	AEC Regent V 3D2RA	Neepsend H40/30R	Southampton Corporation	402	RP
PCG 888G	1968	AEC Reliance 6U3ZR	Plaxton C55F	Coliseum Coaches of Southampton		A
PCG 889G	1968	AEC Reliance 6MU3R	Plaxton C45F	Coliseum Coaches of Southampton		A
TTR 167H	1970	Leyland Atlantean PDR1A/1	East Lancs H45/31F	Southampton Corporation	133	R
HNP 989J	1971	Leyland Atlantean PDR1A/1	East Lancs O45/31F	Southampton Corporation	139	R
BCR 379K	1972	Seddon Pennine RU	Pennine B44F	Southampton Corporation	15	RP
NLP 389V	1980	Leyland National 2 NL116L11/3R	Leyland National B49F	British Airways	C279	R

Notes:

FTR 511	originally H30/26R; owned by Southampton City Museums
LOW 217	owned by Southampton City Museums
JOW 928	originally B36D
PCG 888G	originally C57F
HNP 989J	originally H45/31F, registered WOW 531J; preserved in Guide Friday livery
NLP 389V	originally B33T; preserved in traditional Provincial livery

Southdown Historic Vehicle Group

Contact address: 73 Cuckfield Crescent, Worthing, West Sussex

E-mail: southdownqueenmary@ntlworld.com

Website: http://home.fastnet.co.uk/gerrycork/worthingbusrally/worthingbusrally.htm

Brief description: A private collection of vehicles, most of which operated for Southdown Motor Services or have South Coast connections. The collection is not on public view, but vehicles are rallied and often appear in service on running days.

Registration	Date	Chassis	Body	New to	Fleet No	Status
GUF 191	1945	Guy Arab II	Northern Counties O30/26R	Southdown Motor Services	451	RP
GFY 406	1950	Leyland Titan PD2/3	Leyland H30/26R	Southport Corporation	106	RP
LRV 992	1956	Leyland Titan PD2/12	Metro-Cammell O33/26R	Portsmouth Corporation	2	R
YTG 304	1958	Leyland Titan PD3/4	Massey H—/—F	Llynfi Motors of Maesteg	72	A
XUF 141	1960	Leyland Tiger Cub PSUC1/2	Weymann C41F	Southdown Motor Services	1141	R
70 AUF	1962	Commer Avenger IV	Harrington C—F	Southdown Motor Services	70	A
XWV 416A	1963	AEC Regent V 2D3RV	East Lancs H32/28R	Eastbourne Corporation	68	RP
8859 VR	1964	AEC Regent V 2D3RA	Neepsend H41/32R	A. Mayne & Son of Manchester		RP
972 CUF	1964	Leyland Titan PD3/4	Northern Counties FH39/30F	Southdown Motor Services	972	R
401 DCD	1964	Leyland Titan PD3/4	Northern Counties FCO39/30F	Southdown Motor Services	401	R
412 DCD	1964	Leyland Titan PD3/4	Northern Counties FCO39/30F	Southdown Motor Services	412	R
416 DCD	1964	Leyland Titan PD3/4	Northern Counties FCO39/30F	Southdown Motor Services	416	R
419 DCD	1964	Leyland Titan PD3/4	Northern Counties FCO39/30F	Southdown Motor Services	419	R
PRX 187B	1964	Leyland Titan PD3/4	Northern Counties FCO39/30F	Southdown Motor Services	415	RP
BUF 122C	1965	Leyland Leopard PSU3/1RT	Marshall B45F	Southdown Motor Services	122	R
BUF 260C	1965	Leyland Titan PD3/4	Northern Counties FC39/30F	Southdown Motor Services	260	R
BUF 277C	1965	Leyland Titan PD3/4	Northern Counties FC39/30F	Southdown Motor Services	277	R
BUF 426C	1965	Leyland Titan PD3/4	Northern Counties FCO39/30F	Southdown Motor Services	426	R
BJK 672D	1966	Leyland Titan PD2A/30	East Lancs H32/28R	Eastbourne Corporation	72	R
FCD 294D	1966	Leyland Titan PD3/4	Northern Counties FH39/29F	Southdown Motor Services	294	R
DHC 784E	1967	Leyland Titan PD2A/30	East Lancs O32/28R	Eastbourne Corporation	84	R
KUF 199F	1968	Leyland Leopard PSU3/1RT	Willowbrook B45F	Southdown Motor Services	199	R
LFS 296F	1968	Bristol VRTLL6LX	ECW O43/31F	Scottish Omnibuses (Eastern Scottish)	AA296	R
PUF 165H	1969	Leyland Leopard PSU3/1RT	Northern Counties DP49F	Southdown Motor Services	465	R
TCD 374J	1970	Daimler Fleetline CRG6LX	Northern Counties H—/—F	Southdown Motor Services	374	RP
TCD 383J	1970	Daimler Fleetline CRG6LX	Northern Counties H—/—F	Southdown Motor Services	383	RP
TCD 481J	1970	Bristol RESL6L	Marshall B45F	Southdown Motor Services	481	R
TCD 490J	1970	Bristol RESL6L	Marshall B45F	Southdown Motor Services	490	RP
UUF 116J	1971	Bristol VRTSL6LX	ECW H39/31F	Southdown Motor Services	516	R
UUF 335J	1971	Leyland Leopard PSU3B/4RT	Plaxton C47F	Southdown Motor Services	1835	R
SCD 731N	1974	Leyland Atlantean AN68/1R	Park Royal - Roe H43/30F	Southdown Motor Services	731	R
RUF 37R	1977	Leyland National 11351A/2R	Leyland National B44D	Southdown Motor Services	37	R
ANJ 306T	1978	Leyland Leopard PSU3E/4RT	Plaxton C49F	Southdown Motor Services	1306	R
HNP 154S	1978	Leyland Atlantean AN68A/1R	East Lancs O43/31F	Brighton Borough Transport	3	A
TYJ 4S	1978	Leyland Atlantean AN68A/1R	East Lancs H43/31F	Brighton Borough Transport	4	R
USV 324	1979	Leyland Leopard PSU3E/4RT	Plaxton C48F	Southdown Motor Services	1320	RP
OPV 821	1979	Leyland Leopard PSU3E/4RT	Plaxton C48F	Southdown Motor Services	1321	RP

Notes:

GUF 191	originally H30/26R
LRV 992	originally H33/26R
YTG 304	originally H41/31F
70 AUF	originally C35F
XWV 416A	originally registered KHC 368
PRX 187B	originally registered 415 DCD
DHC 784E	originally H32/28R

LFS 296F	originally H47/36F; acquired by Southdown (544) in 1973
TCD 374J	originally H40/31F
TCD 383J	originally H40/31F
HNP 154S	originally H43/31F, registered TYJ 3S
USV 324	originally registered BYJ 920T
OPV 821	originally registered EAP 921V

St Margaret's Transport Society

Contact information: St Margaret's High School, Aigburth Raod, Liverpool L17 6AB

Telephone: 0151 427 1825

Affiliation: NARTM

Brief description: Formed in 1979, the Society specialises in single deck half-cabs from the 1940s and 1950s. Meetings are held regularly to carry out restoration of the vehicles. Visitors are welcome but prior appointment is essential. Please contact the address given.

Registration	Date	Chassis	Body	New to	Fleet No	Status
CMS 201	1949	Leyland Tiger PS1	Alexander C35F	W. Alexander & Sons	PA133	R
GWM 816	1951	Crossley SD42/7	Crossley B32F	Southport Corporation	116	RP

Telford Bus Group

Contact address: 2 Clifton Avenue, Brownhills, Walsall, West Midlands WS8 7DU

Contact number: 07968 410306

Website: www.telfordbus.org.uk

Brief description: The Telford Bus Group has a collection of privately owned buses and coaches in various parts of England. The Group has become known for its Bedford VALs, of which 12 are preserved, including examples of several body types. Other vehicles include Daimler Fleetline ('Mancunian'), Seddon Pennine VI, Commer Avenger and Leyland Leopard (Midland Red 'S27' type)
Not all vehicles are restored, and some are long-term projects.

Registration	Date	Chassis	Body	New to	Fleet No	Status
LFM 404	1950	Bedford OB	Duple C29F	Crosville Motor Services	SL67	A
386 DD	1961	Bedford J2	Plaxton C20F	Talbott of Moreton-in-Marsh		RP
3190 UN	1962	Commer Avenger IV	Plaxton C41F	Wright of Penycae		R
9797 DP	1964	Bedford VAL14	Duple C52F	Smiths of Reading		RP
CTT 774C	1965	Bedford VAS1	Duple C29F	Heard of Bideford		A
EHL 472D	1966	Bedford VAL14	Plaxton C52F	West Riding Automobile Co	3	R
JTH 100F	1968	Bedford VAM14	Duple C45F	Davies Bros of Pencader		RP
RBC 345G	1969	Bedford VAL70	Duple C52F	Cook of Dunstable		RP
WWY 115G	1969	Bedford VAL70	Plaxton C53F	Abbey Coachways of Selby		R
BWP 727H	1970	Bedford VAM70	Plaxton C37F	Regent Motors of Redditch		A
FYG 663J	1970	Bedford VAL70	Willowbrook B56F	Wigmore of Dinnington		RP
VBD 310H	1970	Bedford VAL70	Plaxton C48F	Coales of Woolaston		R
BHO 670J	1971	Bedford VAL70	Duple C53F	Castle Coaches of Waterlooville		R
RNA 236J	1971	Daimler Fleetline CRG6LXB-33	Park Royal H47/29D	SELNEC PTE	2236	R
TUX 906J	1971	Bedford YRQ	Duple C45F	Corvedale of Ludlow	6	A
CDC 166K	1972	Seddon Pennine VI	Plaxton C45F	Bob's of Middlesbrough	26	RP
CDC 167K	1972	Seddon Pennine VI	Plaxton C—F	Bob's of Middlesbrough	27	A
CDC 168K	1972	Seddon Pennine VI	Plaxton C41F	Bob's of Middlesbrough	28	RP
FAR 724K	1972	Bedford VAL70	Duple C53F	Langley Coaches of Slough		RP
XUR 290K	1972	Bedford VAL70	Plaxton C53F	Morgan of Bognor Regis		R
DNT 174L	1973	Bedford YRQ	Duple C45F	Price of Bishop's Castle		A
JHA 227L	1973	Leyland Leopard PSU3B/2R	Marshall DP49F	Midland Red Omnibus Co	227	RP
HNT 945N	1975	Bedford VAS5	Duple C29F	Corvedale of Ludlow	42	A
BOK 1V	1979	MCW Metrobus DR102/12	MCW H43/30F	West Midlands PTE	2001	RP
UIB 5303	1983	MCW Metroliner CR126/1	MCW C51F	East Kent Road Car Co	8846	RP
D536 NDA	1986	Freight Rover Sherpa FR350	Carlyle B18F	West Midlands PTE	536	RP
G918 LHA	1989	Leyland Olympian ONLXB/1RZ	East Lancs H45/29F	Midland Red (North)	1918	R

Notes:

CDC167K	originally C45F
CDC168K	originally C45F
UIB 5303	originally registered FKK 846Y

TH Collection

Contact information: Telephone 01263 834829

E-mail: thecollection@dsl.pipex.com

Affiliation: NARTM

Brief description: A private collection representing coachwork built by Thomas Harrington of Hove. It is believed the vehicles are now all unique examples of the chassis and body combination.

Opening days/times: The collection is not on public view and all vehicles are at varying stages of restoration. Arrangements to visit can be made, strictly by appointment, telephoning first for details.

Registration	Date	Chassis	Body	New to	Fleet No	Status
KD 5296	1928	Leyland Tiger TS2	Harrington C31F	Imperial Motor Services of Liverpool		A
VRF 372	1951	Foden PVRF6	Harrington C41C	Bassett's Coaches of Tittensor		A
JAP 698	1954	Harrington Contender	Harrington C41C	Audawn Coaches of Corringham		RP
YYB 118	1957	Dennis Lancet UF	Harrington B42F	Hutchings & Cornelius Services of South Petherton		RP
PFR 747	1959	Bedford SB3	Harrington C41F	J. Abbott & Son of Blackpool		A
487 GFR	1964	AEC Reliance 2U3RA	Harrington C34F			R

Notes:

KD 5296	rebodied 1939
JAP 698	former Harrington demonstrator

Three Counties Bus & Commercial Vehicle Museum

Contact address: 83 Millwright Way, Flitwick, Beds MK45 1BQ

Phone: 01525 712091

E-mail: nick.doolan@btopenworld.com

Web site: www.3cbcvm.org.uk

Affiliation: NARTM

Brief description: Established to provide a focus for the preservation of buses in Bedfordshire, Buckinghamshire and Hertfordshire. Seeks to ensure a long-term future for the vehicles.

Events planned: Please see enthusiast press for planned Operating Days. Operational vehicles frequently attend local rallies

Registration	Date	Chassis	Body	New to	Fleet No	Status
FXT 122	1939	Leyland Cub REC	LPTB B20F	London Transport	CR16	RP
DBL 154	1946	Bristol K6A	ECW L27/28R	Thames Valley Traction Co	446	R
CFN 104	1947	Leyland Tiger PS1/1	Park Royal C32R	East Kent Road Car Co		R
JWU 307	1950	Bedford OB	Duple C29F	Lunn of Rothwell		RP
LYR 915	1952	AEC Regent III O961	Weymann H30/26R	London Transport	RT3496	R

Registration	Date	Chassis	Body	New to	Fleet No	Status
MXX 434	1952	AEC Regal IV 9821LT	Metro-Cammell B39F	London Transport	RF457	R
MXX 332	1953	Guy Special NLLVP	ECW B26F	London Transport	GS32	R
MXX 489	1953	AEC Regal IV 9821LT	Metro-Cammell B39F	London Transport	RF512	RP
RSJ 747	1956	Albion Victor FT39AN	Heaver C27F	Guernsey Motor Co	69	R
VYO 767	1959	Bristol MW6G	ECW C41F	Tilling		RP
OVL 473	1960	Bristol Lodekka FS5G	ECW H33/27RD	Lincolnshire Road Car Co	2378	R
EFM 631C	1965	Bristol Lodekka FS6G	ECW H33/27RD	Crosville Motor Services	DFG182	R
DEK 3D	1966	Leyland Titan PD2/37	Massey H37/27F	Wigan Corporation	140	R
KBD 712D	1966	Bristol Lodekka FS6G	ECW H33/27RD	United Counties Omnibus Co	712	R
OWC 182D	1966	Bristol MW6G	ECW C41F	Tilling's Transport	182	R
NBD 311F	1967	Bristol RELL6G	ECW B53F	United Counties Omnibus Co	311	RP
RBD 319G	1968	Bristol RELL6G	ECW B53F	United Counties Omnibus Co	319	RP
UXD 129G	1969	Bristol RELL6L	ECW B48D	Luton Corporation	129	RP
VLW 444G	1969	AEC Swift 4P2R	MCW B25D	London Transport	MBS444	A
UBD 757H	1969	Bristol VRTSL6LX	ECW H39/31F	United Counties Omnibus Co	757	A
VMO 234H	1969	Bristol LH6L	ECW B41F	Thames Valley Traction Co	214	RP
WRP 767J	1970	Bristol VRTSL6LX	ECW H39/31F	United Counties Omnibus Co	767	RP
ANV 775J	1971	Bristol VRTSL6LX	ECW H39/31F	United Counties Omnibus Co	775	RP
JPL 153K	1972	Leyland Atlantean PDR1A/1 Special	Park Royal H43/29D	London Country Bus Services	AN53	RP
RBD 111M	1974	Bedford YRT	Willowbrook B53F	United Counties Omnibus Co	111	A
UPE 203M	1974	Leyland National 10351/1R	Leyland National B41F	London Country Bus Services	SNB103	A
GPD 313N	1974	Bristol LHS6L	ECW B35F	London Country Bus Services	BN45	RP
HPF 318N	1975	Leyland National 10351/1R/SC	Leyland National DP39F	London Country Bus Services	SNC168	R
SBD 525R	1977	Leyland National 11351A/1R	Leyland National B49F	United Counties Omnibus Co	525	RP
SOA 674S	1977	Leyland Leopard PSU3E/4R	Plaxton C49F	Midland Red Omnibus Co	674	R
UPB 312S	1977	Leyland National 10351A/1R	Leyland National B41F	London Country Bus Services	SNB312	R
GCK 279S	1978	Bedford YLQ	Plaxton C45F	Florence ('Battersby Silver Grey') of Morecambe		RP
XPK 51T	1978	AEC Reliance 6U2R	Duple C53F	London Country Bus Services	RB51	R
HBD 919T	1979	Bristol VRTSL3/6LXB	ECW DPH40/28F	United Counties Omnibus Co	919	R
SVV 587W	1980	Leyland National 2 NL116L11/1R	Leyland National B49F	United Counties Omnibus Co	587	R
GUW 443W	1981	Leyland National 2 NL106AL11/2R	Leyland/East Lancs B25D	London Transport	GLS443	A
GUW 444W	1981	Leyland National 2 NL106AL11/2R	Leyland National DP43F	London Transport	LS444	RP
TPD 109X	1982	Leyland Olympian ONTL11/1R	Roe H43/29F	London Country Bus Services	LR9	A
C24 NVV	1985	Ford Transit 190D	Carlyle B16F	United Counties Omnibus Co	24	A

Notes:

RSJ 747	Guernsey registration 1529
OWC 182D	passed to Eastern National (392) in 1968 and to Tilling's Travel (9392) in 1971
UXD 129G	passed unused to United Counties (389) in 1970
ANV 775J	rebuilt by United Counties to Series 3 specification
HBD 919T	originally H43/31F
GUW 443W	originally numbered LS443; rebuilt by East Lancs as National Greenway (with Gardner engine) in 1994
GUW 444W	originally B25D; now fitted with Volvo engine

Transport Yorkshire Preservation Group

Contact address: Secretary, Unit 591, 57 Great George Street, Leeds LS1 3AJ

E-Mail: info@typg.org.uk

Web: www.typg.org.uk

Affiliation: NARTM

Brief description: Transport Yorkshire Preservation Group is a not-for-profit organisation set up in 2004 to look after a growing collection of former Leeds City Transport / West Yorkshire PTE / Yorkshire Rider vehicles.

Events planned: 'Leeds 2009' on 19 July 2009. Please refer to web site for details.

Registration	Date	Chassis	Body	New to	Fleet No	Status
SUG 591M	1974	Leyland Atlantean AN68/2R	Roe H45/33D	West Yorkshire PTE	591	RP
C507 KBT	1985	Leyland Olympian ONTL11/1R	Optare DPH43/27F	West Yorkshire PTE	5507	RP
C807 KBT	1986	Leyland Cub CU435	Optare B33F	West Yorkshire PTE	1807	RP
D705 HUA	1986	Freight Rover Sherpa FR350	Optare B16F	Yorkshire Rider	1705	RP
D515 HUB	1987	Leyland Olympian ONTL11/1R	Optare DPH43/27F	Yorkshire Rider	515	RP
E204 PWY	1987	Mercedes-Benz 811D	Optare DP29F	Yorkshire Rider	2004	RP
G254 JYG	1989	DAF SB220LC550	Optare B47F	Yorkshire Rider	1254	RP

Notes:
SUG 591M   ordered by Leeds City Transport

Vintage Yellow Buses of Devon

Contact Address: The Chalet, Church Hill, Kingswear, Dartmouth, Devon, TQ6 0BX

Brief Description: A small collection of privately owned buses from Bournemouth and Devon.

Opening days/times: Not normally open, but visitors are welcome, strictly by prior arrangement.

Registration	Date	Chassis	Body	New to	Fleet No	Status
RRU 903	1955	Leyland Tiger Cub PSUC1/1	Park Royal B42F	Bournemouth Corporation	266	R
8159 EL	1960	Leyland Titan PD3/1	Weymann H37/25D	Bournemouth Corporation	159	RP
MSJ 499	1961	Leyland Atlantean PDR1/1	Metro-Cammell O44/31F	Devon General Omnibus & Touring Co	DL925	R
H262 MFX	1991	Dennis Dominator DDA1033	East Lancs H47/33F	Bournemouth Transport ('Yellow Buses')	262	R

Notes:
RRU 903   originally B41D; rebuilt and converted for OMO in 1957, renumbered 98
MSJ 499   originally CO44/31F, registered 925 GTA

Wealdstone & District Vintage Vehicle Collection

Contact address: 91 Graham Road, Wealdstone, Middx HA3 5RE

E-mail: oldbusgarage@sftt.co.uk

Web site: www.sftt.co.uk/busgarage

Brief description: A small collection of mainly London buses from the 1950s, examples of which regularly attend rallies. Anyone wishing to visit or assist with the vehicles is welcome. Please write to the address given.

Registration	Date	Chassis	Body	New to	Fleet No	Status
DL 9706	1935	Dennis Lancet	ECW B36R	Southern Vectis Omnibus Co	516	RP
KYY 622	1950	AEC Regent III O961	Park Royal H30/26R	London Transport	RT1784	R
MLL 817	1952	AEC Regal IV 9821LT	Metro-Cammell B37F	London Transport	RF280	R
MXX 410	1953	AEC Regal IV 9821LT	Metro-Cammell B41F	London Transport	RF433	R
MXX 430	1953	AEC Regal IV 9821LT	Metro-Cammell B39F	London Transport	RF453	R
NLE 939	1953	AEC Regent III O961	Park Royal H30/26R	London Transport	RT4275	RP

Notes:
DL 9706   rebodied 1944

The West Country Historic Omnibus & Transport Trust

Contact address: Membership Secretary, 6 Oak Drive, Portishead BS20 6SS

Web site: www.busmuseum.org.uk

Affiliation: NARTM

Brief description: An Historic Bus, Coach and Commercial Vehicle Rally is held annually in September. The Trust plans to establish a restoration and storage centre and has already established an archive of West Country commercial road transport material.

Registration	Date	Chassis	Body	New to	Fleet No	Status
LTA 772	1951	Bristol LWL5G	ECW B39R	Western National Omnibus Co	1613	R
OTT 98	1952	Bristol LS6G	ECW C39F	Southern National Omnibus Co (Royal Blue)	1299	R
86 GFJ	1963	Leyland Titan PD2A/30	Massey H31/26R	Exeter City Transport	86	R
OTA 632G	1969	Bristol RELH6G	ECW C45F	Southern National Omnibus Co (Royal Blue)	1460	R
TDV 217J	1970	Leyland Panther PSUR1B/1R	Marshall B—D	Devon General Omnibus & Touring Co	217	R
VDV 137S	1977	Bristol VRTSL3/6LXB	ECW CO43/31F	Western National Omnibus Co (Devon General)	937	R
AFJ 726T	1979	Bristol LH6L	Plaxton C41F	Western National Omnibus Co	3306	A
AFJ 727T	1979	Bristol LH6L	Plaxton C41F	Western National Omnibus Co	3307	RP
AFJ 764T	1979	Bristol VRTSL3/6LXB	ECW H43/31F	Western National Omnibus Co	1157	R
A927 MDV	1983	Ford Transit 160D	Carlyle B16F	Devon General Ltd	7	R
C801 FRL	1985	Mercedes-Benz L608D	Reeve Burgess B20F	Western National Ltd	104	A
C705 FFJ	1986	Ford Transit 190D	Robin Hood B16F	Devon General Ltd	705	RP
L929 CTT	1994	Iveco 59-12	Mellor B21D	Devon General Ltd	1000	R
M627 HDV	1994	Iveco 59-12	Wadham Stringer B21D	Devon General Ltd	1029	A

Notes:
TDV 217J   ordered by Exeter Corporation; originally B47D, converted to publicity vehicle by Western National in 1980
VDV 137S   named *Victory*

West Midlands Bus Preservation Society

Contact address: Secretary, 22 Beaumont Way, Norton Canes, Cannock WS11 9FQ

Brief description: The main core of the collection is of vehicles from the West Midlands PTE in the period 1969 to 1986. Other artefacts are being collected for inclusion in a planned transport museum.

Opening days/times: Vehicles can be viewed by special arrangement, contact secretary.

Registration	Date	Chassis	Body	New to	Fleet No	Status
DUK 278	1946	Guy Arab II	Roe H31/25R	Wolverhampton Corporation	378	A
UHY 362	1955	Bristol KSW6B	ECW H32/28R	Bristol Tramways & Carriage Co	C8322	R
436 KOV	1964	Daimler Fleetline CRG6LX	Park Royal H43/33F	Birmingham City Transport	3436	A
NOV 880G	1969	Daimler Fleetline CRG6LX	Park Royal H43/29D	Birmingham City Transport	3880	R
TOB 997H	1970	Daimler Fleetline CRG6LX-33	Park Royal H47/33D	West Midlands PTE	3997	A
HHA 101L	1972	Leyland National 10151/1R/2501	Leyland National B50F	BMMO ('Midland Red')	101	RP
TOE 527N	1974	Volvo Ailsa B55-10	Alexander H44/35F	West Midlands PTE	4527	RP
JOV 738P	1976	Volvo Ailsa B55-10	Alexander H44/35F	West Midlands PTE	4738	R
NOC 600R	1976	Leyland Fleetline FE30AGR	Park Royal H43/33F	West Midlands PTE	6600	R

Notes:
DUK 278   body built 1952
TOB 997H   Gardner 6LXB engine fitted after acquisition by C. J. Partridge & Son of Hadleigh

West of England Transport Collection

Contact address: 15 Land Park, Chulmleigh, Devon, EX18 7BH

Phone: 01769 580811

Website: www.winkleigh.net

Affiliation: NARTM

Brief description: A large private collection of vehicles, mainly from West Country major operators. The collection includes buses, coaches and transport memorabilia.

Opening days/times: Viewing by prior arrangement with Colin Shears (tel 01769 580811).

Registration	Date	Chassis	Body	New to	Fleet No	Status
UO 2331	1927	Austin 20 5PL	Tiverton B13F	Sidmouth Motor Co		RP
LJ 500	1929	Karrier WL6/1	Hall Lewis B40D	Bournemouth Corporation	33	RP
PSL 234	1931	Maudslay ML3BC	Thurgood C31F	Church ('Royal Blue') of Pytchley		A
JY 124	1932	Tilling-Stevens B10A2 Express	Beadle B—R	Western National Omnibus Co	3379	RP
OD 5489	1933	Vauxhall Cadet VY	Mount Pleasant 7-seat	Davis of Rockbeare		R
OD 5868	1933	Leyland Lion LT5	Weymann B31F	Devon General Omnibus & Touring Co	68	A
OD 7500	1934	AEC Regent O661	Brush H30/26R	Devon General Omnibus & Touring Co	DR213	R
ADV 128	1935	Bristol JO5G	Beadle B—R	Western National Omnibus Co	222	RP
ATT 922	1935	Bristol JJW6A	Beadle B35R	Western National Omnibus Co	172	RP
AUO 74	1935	Leyland Lion LT5A	(chassis only)	Devon General Omnibus & Touring Co	SL79	A
FV 5737	1936	Leyland Tiger TS7	Duple C31F	Ribble Motor Services	753	R
JK 5605	1936	Leyland Titan TD4	Leyland O28/24R	Eastbourne Corporation	95	R
ADR 813	1938	Leyland Titan TD5c	Leyland L27/26R	Plymouth Corporation	141	R
BOW 162	1938	Bristol L5G	-	Hants & Dorset Motor Services	TS662	A
BOW 169	1938	Bristol L5G	-	Hants & Dorset Motor Services	TS676	A
EFJ 241	1938	Leyland Titan TD5	Leyland H30/26R	Exeter Corporation	26	RP
EFJ 666	1938	Leyland Tiger TS8	Cravens B32R	Exeter Corporation	66	R
ETT 946	1938	Bristol L5G	Beadle B36R	Southern National Omnibus Co	280	A
EUF 204	1938	Leyland Titan TD5	Park Royal H28/26R	Southdown Motor Services	204	A
DOD 474	1940	AEC Regal O662	Weymann B35F	Devon General Omnibus & Touring Co	SR474	RP
ETJ 108	1940	Leyland Tiger TS11	Roe -	Leigh Corporation	79	A
GTA 395	1941	Bristol LL5G	BBW B39R	Southern National Omnibus Co	373	RP
FRU 224	1944	Guy Arab II		Bournemouth Corporation	40	A
JK 9115	1947	Leyland Titan PD1	East Lancs O30/26R	Eastbourne Corporation	17	A
FFY 401	1947	Leyland Titan PD2/3	Leyland O30/26R	Southport Corporation	84	RP
KHU 624	1947	Bristol K6B	ECW H30/26R	Bristol Omnibus Co	3705	RP
GLJ 957	1948	Leyland Titan PD1A	ECW L27/26R	Hants & Dorset Motor Services	PD959	A
HHP 755	1948	AEC Regal III 9621E	Duple FC33F	Greenslades Tours of Exeter		A
JFJ 606	1949	Daimler CVD6	Brush H30/26R	Exeter Corporation	43	A
KGU 434	1949	Leyland Titan 7RT	Park Royal H30/26R	London Transport	RTL358	RP
LTV 702	1951	AEC Regal III 9621E	East Lancs B35R	Nottingham City Transport	702	A
Q995 CPE	1953	AEC Regent III O961	Park Royal O30/26R	London Transport	RT4588	A
MCO 669	1956	Leyland Titan PD2/12	Metro-Cammell H30/26R	Plymouth Corporation	69	A
TFJ 808	1956	Guy Arab IV	Massey H30/26R	Exeter Corporation	50	A
WRL 16	1956	Rowe Hillmaster	Reading B42F	Millbrook Steamboat & Trading Co		A
ONV 425	1957	Bristol SC4LK	ECW B35F	United Counties Omnibus Co	125	RP
974 AFJ	1960	Guy Arab IV	Massey H31/26R	Exeter Corporation	74	R
1925 WA	1961	AEC Bridgemaster 2B3RA	Park Royal H43/29F	Sheffield Transport	525	R
484 EFJ	1962	Leyland Titan PD2A/30	Massey H31/26R	Exeter City Transport	84	A
815 KDV	1963	Bristol Lodekka FLF6B	ECW H38/30F	Western National Omnibus Co	2010	A
991 MDV	1963	AEC Reliance 2MU3RV	Marshall B41F	Devon General Omnibus & Touring Co	991	A

Registration	Date	Chassis	Body	New to	Fleet No	Status
HDV 626E	1967	Bristol RELL6G	ECW B53F	Southern National Omnibus Co	2700	R
VTY 543J	1970	Leyland Leopard PSU3A/4R	Plaxton C45F	Tyne Valley Coaches of Acomb		A
MPX 945R	1977	Ford Transit	Robin Hood C—F	Angela of Bursledon		A
PTT 106R	1977	Bristol LH6L	Plaxton C37F	Western National Omnibus Co	3406	RP
CRM 927T	1979	Leyland-DAB	Leyland AB64T	Leyland Vehicles (demonstrator)		A
DBV 43W	1980	Leyland Leopard PSU4E/4R	East Lancs B47F	Burnley & Pendle Transport	43	A
RLN 237W	1981	Leyland-DAB 6-35-690/4	Roe AB—T	British Airways	C310	A
YNW 33X	1982	Leyland Leopard PSU3E/4R	Plaxton C51F	Shilton of Leeds		R
A749 NTA	1984	Ford Transit	Ford M8l	Devon County Council		A
K361 LWS	1992	Leyland-DAF 400	Leyland-DAF/G&M M16	Rothwell of Plymouth		A
L512 BOD	1993	Leyland-DAF 400	Leyland-DAF M16	Okehampton College		RP

Notes:

UO 2331	body new 1940	EFJ 666	used as a snowplough 1952-6
PSL 234	body new 1948; originally registered NV 30	EFJ 241	converted to tree-lopper in 1958
JY 124	new body and engine fitted in 1947	ADR 813	rebodied 1953; original torque-convertor replaced with crash gearbox
OD 5489	body fitted 1946		
OD 7500	rebodied 1949	ETJ 108	breakdown vehicle
ATT 922	rebodied in the late 1940s	GTA 395	lengthened and rebodied in 1954
ADV 128	rebodied 1950	FRU 224	converted to mobile crane for traction poles
AUO 74	front end of chassis only	JK 9115	originally H30/26R
FV 5737	rebodied 1950	FFY 401	originally H30/26R
ETT 946	rebodied 1950	HHP 755	former demonstrator, badged as Maudslay for exhibition at 1948 Commercial Motor Show
BOW 162	new with Beadle body; converted to breakdown vehicle following withdrawal in 1953		
		Q995 CPE	originally H30/26R, registered NLP 581
BOW 169	new with Beadle body; acquired by Wilts & Dorset Motor Services (505) in 1952 and converted to breakdown vehicle in 1956	CRM 927T	operated by South Yorkshire PTE (2006)
		RLN 237W	front portion converted to playbus
		K361 LWS	originally a British Gas van

Workington Heritage Transport Trust

Contact information: 22 Calva Road, Seaton, Workington, Cumbria, CA14 1DF

Telephone: 01900 67389

E-mail: wthc@btopenworld.com

Affiliation: NARTM, Transport Trust

Brief description: A collection based around buses and rail vehicles from the West Cumberland area. It is the aim to open to the public once a suitable building and funding have been arranged.

Registration	Date	Chassis	Body	New to	Fleet No	Status
RAO 733	1956	Bristol Lodekka LD6G	ECW H33/27RD	Cumberland Motor Services	369	R
109 DRM	1961	Bristol Lodekka FS6G	ECW H33/27RD	Cumberland Motor Services	C416	R
AAO 34B	1964	Bristol MW6G	ECW B45F	Cumberland Motor Services	231	R
DAO 295K	1972	Bristol RELL6L	ECW B53F	Cumberland Motor Services	295	RP
GRM 353L	1973	Leyland National 1151/1R/0401	Leyland National B52F	Cumberland Motor Services	353	RP
HHH 272N	1975	Bristol VRTSL6LX	ECW O43/34F	Cumberland Motor Services	401	RP
VKU 78S	1978	Leyland National 11351A/1R	Leyland National B49F	Chesterfield Transport	78	RP
KHH 378W	1980	Leyland National 2 NL116L11/1R	Leyland National B52F	Cumberland Motor Services	378	R
PHH 149W	1980	Bristol VRTSL3/6LXB	ECW H43/31F	Cumberland Motor Services	431	R
F251 JRM	1989	Leyland Lynx LX112L10ZR1R	Leyland B51F	Cumberland Motor Services	251	R

Notes:

RAO 733	renumbered 416 in 1961	KHH 378W	restored to post-NBC 'CMS Cumberland' livery
109 DRM	renumbered 550 in 1961	PHH 149W	originally registered KRM 431W
HHH 272N	originally H43/34F		

Left: The North East Bus Preservation Trust is the custodian of Northern General 2099 (originally registered RCN 699 but now PCN 762). Following withdrawal by Northern this forward-entrance AEC Routemaster saw further service with both Stevensons of Spath and Stagecoach of Perth but has now been restored to original livery. *Philip Lamb*

Below: New in 1963 and recently restored by the Bolton Bus Preservation Group, Bolton 185 (UWH 185) was the first of its former operator's renowned fleet of Leyland Atlanteans and the first of its type with East Lancs bodywork. *Philip Lamb*

Above right: Modernised Green Line RF48 (LYF 399) can often be found on reincarnations of classic routes when heritage running days take place based on London suburbs; the first such was the successful Hackney-area event of 16 April 2006. *Matthew Wharmby*

Right: Former East Kent AEC Regent V/Park Royal GJG 750D became RV1 when acquired by London Buses Ltd's Leaside Buses division, and continues to turn out in private preservation. In this shot it is attending the 2006 incarnation of Cobham bus rally. *Matthew Wharmby*

Part 3
Privately Preserved Buses

PRIVATELY PRESERVED BUSES

This section is included with the help and co-operation of the British Bus Preservation Group (BBPG). There are known to be many excellent privately preserved buses, coaches and some trolleybuses in this country and the list which follows is prepared from data provided by the Group. All the vehicles are owned by BBPG members and every effort has been made to ensure that the information given is correct at the time of going to press.

Condition of the vehicles varies, some having been fully restored (even to public operational standard in some cases); others are undergoing restoration, often a lengthy job with limited resources; some awaiting their turn for the day when the restoration task can be started. Those vehicles which are restored generally make visits to bus rallies up and down the country and details of such events can be found in the bus enthusiast magazines, regularly published.

If you are the owner of a preserved bus, coach or trolleybus which is not listed, you may wish to become a member of the BBPG. Services to their members include a regular Newsletter 'British Bus News', the chance to contact others with similar interests and the ability to share information on vehicle restoration problems, projects and, of course, sources of spare parts. Membership costs is £13 per annum and the BBPG may be contacted at the address below.

British Bus Preservation Group

Contact address: BBPG, 7 Dukeries Lane, Oakwood, Derby DE21 2HA..
E-mail: info@bbpg.co.uk
Web site: www.bbpg.co.uk
Affiliation: NARTM

Registration	Date	Chassis	Body	New to	Fleet No	Status
PY 6170	1926	Morris Commercial Z 15.9hp	Ch16	Robinsons of Scarborough		R
FM 6397	1931	Leyland Titan TD1	Leyland L51R	Crosville Motor Services	45	RP
FM 6435	1931	Leyland Lion LT2	Leyland B32F	Crosville Motor Services	L7	RP
FM 7443	1932	Leyland Cub KP2	Brush B20F	Crosville Motor Services	716	RP
AOG 638	1934	Daimler COG5		Birmingham City Transport	51	RP
AUF 670	1934	Leyland Titan TD3	East Lancs H26/26R	Southdown Motor Services	970	R
FM 9984	1936	Leyland Tiger TS7	Harrington C32F	Crosville Motor Services	K101	RP
JA 5528	1936	Bristol JO5G	Brush B31R	North Western Road Car Co	728	RP
BFM 144	1937	Leyland Tiger TS7	ECW B32F	Crosville Motor Services	KA27	R
JA 7770	1938	Bristol L5G	Burlingham B35R	North Western Road Car Co	346	RP
JK 8418	1939	Leyland Lion LT9	Leyland B32F	Eastbourne Corporation	12	R
EFM 581	1940	Leyland Tiger TS8	ECW B32F	Crosville Motor Services	KA158	RP
HHA 26	1944	Guy Arab II	Weymann H30/26R	BMMO ('Midland Red')	2574	RP
HKE 867	1945	Bristol K6A	Weymann H30/26R	Maidstone & District Motor Services	DH159	R
ACH 627	1947	Daimler CVD6	Brush H30/26R	Derby Corporation	27	A
ANH 154	1947	Daimler CVG6	Northern Coachbuilders H30/26R	Northampton Corporation	154	R
GOE 486	1947	Daimler CVA6	Metro-Cammell H30/24R	Birmingham City Transport	1486	RP
JXN 46	1948	AEC Regent III O961	Weymann H30/26R	London Transport	RT1018	R
KHA 311	1948	BMMO C1	Duple C30C	BMMO ('Midland Red')	3311	R
KNN 254	1948	Leyland Titan PD1A	Duple L29/26F	Barton Transport of Chilwell	580	RP
FUT 58	1949	Bedford OB	Duple C29F	Smiths of Syston		RP
KNN 959	1949	Daimler CVD6	Roberts H30/26RD	Gash of Newark	DD6	RP
LHY 937	1949	Bristol K6B	ECW H31/28R	Bristol Tramways	3774	RP
JOJ 231	1950	Leyland Tiger PS2	Weymann B34F	Birmingham City Transport	2231	RP
KYY 529	1950	AEC Regent III O961	Park Royal H30/26RD	London Transport	RT1702	R
FFN 446	1951	Beadle-Leyland	Beadle C35F	East Kent Road Car Co		RP
JND 629	1951	Leyland Titan PD2/3	Metro-Cammell H32/26R	Manchester Corporation	3228	R
JOJ 707	1951	Daimler CVD6	Metro-Cammell H30/24R	Birmingham City Transport	2707	R
KXW 123	1951	AEC Regent III O961	Weymann O30/26R	London Transport	RT2494	R
LYF 104	1951	Leyland Titan 7RT	Park Royal H30/26R	London Transport	RTL1163	R
LYF 282	1951	AEC Regent III O961	(chassis only)	London Transport	RT2557	RP

Registration	Date	Chassis	Body	New to	Fleet No	Status
LYF 399	1951	AEC Regal IV 9821LT	Metro-Cammell B39F	London Transport	RF 48	R
LYR 672	1951	AEC Regent III O961	Park Royal H30/26R	London Transport	RT2688	RP
MFM 39	1951	Bedford OB	Duple C29F	Crosville Motor Services	SL71	R
RSK 615	1951	Leyland Royal Tiger PSU1/15	Duple DP41F	Jackson of Castle Bromwich		A
URE 281	1951	AEC Regal III 9612A	Harrington FC33F	Lymers of Tean		R
LTX 311	1952	Leyland Tiger PS2/5	Massey B35F	Caerphilly Corporation	1	R
MLL 722	1952	AEC Regal IV 9822E	Park Royal RC37C	British European Airways		A
JDL 760	1953	Bristol LS6B	ECW C39F	Southern Vectis Omnibus Co	311	R
RFM 435	1954	Bristol Lodekka LD6B	ECW H33/25R	Crosville Motor Services	ML690	RP
395 DEL	1955	Albion Victor FT39AN	Heaver B35F	Guernsey Motor Co	71	RP
783 EFM	1957	Bristol SC4LK	ECW B35F	Crosville Motor Services	SC13	R
XCV 326	1957	Bedford SBG	Duple B42F	Harper & Kellow of St Agnes		A
GEN 201	1958	Leyland Titan PD3/6	Weymann H41/32RD	Bury Corporation	201	R
PFW 935	1958	Bristol SC4LK	ECW B35F	Lincolnshire Road Car Co	2453	RP
UNB 524	1958	Leyland Titan PD2/40	Metro-Cammell H37/28R	Manchester Corporation	3524	R
VFJ 995	1958	Leyland Titan PD2/40	Weymann H31/26R	Exeter Corporation	60	R
129 DPT	1959	AEC Reliance 2MU3RA	Plaxton C41F	OK Motor Services of Bishop Auckland		R
PBN 668	1960	Daimler CVG6-30	East Lancs H41/32F	Bolton Corporation	150	RP
VLT 250	1960	AEC Routemaster R2RH	Park Royal H36/28R	London Transport	RM244	R
107 GYC	1960	Bedford SB3	Duple C41F	Bowerman of Taunton		RP
314 PFM	1960	Bristol Lodekka FS6G	ECW H33/27R	Crosville Motor Services	DFG33	R
AKG 307A	1960	Bristol Lodekka FL6G	ECW H37/33RD	Red & White Services	L2060	R
387 HRR	1961	Leyland Leopard L1	Willowbrook B45F	East Midland Motor Services	R387	A
WKG 284	1961	AEC Reliance 2MU3RA	Willowbrook DP41F	Western Welsh Omnibus Co	1284	R
WS 337	1961	AEC Regent V LD2LA	UTIC H36/31F	Lisbon Electric Tramways	426	RP
811 BWR	1962	Bristol SUL4A	ECW B36F	West Yorkshire Road Car Co	SMA5	R
103 GAA	1963	Bedford SB5	Plaxton C41F	Princess Coaches of Southampton		RP
BKG 713B	1964	AEC Renown 3B3RA	Northern Counties H38/29F	Western Welsh Omnibus Co	713	RP
TFA 987	1964	Daimler CCG5	Massey H33/28R	Burton upon Trent Corporation	87	R
BNH 246C	1965	Daimler CVG6	Roe H33/26R	Northampton Corporation	246	R
CUV 116C	1965	AEC Routemaster R2RH	Park Royal H36/28R	London Transport	RM2116	R
FDB 328C	1965	Leyland Titan PD2/40	East Lancs H36/28R	Stockport Corporation	28	RP
GJG 750D	1966	AEC Regent V 2D3RA	Park Royal H40/32F	East Kent Road Car Co		R
HHW 452D	1966	Bristol MW5G	ECW B45F	Bristol Omnibus Co	2636	RP
JJD 394D	1966	AEC Routemaster R2RH/1	Park Royal H40/32R	London Transport	RML2394	RP
JJD 414D	1966	AEC Routemaster R2RH/1	Park Royal H40/32R	London Transport	RML2414	R
JJD 499D	1966	AEC Routemaster R2RH/1	Park Royal H40/32R	London Transport	RML2499	RP
JJD 539D	1966	AEC Routemaster R2RH/1	Park Royal H40/32R	London Transport	RML2539	RP
LAX 101E	1967	Bristol RESL6L	ECW B46F	Red & White Services	RS167	R
NDM 950E	1967	Bedford VAM14	Duple Midland DP45F	Phillips of Holywell		A
SMK 716F	1967	AEC Routemaster R2RH/1	Park Royal H40/32R	London Transport	RML2716	R
SMK 747F	1967	AEC Routemaster R2RH/1	Park Royal H40/32R	London Transport	RML2747	A
JVV 267G	1968	Daimler CVG6	Roe H33/26R	Northampton Corporation	267	RP
YNU 351G	1968	Bristol Lodekka FLF6G	ECW H38/32F	Midland General Omnibus Co	313	RP
SVF 896G	1969	Bristol RELH6G	ECW C47F	Eastern Counties Omnibus Co	RE896	RP
WYP 203G	1969	AEC Reliance 6MU3R	Plaxton C41F	Surrey Motors of Sutton		R
UHA 963H	1969	BMMO S23	BMMO/Plaxton B51F	BMMO ('Midland Red')	5963	R
TTA 400H	1970	Bedford SB5	Duple C41F	Otter Coaches of Ottery St Mary		R
CRR 537J	1970	Bristol RELL6L	Marshall B—F	East Midland Motor Services	O537	A
PKW 434J	1970	Daimler Fleetline CRG6LX-33	Alexander H—/—C	Bradford City Transport	434	A
IJI 5367	1971	Bristol RELH6L	Plaxton C49F	Greenslades Tours	300	RP
STL 725J	1971	Bedford YRQ	Willowbrook DP43F	Simmonds of Great Gonnerby	434	RP
TRU 947J	1971	Bristol RELL6G	ECW DP50F	Wilts & Dorset Motor Services	846	R
VOD 123K	1971	Bristol LHS6L	Marshall B33F	Western National Omnibus Co	1253	RP
XRD 23K	1971	Bristol VRTLL6LX	Northern Counties H47/30D	Reading Corporation	23	R
JMC 123K	1972	AEC Reliance 6MU4R	Plaxton C34F	Glenton Tours of London	123	RP
RWC 637K	1972	Bedford YRQ	Plaxton C37F	Harris of Grays		RP
RVO 668L	1973	Leyland Leopard PSU3B4R	Plaxton C53F	Barton Transport of Chilwell	1246	R
OWC 720M	1973	Bristol RELL6L	ECW B53F	Colchester Corporation	20	A

Registration	Date	Chassis	Body	New to	Fleet No	Status
PKH 600M	1974	Bedford VAS5	Plaxton C29F	Hull City Football Club		R
RPU 869M	1974	Bristol RELH6G	ECW DP49F	National Travel (South East)		RP
GUG 547N	1974	Leyland Atlantean AN68/1R	Roe PO—/—F	West Yorkshire PTE	6020	RP
GNM 235N	1975	Bristol LH6L	Plaxton C51F	G&M Coaches, East Sheen	74	A
KTT 316P	1975	Volvo B58-56	Duple C53F	Trathens of Yelverton		A
LWB 377P	1976	Ailsa B55-10	Van Hool McArdle H44/31D	South Yorkshire PTE	377	RP
NDP 31R	1976	Bristol VRTLL3/6LXB	Northern Counties H47/29D	Reading Transport	31	RP
NDP 38R	1976	Bristol VRTLL3/6LXB	Northern Counties H47/29D	Reading Transport	38	R
WYL 137	1976	Bristol LH6L	ECW B39F	London Transport	BL49	R
LOI 1859	1977	Bedford YLQ	Alexander B45F	Ulsterbus	1859	RP
PCD 80R	1977	Leyland National 11351A/1R	Leyland National B49F	Southdown Motor Services	34	A
UVX 7S	1977	Bristol LH6L	ECW B43F	Eastern National Omnibus Co	1103	RP
VKE 566S	1977	Leyland National 11351A/1R	Leyland National B49F	Maidstone & District Motor Services	3566	R
THX 220S	1978	Leyland National 10351A/2R	Leyland National B36D	London Transport	LS220	RP
WKO 138S	1978	Bristol VRTSL3/6LXB	ECW H43/31F	Maidstone & District Motor Services	5138	RP
DAR 120T	1978	Leyland National 11351A/1R	Leyland National B49F	Eastern National Omnibus Co	1898	RP
AYJ 100T	1979	Leyland National 11351A/1R	Leyland National B52F	Southdown Motor Services	100	RP
EWW 207T	1979	Leyland Leopard PSU3E/4R	Plaxton C49F	Wallace Arnold Tours of Leeds		RP
HIL 7081	1979	Bedford CFL	Plaxton C17F	Golden Miller of Feltham		R
JIW 4045	1979	AEC Reliance 6U3ZR	Plaxton C57F	Randall Enterprises of London		RP
HFG 923V	1980	Leyland National 2 NL116L11/1R	Leyland National B52F	Southdown Motor Services	123	R
PUA 294W	1980	Leyland Atlantean AN68C/1R	Roe H43/33F	West Yorkshire PTE	6294	RP
VIB 5069	1980	Leyland Leopard PSU3E/4R	Duple C49F	Grey-Green of London		RP
RLN 230W	1981	Bristol LHS6L	Plaxton C26F	British Airways	C303	RP
RNE 692W	1981	Bedford CF	Plaxton C17F	Shearings Coaches of Altrincham		R
PSX 189Y	1982	Leyland Leopard PSU3G/4R	Alexander B53F	W. Alexander & Sons (Fife)	FPE189	RP
VCO 802	1983	Leyland Tiger TRCTL11/3R	Plaxton C53F	East Kent Road Car Co	8840	R
A658 OCX	1984	Leyland Olympian ONLXB/1R	ECW H45/32F	Yorkshire Traction Co	658	R
B361 LOY	1984	Leyland National 2 NL116TL11/3R	Leyland National B33T	British Airways	BU397	RP
C724 FKE	1986	Ford Transit 190D	Dormobile B16F	East Kent Road Car Co	24	RP
G645 WDV	1990	Volkswagen LT31	Devon Conversions M10	Help the Aged, Crediton		A
VCO 772	1991	Mercedes-Benz 814D	Dormobile DP3F	Pathfinder of Newark	2	R
J7 FTG	1992	Mercedes-Benz 811D	PMT C33F	Flights Coach Travel of Birmingham		R
K727 UTT	1993	Iveco 59-12	Mellor B29F	Thames Transit	2026	R
K729 GBE	1993	Mercedes-Benz 814D	Autobus Classique C25F	Classic Coaches of Annfield Plain		R
L932 CTT	1994	Iveco 59-12	Mellor B21D	Devon General Ltd	1003	R

Notes:

AOG 638	lorry conversion	IJI 5367	originally registered UFJ 229J
LHY 937	renumbered 1541 in 1964	RPU 869M	passed unused to Eastern Counties (RE849)
KXW 123	originally H30/26R	GUG 547N	originally H43/33F
RSK 615	originally registered LOE 300	WYL 137	originally registered OJD 49R
FFN 446	rebuild using chassis parts from 1938 Leyland TD5	VKE 566S	passed to Hastings & District (366) in 1983; now fitted with Volvo engine and preserved in H&D 'Arrow' livery
395 DEL	Guernsey registration 2027		
VLT 250	originally registered VLT 244	HIL 7081	originally registered DJF 631T
314 PFM	restored in Brighton, Hove & District livery	JIW 4045	originally registered EBM 459T
AKG 307A	originally registered 20 AAX	VIB 5069	originally registered FYX 817W
WS 337	Portuguese registration HH-97-96	VCO 802	originally registered FKK 840Y
WYP 203G	rebodied 1974 for Edward Thomas of West Ewell	VCO 772	originally registered J914 HGD
CRR 537J	originally B49F	J7 FTG	originally registered J457 UFS
PKW 434J	originally H47/29D		

Above right: Still bearing Blue Triangle fleetnames, AEC Routemaster coach RCL2260 (CUV 260C) pays a visit to Ensignbus's X80 Running Day of 2 December 2006. *Matthew Wharmby*

Right: RTW75 (KGK 575) of The London Bus Company (formerly Blue Triangle). has just completed its run back from LOTS' Harrow event to Colindale station on 4 November 2006. *Matthew Wharmby*

Part 4

Heritage Bus Services

Buckland Omnibus Co
Woodbridge

Contact address: Ivy Cottage, 28 Marlesford Road, Hacheston, Woodbridge, Suffolk IP13 0DP
Phone: 01728 747093
E-mail: bucklandcoaches@yahoo.co.uk
Web site: www.bucklandbuses.co.uk
Operations planned for 2009: Vehicles available for private hire. OccasiFelixstowe seafront service — phone for details.

Registration	Date	Chassis	Body	New to	Fleet No	Status
TE 7870	1929	Dennis ES	Brush B29D	Accrington Corporation	57	R
GRP 260D	1966	Bristol MW6G	ECW C39F	United Counties Omnibus Co	260	R

Notes:
TE 7870   body rebuilt 1974 by Wyatt

Carmel Coaches
Okehampton

Contact address: Mr A. G. Hazell, Northlew, Okehampton, Devon.
Phone: 01409 221237
Operations planned for 2009: LOD 495 is a licensed PSV and available for private hire

Registration	Date	Chassis	Body	New to	Fleet No	Status
LOD 495	1950	Albion Victor FT39N	Duple C31F	Way of Crediton		R
MTT 640	1951	Leyland Titan PD2/1	Leyland L27/26R	Devon General Omnibus & Touring Co	DL640	R

Classic Southdown Omnibuses

Contact address: Dormy Cottage, 2 Alan Road, Wimbledon Village, London SW19 7PT
Affiliation: NARTM
Brief description: One of the largest single privately owned collections of Southdown vehicles in the country, ranging from a 1939 Leyland Titan TD5 to the last Bristol VR delivered new to the company in 1981.
Events planned: The operational vehicles will attend events in the South of England during the rally season as well as being used for private-hire work.

Registration	Date	Chassis	Body	New to	Fleet No	Status
GCD 48	1939	Leyland Titan TD5	Park Royal H28/26R	Southdown Motor Services	248	R
RUF 186	1956	Leyland Titan PD2/12	Beadle H33/26R	Southdown Motor Services	786	R
410 DCD	1964	Leyland Titan PD3/4	Northern Counties FCO39/30F	Southdown Motor Services	410	R
422 DCD	1964	Leyland Titan PD3/4	Northern Counties FCO39/30F	Southdown Motor Services	422	R
HCD 347E	1967	Leyland Titan PD3/4	Northern Counties FH39/30F	Southdown Motor Services	347	R
UUF 110J	1971	Bristol VRTSL6LX	ECW H39/31F	Southdown Motor Services	510	RP
WTG 360T	1979	Bristol VRTSL3/6LXB	Alexander O44/31F	City of Cardiff	360	
GRU 163V	1980	Leyland Fleetline FE30AGR	Alexander O43/31F	Bournemouth Transport	163	
GRU 164V	1980	Leyland Fleetline FE30AGR	Alexander O43/31F	Bournemouth Transport	164	

Registration	Date	Chassis	Body	New to	Fleet No	Status
JWV 976W	1981	Bristol VRTSL3/680	ECW H43/31F	Southdown Motor Services	276	R
DCA 528X	1981	Bristol VRTSL3/6LXB	ECW O43/31F	Crosville Motor Services	DVG528	

Notes:

GCD 48	rebodied 1950
RUF 186	body built on Park Royal frames
WTG 360T	originally CO44/31F
GRU 163V	originally H43/31F
GRU 164V	originally H43/31F
JWV 976W	fitted with Gardner 6LXB engine
DCA 528X	originally H43/31F

Cumbria Classic Coaches
Kirkby Stephen

Contact address: Bowber Head, Ravenstonedale, Kirkby Stephen, Cumbria, CA17 4NL.

Phone: 015396 23254

Website: www.cumbriaclassiccoaches.co.uk

E-mail: coaches@cumbriaclassiccoaches.co.uk

Operations planned for 2009:
Route 40: Kendal Clipper, half-hourly, five days a week during school summer holidays.
Route 569: Ravenstonedale–Kirkby Stephen–Hawes, Tuesdays (Hawes market day) 14 April to 27 October.
Route 570: Hawes to Ribblehead viaduct, Tuesdays 7 July to 27 October.
Route 572: Ravenstonedale–Kirkby Stephen–Middleton-in-Teesdale–Barnard Castle, Wednesdays 15 April to 28 October and 4 November to 8 April 2010.

Registration	Date	Chassis	Body	New to	Fleet No	Status
JTB 749	1948	AEC Regal III O962	Burlingham C33F	Florence Motors of Morecambe		R
CRN 80	1949	Leyland Tiger PS1	East Lancs B34R	Preston Corporation	75	R
TSK 736	1949	Commer Commando	Scottish Aviation C29F	David Lawson	C8	RP
CWG 286	1950	Leyland Tiger PS1/1	Alexander C35F	W. Alexander & Sons	PA184	R
MTJ 84	1951	Guy Arab III	Roe C31F	Lancashire United Transport	440	R
UTC 672	1954	AEC Regent III 9613S	East Lancs L27/28RD	Bamber Bridge Motor Services	4	R
627 HFM	1959	Bristol Lodekka LD6B	ECW CO33/27RD	Crosville Motor Services	DLB978	R

Notes:

TSK 736	originally registered CMS 9

The London Bus Co
Rainham

Contact address: Unit 3C, Denver Industrial Estate, Ferry Lane, Rainham, Essex, RM13 7MD

Phone: 01708 631001

Website: www.thelondonbuscompany.com

Operations planned for 2009: Scheduled heritage services not finalised at time of publication. Please see website for details.
Vehicles appear on rail-replacement services.

Registration	Date	Chassis	Body	New to	Fleet No	Status
JXN 371	1949	Leyland Titan 7RT	Park Royal H30/26R	London Transport	RTL48	A
KGK 709	1949	AEC Regent III O961	Weymann H30/26R	London Transport	RT1240	A
KGK 959	1949	AEC Regent III O961	Weymann H30/26R	London Transport	RT2150	R
KLB 569	1950	AEC Regent III O961	Saunders H30/26R	London Transport	RT1320	A

Registration	Date	Chassis	Body	New to	Fleet No	Status
KXW 171	1950	AEC Regent III O961	Saunders H30/26R	London Transport	RT3062	R
KXW 22	1950	Leyland Titan 7RT	Metro-Cammell H30/26R	London Transport	RTL672	A
KXW 302	1950	AEC Regent III O961	Saunders H30/26R	London Transport	RT1656	A
KXW 488	1950	AEC Regent III O961	Weymann H30/26R	London Transport	RT1389	A
KYY 527	1950	AEC Regent III O961	Weymann H30/26R	London Transport	RT1700	R
LLU 670	1950	AEC Regent III O961	Park Royal H30/26R	London Transport	RT3871	R
LLU 732	1950	AEC Regent III O961	Park Royal H30/26R	London Transport	RT3933	RP
LYR 854	1950	AEC Regent III O961	Weymann O30/26R	London Transport	RT3435	R
LYR 969	1952	AEC Regent III O961	Weymann H30/26R	London Transport	RT2799	R
MLL 658	1952	AEC Regent III O961	Park Royal H30/26R	London Transport	RT2911	R
MXX 289	1952	AEC Regal IV 9821LT	Metro-Cammell B39F	London Transport	RF401	RP
MXX 360	1953	Guy Special NLLVP	ECW B26F	London Transport	GS60	R
OLD 587	1954	AEC Regent III O961	Saunders H30/26R	London Transport	RT4823	A
SLT 59	1957	Leyland Routemaster	ECW H32/25RD	London Transport	RMC4	R
VLT 85	1959	AEC Routemaster R2RH	Park Royal H36/28R	London Transport	RM85	R
VLT 111	1959	AEC Routemaster R2RH	Park Royal H36/28R	London Transport	RM111	RP
VLT 268	1960	AEC Routemaster R2RH	Park Royal H36/28R	London Transport	RM268	A
VLT 298	1960	AEC Routemaster R2RH	Park Royal H36/28R	London Transport	RM298	R
WLT 646	1961	AEC Routemaster R2RH	Park Royal H36/28R	London Transport	RM646	RP
WLT 893	1961	AEC Routemaster R2RH	Park Royal H40/32R	London Transport	RML893	RP
OPV 47	1962	AEC Regent V 2D2RA	East Lancs H37/28R	Ipswich Corporation	47	RP
215 UXJ	1962	AEC Routemaster R2RH/1	Park Royal H40/32R	London Transport	RML899	R
WLT 900	1962	AEC Routemaster R2RH/1	Park Royal H36/28R	London Transport	RML900	R
WLT 902	1962	AEC Routemaster R2RH/1	Park Royal H40/32R	London Transport	RML902	RP
9 CLT	1962	AEC Routemaster 2R2RH	Park Royal H36/28R	London Transport	RM1009	RP
516 CLT	1963	AEC Routemaster R2RH	Park Royal H32/25RD	London Transport	RMC1516	RP
ALD 936B	1964	AEC Routemaster 2R2RH	Park Royal H36/28R	London Transport	RM1936	RP
ALD 979B	1964	AEC Routemaster 2R2RH	Park Royal H36/28R	London Transport	RM1979	RP
CUV 260C	1965	AEC Routemaster R2RH/1	Park Royal H36/29RD	London Transport	RCL2260	R
CUV 331C	1965	AEC Routemaster R2RH/1	Park Royal H40/32R	London Transport	RML2331	RP
JJD 413D	1966	AEC Routemaster R2RH/1	Park Royal H40/32R	London Transport	RML2413	RP
NMY 631E	1967	AEC Routemaster R2RH/2	Park Royal H33/24F	British European Airways		R
KOW 902F	1967	AEC Regent V 3D2RA	Neepsend H40/30R	Southampton Corporation	394	RP
AML 1H	1970	AEC Swift 4MP2R	Marshall B42F	London Transport	SM1	RP
AML 88H	1970	AEC Swift 4MP2R	Park Royal B42D	London Transport	SMS88	RP
JPF 108K	1971	AEC Swift 3MP2R	Alexander DP45F	London Country Bus Services	SMA8	A
THM 684M	1974	Daimler Fleetline CRL6	MCW O44/27D	London Transport	DMS1684	R
GHV 52N	1975	Daimler Fleetline CRL6	Park Royal H44/27D	London Transport	DM1052	R
THX 271S	1977	Leyland Fleetline FE30ALRSp	MCW O44/27D	London Transport	DMS2271	A
THX 402S	1978	Leyland Titan TNLXB2RRSp	Park Royal H44/26D	London Transport	T2	R
WYV 4T	1978	Leyland Titan TNLXB2RRSp	Park Royal H44/26D	London Transport	T4	R
WYW 28T	1979	MCW Metrobus DR101/8	MCW H43/28D	London Transport	M28	RP
A103 SUU	1984	Volvo Ailsa B55-10 Mk III	Alexander H36/28D	London Transport	V3	R

Notes:

LYR 854	converted to open-top following de-roofing in 1976
SLT 59	originally numbered CRL4
215 UXJ	originally registered WLT 899
NMY 631E	acquired by London Transport (RMA48) in 1979
AML 88H	originally B33D; upseated in 1976 and renumbered SMD88
THM 684M	originally H44/24D; converted to open-top by Blue Triangle in 1991
THX 271S	originally H44/24D; fitted with Iveco engine in 1988 and converted to open-top by Blue Triangle in 1992
WYV 4T	originally H44/22D

MacTours and Majestic Tour Edinburgh

Contact address: Edinburgh Vintage Bus Company, 11A James Court, Lawnmarket, Edinburgh EH1 2PB.
Phone: 0131 477 4771
Operations planned for 2009: Hop-on, hop-off open-top tours of Edinburgh operate seven days a week, most of the year.

Registration	Date	Chassis	Body	New to	Fleet No
YSL 334	1951	Leyland Tiger PS1	Guernseybus OB34F	Jersey Motor Transport Co	44
LST 873	1958	Leyland Titan PD2/40	Park Royal O27/26RO	Barrow-in-Furness Corporation	165
JSJ 746	1959	AEC Routemaster R2RH	Park Royal O43/32RD	London Transport	RM90
JSJ 747	1959	AEC Routemaster R2RH	Park Royal O43/32RD	London Transport	RM84
JSJ 748	1959	AEC Routemaster R2RH	Park Royal O43/32RD	London Transport	RM80
JSJ 749	1959	AEC Routemaster R2RH	Park Royal O43/32RD	London Transport	RM94
VLT 143	1960	AEC Routemaster R2RH	Park Royal O43/32RD	London Transport	RM143
VLT 163	1960	AEC Routemaster R2RH	Park Royal O43/32RD	London Transport	RM163
VLT 235	1960	AEC Routemaster R2RH	Park Royal O43/32RD	London Transport	RM235
VLT 237	1960	AEC Routemaster R2RH	Park Royal O43/32RD	London Transport	RM237
VLT 242	1960	AEC Routemaster R2RH	Park Royal O43/32RD	London Transport	RM242
VLT 281	1960	AEC Routemaster R2RH	Park Royal O43/32RD	London Transport	RM281
WLT 371	1960	AEC Routemaster R2RH	Park Royal O36/28RD	London Transport	RM371
858 DYE	1961	AEC Routemaster R2RH	Park Royal O36/28RD	London Transport	RM727
803 DYE	1961	AEC Routemaster R2RH	Park Royal O36/28RD	London Transport	RM1010
485 CLT	1962	AEC Routemaster R2RH	Park Royal H32/25RD	London Transport	RMC1485
CUV 203C	1965	AEC Routemaster R2RH	Park Royal H36/28RD	London Transport	RM2203
CUV 210C	1965	AEC Routemaster R2RH	Park Royal O36/28RD	London Transport	RM2210
CUV 241C	1965	AEC Routemaster R2RH/1	Park Royal PO36/29RD	London Transport	RCL2241
CUV 248C	1965	AEC Routemaster R2RH/1	Park Royal PO36/29RD	London Transport	RCL2248
NMY 634E	1967	AEC Routemaster R2RH/2	Park Royal H32/24F	British European Airways	
NMY 646E	1967	AEC Routemaster R2RH/2	Park Royal H32/24F	British European Airways	
OSJ 636R	1977	Leyland Leopard PSU3C/3R	Alexander OB49F	Western SMT Co	L2636

Notes:

YSL 334	originally registered J 5567 and fitted with Reading B34F body
LST 873	originally H33/28R, registered CEO 952
JSJ 746	originally H36/28R, registered VLT 90; converted to open-top in 1986 and extended in 1990
JSJ 747	originally H36/28R, registered VLT 84; converted to open-top in 1986 and extended in 1990
JSJ 748	originally H36/28R, registered VLT 80; converted to open-top in 1986 and extended in 1990
JSJ 749	originally H36/28R, registered VLT 94; converted to open-top in 1986 and extended in 1990
VLT 143	originally H36/28R; converted to open-top in 1986 and extended in 1990
VLT 163	originally H36/28R; converted to open-top in 1986 and extended in 1990
VLT 237	originally H36/28R; converted to open-top in 1986 and extended in 1990
VLT 235	originally H36/28R; converted to open-top in 1986 and extended in 1990
VLT 242	originally H36/28R; converted to open-top in 1986 and extended in 1990
VLT 281	originally H36/28R; converted to open-top in 1986 and extended in 1990
WLT 371	originally H36/28R; converted to open-top by Mac Tours in 2001
858 DYE	originally H36/28R, registered WLT 727; converted to open-top for East Yorkshire (817) in 1996
803 DYE	originally H36/28R, registered 10 CLT; converted to open-top for East Yorkshire (819) in 1996
CUV 210C	originally H36/28R; converted to open-top converted to open-top for East Yorkshire (816) in 1996
CUV 241C	originally H36/29RD; rebuilt in 1991 as convertible open-top and later as partial open-top
CUV 248C	originally H36/29RD; rebuilt in 1991 as convertible open-top and later as partial open-top
NMY 646E	acquired by London Transport (RMA9) in 1975
NMY 634E	acquired by London Transport (RMA50) in 1979 and by Stagecoach at Perth in 1987
OSJ 636R	originally B49F

Memory Lane Vintage Omnibus Services
Maidenhead

Contact address: 78 Lillibrooke Crescent, Maidenhead, Berkshire, SL6 3XQ.

Phone: 01628 825050

Fax: 01628 825851

E-mail: info@memorylane.co.uk

Web site: www.memorylane.co.uk

Registration	Date	Chassis	Body	New to	Fleet No	Status
KGU 290	1949	AEC Regent III O961	Weymann H30/26R	London Transport	RT1530	RP
KYY 628	1950	AEC Regent III O961	Park Royal H30/26R	London Transport	RT1790	R
LYF 377	1951	AEC Regal IV 9821LT	Metro-Cammell B37F	London Transport	RF26	R
NLE 643	1953	AEC Regal IV 9821LT	Metro-Cammell B39F	London Transport	RF643	RP
VLT 216	1960	AEC Routemaster R2RH	Park Royal H36/28R	London Transport	RM216	R

Midland Classic Ltd
Swadlincote

Contact Address: Kiln Way, Swadlincote, Derbyshire, DE11 8ED

Telephone: 01283 213869

Web site: www.midlandclassic.com

E-mail: info@midlandclassic.com

Brief Description: Midland Classic have a range of restored vehicles available for hire and also operate bus services in the Swadlincote / Burton upon Trent area.

Operations planned for 2009: Routes 15 Swadlincote–Stretton (via Newhall and Burton), 21 Swadlincote–Stretton (via Gresley Lidton and Burton) and 29 Ashby de la Zouch–Loughborough. Some 'modern' vehicles are now in service.

Registration	Date	Chassis	Body	New to	Fleet No	Status
798 UXA	1962	AEC Routemaster 2R2RH	Park Royal H36/28R	London Transport	RM1168	R
TOJ 592S	1977	MCW Metrobus DR101/2	MCW H43/30F	MCW (demonstrator)		R
WDA 4T	1978	Leyland Titan TNLXB1RF	Park Royal H43/29F	West Midlands PTE	7004	R
GBU 6V	1979	MCW Metrobus DR101/6	MCW H43/30F	Greater Manchester PTE	5006	R
GBU 7V	1979	MCW Metrobus DR101/6	MCW H43/30F	Greater Manchester PTE	5007	RP
HXI 3009	1986	Leyland Lynx LX563LXB FR	Alexander (Belfast) B49F	Citybus	3009	R
E72 KBF	1988	Leyland Lynx LX112L10ZR1R	Leyland B51F	Stevensons of Uttoxeter	72	R
H851 NOC	1991	Dennis Dart 9.8SDL3004	Carlyle B43F	Thanet Bus of Ramsgate		R

Notes:

798 UXA	originally registered 168 CLT
TOJ 592S	prototype Metrobus, originally H43/28D; acquired by Stevensons of Uttoxeter (80) in 1989 and rebuilt in 1990
WDA 4T	originally H47/26F
HXI 3009	acquired by Stevensons (259) in 1992
H851 NOC	acquired by Stevensons (308) in 1992

Quantock Heritage
Wiveliscombe

Contact address: Bishop's Lydeard, Somerset.
Phone: 01823 251140
Affiliations: NARTM
Operations planned for 2009: Please telephone for details

Registration	Date	Chassis	Body	New to	Fleet No	Status
JG 9938	1937	Leyland Tiger TS8	Park Royal C32R	East Kent Road Car Co		R
AJA 132	1938	Bristol L5G	Burlingham B35R	North Western Road Car Co	372	R
GNU 750	1939	Daimler COG5/40	Willowbrook DP35F	Tailby & George ('Blue Bus Services') of Willington	DR5	RP
CCX 777	1945	Daimler CWA6	Duple L27/26R	Huddersfield Joint Omnibus Committee	217	RP
EMW 893	1947	Daimler CVD6	Park Royal B35C	Swindon Corporation	57	A
HUO 510	1947	AEC Regal I O662	Weymann B35F	Devon General Omnibus & Touring Co	SR510	A
JUO 992	1947	Leyland Titan PD1	ECW L27/26R	Southern National Omnibus Co	2932	A
ACH 441	1948	AEC Regal III O682	Windover C32F	Trent Motor Traction Co	611	R
CCK 359	1948	Leyland Titan PD2/3	Leyland L27/26R	Ribble Motor Services	2584	A
JFM 575	1948	AEC Regal III 6821A	Strachan B35R	Crosville Motor Services	TA5	R
JNN 384	1948	Leyland Titan PD1	Duple L29/26F	Barton Transport of Chilwell	467	RP
JTE 546	1948	AEC Regent III 6811A	Park Royal H33/26R	Morecambe & Heysham Corporation	20	R
KTF 594	1949	AEC Regent III 9621E	Park Royal O33/26R	Morecambe & Heysham Corporation	65	R
LJH 665	1949	Dennis Lancet III	Duple C35F	Lee of Barnet		R
JFJ 875	1950	Daimler CVD6	Weymann B35F	Exeter Corporation	75	R
KEL 131	1950	Leyland Titan PD2/3	Weymann FH33/25D	Bournemouth Corporation	131	RP
KFM 893	1950	Bristol L5G	ECW DP31R	Crosville Motor Services	KG131	R
LFM 302	1950	Leyland Tiger PS1	Weymann B35F	Crosville Motor Services	KA226	R
LFM 717	1950	Bristol L5G	ECW B35R	Crosville Motor Services	KG136	A
LFM 734	1950	Bristol LL5G	ECW B39R	Crosville Motor Services	KG153	A
LUO 692	1950	Leyland Tiger PS2/3	Burlingham C33F	Pridham of Lamerton		A
DCK 219	1951	Leyland Titan PD2/3	East Lancs FCL27/22RD	Ribble Motor Services	1248	R
HJG 17	1954	Dennis Lancet UF	Duple C41C	East Kent Road Car Co		A
BAS 563	1956	Bristol Lodekka LD6G	ECW O33/27R	Southern Vectis Omnibus Co	542	R
701 AEH	1957	Leyland Titan PD3/4	Metro-Cammell O36/32F	Potteries Motor Traction Co	H701	RP
VDV 752	1957	Bristol Lodekka LDL6G	ECW O37/33RD	Western National Omnibus Co	1935	R
VDV 753	1957	Bristol Lodekka LDL6G	ECW O37/33RD	Western National Omnibus Co	1936	R
NDB 356	1958	Leyland Tiger Cub PSUC1/1	Crossley B44F	Stockport Corporation	403	R
890 ADV	1959	AEC Reliance 2MU3RV	Willowbrook C41F	Devon General Omnibus & Touring Co (Grey Cars)	TCR890	R
805 EVT	1960	AEC Reliance 2MU3RV	Weymann DP41F	Potteries Motor Traction Co	SL805	R
851 FNN	1960	AEC Regent V 2D3RA	Northern Counties FL37/33F	Barton Transport of Chilwell	851	R
572 CNW	1962	Daimler CVG6LX-30	Roe H—/—F	Leeds City Transport	572	A
7682 LJ	1962	Bristol Lodekka FL6G	ECW H37/33RD	Hants & Dorset Motor Services	1482	RP
DEL 893C	1965	Bristol Lodekka FLF6G	ECW H38/32F	Hants & Dorset Motor Services	1523	R
DPV 65D	1966	AEC Regent V 2D2RA	Neepsend H37/28R	Ipswich Corporation	65	R
XTF 98D	1966	Leyland Titan PD3/4	East Lancs H41/32F	Haslingden Corporation	45	R
HJA 965E	1967	Leyland Titan PD2/40	Neepsend H36/28R	Stockport Corporation	65	R
GNH 258F	1967	Daimler CVG6	Roe H33/26R	Northampton Corporation	258	R
NNC 854P	1976	AEC Reliance 6U3ZR	Plaxton C53F	Yelloway Motor Services of Rochdale		A
WDK 562T	1979	AEC Reliance 6U3ZR	Plaxton C49F	Yelloway Motor Services of Rochdale		R

Notes:

AJA 132	rebodied 1950
KEL 131	built with twin staircases
DCK 219	'White Lady' double-deck coach
BAS 563	originally H33/25R, registered MDL 952; converted to open-top in 1973 and renumbered OT2

701 AEH	originally H36/32F; converted to open-top by Sundekker				
VDV 752	originally H37/33RD				
VDV 753	originally H37/33RD				
572 CNW	originally H39/31F; converted to exhibition vehicle				

Ron Greet Nostalgic Transport
Totnes

Contact address: Ron Greet Nostalgic Transport, Bickaton, Broadhempston, Totnes, Devon, TQ9 6BY

Phone: 01803 813039

Fax: 01803 813613

E-mail: info@rongreet.co.uk

Web site: www.nostalgic-transport.co.uk

Opening days/times: Not normally open but visitors are welcome, strictly by prior arrangement.

Operations planned for 2009: Vintage and classic transport for weddings and special events in Devon.

Registration	Date	Chassis	Body	New to	Fleet No	Status
OD 7497	1934	AEC Regent O661	Short O31/24R	Devon General Omnibus & Touring Co	DR210	R
HTT 487	1946	AEC Regal O662	Weymann B35F	Devon General O&T Co	SR487	R
HOD 66	1949	Beadle-Bedford	Beadle B35R	Western National Omnibus Co	2015	R
KOD 585	1949	AEC Regent III 9612E	Weymann H30/26R	Devon General O&T Co	DR585	R
LTA 906	1949	Bedford OB	Duple C29F	Southern National Omnibus Co	1430	R
MHU 52	1950	Bedford OB	Duple B35F	Bristol Tramways & Carriage Co	210	R
NTT 679	1952	AEC Regent III 9613S	Weymann H30/26R	Devon General O&T Co	DR679	R
898 FUF	1954	Albion Victor FT39AN	Reading B36F	Watson's Greys of St Martin's, Guernsey		R
UFJ 296	1957	Guy Arab IV	Park Royal H31/26R	Exeter Corporation	56	R
VDV 818	1957	AEC Regent V MD3RV	Metro-Cammell O33/26R	Devon General O&T Co	DR818	R
181 ECV	1959	Bedford SB1	Duple C41F	Jennings of Bude		R
532 DWW	1963	Bedford SB5	Plaxton C41F	Barnsley British Co-op		A
4 RDV	1964	AEC Reliance 2U3RA	Harrington C41F	Devon General O&T Co (Grey Cars)	4	A
503 RUO	1964	AEC Regent V 2D3RA	Willowbrook H39/30F	Devon General O&T Co	503	RP
HAD 915D	1966	Bedford VAM5	Plaxton C45F	Princess Mary Coaches of Staple Hill		R

Notes:

OD 7497	originally H30/26R; converted to open-top in 1955
898 FUF	Guernsey registration 1787
VDV 818	originally H33/26R

Thames Valley 748 (JRX 823), a Bristol KSW/ECW new in 1955, is seen in Medstead. *Duncan Egerton*

Indices

Index of Vehicles by Registration Number

Reg	No.	Reg	No.	Reg	No.	Reg	No.	Reg	No.
ATT 922	104	BKC 236K	88	C771 OCN	72	CRU 103C	65	D676 NNE	39
AUD 310J	70	BKC 276K	88	C777 SFS	49	CRU 180C	65	D685 SEM	88
AUF 666	32	BKG 713B	109	C801 FRL	103	CRU 184C	77	D705 HUA	102
AUF 670	108	BLH 123B	24	C807 KBT	102	CRU 197C	65	D901 MWR	75
AUO 74	104	BLV 755A	63	C823 CBU	95	CS 3364	47	D902 CSH	80
AUP 369W	72	BM 2856	45	C877 JWE	73	CSG 29C	48	DAO 295K	105
AUX 296	47	BMS 222	47	CAH 923	31	CSG 43C	48	DAR 120T	110
AVH 470	54	BMS 405	47	CBC 921	18	CSG 773S	49	DB 5070	38
AVX 975G	24	BNC 960T	95	CBR 539	90	CSG 792S	49	DBA 214C	39
AWA 124B	48	BND 874C	38	CC 1087	89	CST 703N	80	DBC 190C	85
AWG 393	47	BNE 729N	95	CC 7745	51	CTF 627B	84	DBE 187	35
AWG 623	47	BNE 751N	95	CC 8671	73	CTP 200	70	DBL 154	100
AWG 639	47	BNE 764N	95	CC 9305	28	CTT 23C	74	DBN 978	50
AXI 2259	82	BNH 246C	109	CCET 613	94	CTT 513C	74	DBU 246	38
AXJ 857	38	BNU 679G	40	CCG 296K	62	CTT 518C	74	DBV 100W	93
AXM 649	86	BOK 1V	99	CCG 704C	78	CTT 774C	99	DBV 43W	105
AXM 693	26	BON 474C	52	CCK 359	117	CU 3593	54	DBV 831W	93
AYJ 100T	110	BOT 303	62	CCK 663	84	CU 4740	47	DBW 613	45
AYJ 379	47	BOW 162	104	CCX 777	117	CUB 331C	33	DBY 001	79
AYV 651	86	BOW 169	104	CCX 801	75	CUL 260	29	DCA 528X	113
AZD 203	24	BP 9822	19	CD 4867	19	CUV 116C	109	DCK 219	117
B100 PKS	80	BPV 9	31	CD 5125	19	CUV 121C	79	DCN 83	90
B101 SJA	95	BR 7132	19	CD 7045	46	CUV 186C	90	DCS 616	47
B106 XJO	46	BRS 37	47	CDB 224	38	CUV 203C	115	DDB 174C	39
B115 ORU	78	BTF 25	92	CDC 166K	99	CUV 208C	75	DDL 50	32
B147 EDP	28	BTN 113	72	CDC 167K	99	CUV 210C	115	DDM 652	64
B177 FFS	80	BTR 361B	70	CDC 168K	99	CUV 218C	45	DDV 446	74
B207 GNL	72	BUF 122C	98	CDJ 878	43	CUV 219C	52	DED 797	43
B349 LSO	49	BUF 260C	98	CDK 409C	85	CUV 220C	77	DEK 3D	101
B361 LOY	110	BUF 277C	98	CDL 479C	32	CUV 226C	77	DEL 893C	117
B401 NJF	18	BUF 426C	98	CDL 792	32	CUV 229C	86	DFE 383	35
B65 PJA	39	BUP 736L	91	CDR 679	47	CUV 241C	115	DFE 963D	67
B900 WRN	93	BUS 181	79	CDT 636	54	CUV 248C	115	DFM 347H	44
B901 TVR	95	BVP 784V	21	CDX 516	26	CUV 260C	114	DFV 146	84
B926 KWM	57	BWB 148H	97	CEO 720W	63	CUV 290C	84	DGS 536	47
BAS 563	117	BWG 39	47	CEO 723W	64	CUV 331C	114	DGS 625	47
BBA 560	38	BWG 833L	48	CEO 956	63	CVF 31T	77	DHC 784E	98
BBK 236B	70	BWO 585B	50	CEO 957	63	CVF 874	31	DHR 192	89
BBW 214Y	46	BWP 727H	99	CFK 340	90	CVH 741	54	DHW 293K	68
BBW 21V	46	BWS 105L	49	CFN 104	100	CVL 850D	35	DJF 349	44
BCD 820L	90	BXA 464B	48	CFN 121	73	CVP 207	51	DJG 619C	76
BCJ 710B	77	BXD 576	86	CFN 154	73	CWG 206	38	DJP 754	38
BCK 367C	43	BXD 628	77	CFV 851	23	CWG 283	47	DKC 301L	44
BCR 379K	97	BXI 2583	82	CGJ 188	26	CWG 286	113	DKC 330L	88
BD 209	89	BXI 339	82	CHF 565	57	CWG 756V	97	DKY 704	68
BDJ 87	54	C 2367	89	CHL 772	79	CWH 717	38	DKY 706	54
BDY 809	29	C101 HKG	69	CHU 419C	66	CWN 629C	67	DKY 712	65
BED 731C	43	C201 CBU	95	CJG 959	76	CWU 146T	57	DKY 735	21
BED 732C	43	C208 FVU	39	CK 3825	38	CWX 671	33	DL 5084	32
BEN 177	38	C225 CBU	95	CK 4474	92	CXX 171	26	DL 9015	73
BFE 419	35	C24 NVV	101	CKC 308L	88	CYJ 252	47	DL 9706	102
BFM 144	108	C255 FRJ	39	CKG 193	54	CZ 7013	56	DLJ 116L	65
BFS 1L	48	C41 HDT	73	CLE 122	86	D103 DAJ	29	DLU 92	26
BFS 463L	49	C416 AHT	67	CLTA 772	103	D122 PTT	46	DM 2583	89
BG 8557	57	C45 HDT	55	CMS 201	99	D275 OOJ	34	DM 6228	92
BG 9225	57	C46 HDT	73	CN 2870	51	D277 JVR	96	DMS 325C	48
BHA 399C	52	C481 CBU	95	CN 4740	90	D278 FAS	40	DMS 348C	80
BHA 656C	52	C507 KBT	102	CN 6100	90	D302 JVR	96	DMS 359C	48
BHL 682	75	C526 DYT	86	CNH 699	67	D320 LNB	96	DMS 820	47
BHO 543C	78	C526 FFJ	74	CNH 860	69	D472 OWE	55	DMS 823	47
BHO 670J	99	C53 HDT	97	CNH 862	69	D479 OWE	55	DNF 204	50
BHT 677A	88	C655 LFT	91	CPM 61	89	D5 CTB	73	DNF 708C	95
BHU 92C	66	C705 FFJ	103	CPU 979G	24	D501 LNA	96	DNT 174L	99
BJA 425	38	C724 FKE	110	CRG 811	79	D509 MJA	96	DNW 840T	34
BJG 674V	28	C724 JJO	46	CRM 927T	105	D515 HUB	102	DOC 26V	53
BJK 672D	98	C729 JJO	70	CRN 80	113	D536 NDA	99	DOD 474	104
BJX 848C	79	C751 YBA	95	CRR 537J	109	D553 NOE	53	DPT 848	90
BK 2986	41	C760 FFJ	74	CRS 834	79	D63 NOF	39	DPV 65D	117

DPV 68D	31	EHA 767D	52	F575 RCW	84	FTN 708W	72	GHT 127	67
DR 4902	89	EHA 775	20	F649 FGE	56	FTN 710W	91	GHT 154	67
DRC 224	29	EHL 336	93	F685 YOG	21	FTO 614	54	GHV 52N	114
DRD 130	54	EHL 344	75	FAE 60	66	FTR 511	97	GJ 2098	25
DRN 289	92	EHL 472D	99	FAM 2	66	FTT 704	67	GJF 301N	85
DSD 936V	49	EHV 65	70	FAR 724K	99	FUF 181	73	GJG 750D	109
DSE 980T	56	EIB 8234	83	FAS 982	48	FUT 240V	85	GJG 751D	28
DSG 169	47	EJR 110W	91	FBG 910	57	FUT 58	108	GJG 757D	28
DTJ 139B	43	EJR 111W	91	FBN 232C	64	FV 5737	104	GJN 509D	24
DTP 823	70	EKA 220Y	88	FBR 53D	72	FVA 854	79	GJX 331	33
DU 4838	45	EKU 743	54	FBU 827	38	FW 5698	35	GK 3192	86
DUK 278	103	EKU 744	54	FCD 294D	98	FW 8990	54	GK 5323	86
DUK 833	21	EKV 966	27	FCI 323	24	FWA 475V	44	GK 5486	86
DWB 54H	97	EKY 558	54	FCK 884	92	FWG 846	47	GKA 74N	88
DWG 526	47	ELP 223	77	FDB 328C	109	FWH 461Y	95	GKD 4347	87
DWH 706W	95	ELP 228	26	FDL 676	32	FWL 371E	46	GKP 511	54
DX 3988	31	EMS 362V	80	FDL 927D	32	FWX 914	33	GKV 94	93
DX 5610	31	EMW 284	67	FDM 724	51	FXH 521	29	GLJ 957	104
DX 5617	31	EMW 893	117	FDO 573	35	FXT 122	100	GLS 265S	49
DX 5629	31	EN 9965	95	FEA 156	21	FXT 183	77	GM 6384	47
DX 6591	31	END 832D	95	FES 831W	49	FYG 663J	99	GN 8242	26
DX 7657	83	ENW 980D	33	FET 617	94	FYS 8	79	GNB 518D	95
DX 7812	31	EO 9051	63	FET 618	54	FYS 839	54	GNC 276N	39
DX 8871	89	EO 9177	63	FFM 135C	43	FYS 988	42	GNF 15V	95
DXI 3343	82	EOD 524D	74	FFN 399	76	FYS 998	42	GNF 16V	95
DY 5029	81	EOI 4857	56	FFN 446	108	FYS 999	79	GNG 125C	31
E186 BNS	80	ERD 145	54	FFU 860	35	FZ 7883	56	GNH 258F	117
E204 PWY	102	ERD 152	54	FFV 447D	48	FZ 7897	56	GNM 232N	24
E48 TYG	73	ERN 700	92	FFY 40	51	G142 HNP	21	GNM 235N	110
E72 KBF	116	ERV 938	29	FFY 401	104	G251 SRG	72	GNU 750	117
E901 DRG	91	ES 5150	79	FFY 404	43	G254 JYG	102	GNY 432C	69
E903 DRG	91	ESF 647W	49	FGE 423X	80	G258 HUH	69	GO 5170	26
EA 4181	20	ESF 801C	48	FGS 59D	47	G292 EOG	21	GO 5198	86
EBB 846W	73	ESG 652	47	FHF 451	57	G545 RDS	80	GOE 486	108
EBO 919	68	ESV 811	40	FHF 456	43	G571 BHP	64	GOU 732	93
EC 8852	64	ET 778	73	FHN 833	35	G571 PNS	80	GOU 845	62
ECD 524	19	ETA 280	64	FHN 923	63	G645 WDV	110	GPD 313N	101
ECU 201E	91	ETJ 108	104	FHU 59D	66	G918 LHA	99	GRD 576D	73
ED 217	23	ETS 964	47	FJF 193	85	GAA 580	62	GRM 353L	105
ED 6141	77	ETT 946	104	FJF 40D	85	GAA 616	62	GRP 260D	112
EDB 549	38	ETT 995	74	FJJ 764	26	GAN 744J	91	GRS 334E	80
EDB 562	38	ETY 91L	72	FJJ 774	36	GAN 745J	91	GRS 343E	48
EDB 575	38	EUD 256K	46	FJW 616	51	GAY 171	85	GRU 163V	112
EDL 657	32	EUF 184	19	FKF 801D	88	GBB 524K	72	GRU 164V	112
EDS 288A	48	EUF 196	32	FKF 835E	88	GBJ 192	29	GRY 48D	85
EDS 320A	48	EUF 204	104	FKF 933G	88	GBU 1V	95	GRY 60D	52
EDS 50A	48	EUI 530	73	FKM 706L	28	GBU 6V	116	GSC 667X	49
EDT 703	54	EUP 405B	72	FKU 758	54	GBU 7V	116	GSO 80V	80
EDW 68D	69	EVA 324	47	FLD 447Y	80	GCD 48	112	GSR 244	90
EE 8128	90	EVL 549E	35	FM 6397	108	GCK 279S	101	GSU 378	47
EF 7380	90	EWM 358	43	FM 6435	108	GCM 152E	57	GTA 395	104
EFJ 241	104	EWS 130D	48	FM 7443	108	GDJ 435	43	GTB 903	84
EFJ 666	104	EWS 168D	48	FM 9984	108	GDL 33	64	GTP 175F	70
EFJ 92	38	EWS 812D	48	FNV 557	93	GDL 764	32	GTV 666	54
EFM 181H	44	EWW 207T	110	FOI 1629	82	GDT 421	54	GUE 247	51
EFM 581	108	EX 1128	90	FON 630	20	GE 2446	46	GUF 191	98
EFM 631C	101	EX 6566	29	FOP 429	23	GEK 14V	44	GUF 727	35
EFN 178L	76	EXV 201	29	FPT 6G	92	GEN 201	109	GUG 547N	110
EFN 568	73	EXV 253	36	FRB 211H	52	GFN 273	76	GUJ 608	20
EFN 584	73	EY 5218	41	FRC 956	52	GFU 692	54	GUP 907N	91
EFN 592	76	EZH 155	25	FRJ 254D	39	GFY 406	98	GUS 926	79
EFS 229S	80	EZH 170	25	FRJ 511	50	GGR 103N	72	GUW 443W	101
EGA 79	42	F115 PHM	86	FRP 692	69	GHA 327D	22	GUW 444W	101
EGN 369J	26	F251 JRM	105	FRP 828	69	GHA 333	51	GVD 47	47
EGO 426	26	F261 YTJ	88	FRU 224	104	GHA 337	51	GW 713	89
EGP 1J	36	F292 NHJ	78	FSC 182	47	GHA 415D	52	GWJ 724	96
EGP 33J	78	F301 DRJ	96	FSL 615W	80	GHN 189	63	GWM 816	99
EHA 424D	93	F305 DRJ	96	FTB 11	38	GHN 574	54	GWY 690N	34

Reg	No.	Reg	No.	Reg	No.	Reg	No.	Reg	No.
GYC 160K	67	HRN 31	92	JJD 413D	114	JTU 588T	49	KGU 434	104
GYS 896D	80	HRN 99N	84	JJD 414D	109	JUD 597W	46	KGY 4D	86
H140 GVM	96	HSC 173X	49	JJD 499D	109	JUE 349	51	KHA 301	20
H262 MFX	102	HSD 86V	80	JJD 524D	75	JUM 505V	34	KHA 311	108
H35 HBG	44	HTB 656	38	JJD 539D	109	JUO 992	117	KHA 352	20
H74 ANG	77	HTF 586	38	JJD 551D	90	JUS 774N	80	KHC 367	87
H851 NOC	116	HTF 644B	43	JK 5605	104	JV 9901	54	KHH 378W	105
HA 3501	51	HTJ 522B	83	JK 8418	108	JVB 908	47	KHU 326P	67
HA 4963	20	HTT 487	118	JK 9115	104	JVF 528	45	KHU 624	104
HA 8047	21	HUD 476S	46	JKC 1787	87	JVO 230	44	KHW 306E	52
HAD 915D	118	HUO 510	117	JKG 497F	69	JVU 755	38	KHW 630	66
HAH 537L	69	HUP 236	72	JLJ 403	65	JVV 267G	109	KHY 383	20
HAX 399N	67	HUY 655	65	JMC 123K	109	JVW 430	23	KID 154	24
HBD 919T	101	HVF 455L	89	JMN 727	54	JWB 416	96	KJ 2578	77
HBF 679D	52	HVM 901F	39	JMS 452E	80	JWS 594	47	KJA 299G	44
HCD 347E	112	HVO 937	40	JN 5783	89	JWU 307	100	KJA 871F	39
HCK 204G	44	HVU 244N	39	JNA 467	38	JWU 886	33	KJD 401P	86
HD 7905	96	HW 6634	66	JNB 416	27	JWV 976W	113	KL 7796	83
HDB 116V	95	HWO 334	51	JND 629	108	JWW 375	54	KLB 569	113
HDG 448	51	HWV 294	69	JND 646	38	JWW 376	54	KLB 721	67
HDM 473	65	HX 2756	86	JND 728	50	JWW 377	54	KLB 881	94
HDV 626E	105	HXI 3009	116	JND 791	38	JXC 194	77	KLB 908	94
HDV 639E	48	HYM 768	86	JNK 681C	85	JXC 288	26	KLB 915	94
HDZ 5488	49	HYM 812	54	JNN 384	117	JXC 323	67	KLJ 346	65
HE 12	89	IB 552	19	JO 5032	45	JXC 432	77	KLJ 749	67
HEK 705	38	IJI 5367	109	JO 5403	45	JXN 371	113	KMN 5017	87
HEN 868N	44	ILI 98	24	JOJ 222	20	JXN 46	108	KMN 5197	87
HET 513	89	IY 7383	24	JOJ 231	108	JY 124	104	KNG 374	31
HF 9126	47	IY 8044	24	JOJ 245	51	JYC 855	93	KNG 718	76
HFG 923V	110	J 2503	42	JOJ 526	20	K232 DAC	27	KNN 254	108
HFR 501E	80	J7 FTG	110	JOJ 533	51	K361 LWS	105	KNN 959	108
HFR 512E	84	JA 5506	73	JOJ 548	20	K727 UTT	110	KNV 337	69
HFR 516E	84	JA 5528	108	JOJ 707	108	K729 GBE	110	KO 117	83
HGA 983D	80	JA 7585	38	JOJ 847	20	K916 VDV	70	KO 54	83
HGC 130	26	JA 7770	108	JOJ 976	52	KAG 856	79	KO 63	90
HGG 359	79	JAA 708	78	JOV 613P	52	KAH 407	31	KO 7311	83
HGM 335E	48	JAP 698	100	JOV 714P	21	KAH 408	29	KOD 585	118
HGM 346E	80	JBN 153	38	JOV 738P	103	KAL 579	51	KOM 150	27
HHA 101L	103	JC 5313	81	JOW 499E	97	KBD 712D	101	KON 311P	52
HHA 26	108	JCK 530	84	JOW 928	97	KBO 961	68	KOU 791P	67
HHA 637	51	JCK 542	92	JP 4712	38	KCG 627L	62	KOW 901F	97
HHH 272N	105	JCP 60F	89	JP 7538	64	KCK 869	92	KOW 902F	114
HHN 202	72	JDC 599	73	JPA 190K	26	KD 5296	100	KOW 910F	97
HHP 755	104	JDL 760	109	JPA 82V	79	KDB 408F	39	KOX 663F	21
HHW 452D	109	JDN 668	35	JPF 108K	114	KDB 696	76	KOX 780F	52
HIL 7081	110	JEL 257	66	JPF 113K	91	KDJ 999	43	KPT 909	89
HJA 965E	117	JF 2378	20	JPL 153K	101	KDL 885F	32	KR 1728	77
HJG 17	117	JFJ 606	104	JPT 901T	91	KDT 393	35	KR 8385	77
HKE 867	108	JFJ 875	117	JPT 906T	72	KED 546F	82	KRN 422	43
HKF 820	57	JFM 238D	30	JRN 29	22	KEL 110	65	KRR 255	40
HKR 11	54	JFM 575	117	JRR 404	51	KEL 131	117	KRU 505F	65
HL 7538	64	JFM 650J	44	JRT 82K	31	KEL 133	65	KSV 102	82
HLJ 44	77	JFT 228N	91	JRX 8237	87	KET 220	96	KSX 102X	49
HLX 410	26	JFT 413X	91	JS 1972	56	KFM 766	69	KTB 672	64
HNB 24N	95	JFV 527	92	JS 8089	56	KFM 775	52	KTD 768	43
HNP 154S	98	JG 669	83	JSC 869E	48	KFM 893	117	KTF 594	117
HNP 989J	97	JG 691	83	JSC 900E	48	KFN 239	76	KTJ 204C	78
HNT 945N	99	JG 8720	73	JSF 928T	49	KGK 529	94	KTJ 502	90
HNW 131D	33	JG 9938	117	JSJ 746	115	KGK 575	94	KTT 316P	110
HOD 66	118	JGA 189N	80	JSJ 747	115	KGK 708	77	KTV 493	54
HOR 590E	78	JHA 227L	99	JSJ 748	115	KGK 709	113	KTV 506	54
HOR 592E	78	JHA 868E	52	JSJ 749	115	KGK 758	77	KUF 199F	98
HOU 904	62	JHL 701	90	JSX 595T	49	KGK 803	26	KUO 963	67
HOV 685	51	JHL 708	75	JTB 749	113	KGK 959	113	KUS 607E	64
HPF 318N	101	JHT 802	66	JTD 300B	43	KGM 664	48	KVF 658E	77
HPW 108	66	JIW 4045	110	JTE 546	117	KGU 142	26	KVH 219	54
HPW 133	35	JJD 394D	109	JTF 920B	55	KGU 284	22	KVH 473E	33
HRG 209	47	JJD 405D	78	JTH 100F	99	KGU 290	116	KVO 429P	45

KW 1961	29	LKT 991	83	MFR 306P	93	NCK 338J	93	NRN 586	92
KW 2260	33	LLU 670	114	MGB 286E	80	NCS 16P	49	NSF 757	79
KW 474	35	LLU 732	114	MHU 193	66	NDB 356	117	NSJ 502	48
KW 6052	54	LLU 829	29	MHU 52	118	NDH 959	54	NTF 466	43
KW 7604	35	LLU 957	94	MHY 765	96	NDK 980	38	NTT 661	74
KWE 255	96	LLU 987	94	MJ 4549	73	NDL 375G	80	NTT 679	118
KXW 123	108	LMA 284	38	MJA 891G	39	NDL 490G	32	NTU 125	93
KXW 171	114	LMJ 653G	89	MJA 897G	39	NDL 637M	32	NTW 942C	23
KXW 22	114	LMS 168W	80	MKB 9947	87	NDL 656R	49	NTY 416F	48
KXW 234	29	LMS 374W	49	MLL 570	76	NDL 769G	63	NUD 105L	70
KXW 302	114	LN 4743	30	MLL 658	114	NDM 950E	109	NUW 567Y	86
KXW 435	94	LN 7270	89	MLL 722	109	NDP 31R	110	NVK 341	72
KXW 488	114	LNA 166G	95	MLL 735	77	NDP 38R	110	NWA 257K	44
KY 9106	33	LNY 903	69	MLL 740	26	NDV 537G	74	NWU 265D	34
KYV 447X	24	LOD 495	112	MLL 817	102	NEA 101F	52	NWW 89E	75
KYV 781X	80	LOG 301	20	MN 2615	86	NEH 453	23	NXL 847	93
KYY 527	114	LOG 302	20	MNC 487W	44	NFN 84R	76	NXP 775	77
KYY 529	108	LOI 1859	110	MNC 525W	95	NFS 176Y	49	NXP 997	86
KYY 622	102	LOU 48	62	MNS 10Y	80	NFW 36V	35	O 9926	51
KYY 628	116	LOW 217	97	MNW 86	33	NG 1109	32	OAE 954M	66
KYY 961	77	LRA 801P	40	MO 9324	19	NHA 744	52	OBN 502R	95
L247 FDV	46	LRN 321J	92	MOD 978	67	NHA 795	52	OBU 163F	43
L512 BOD	105	LRV 992	98	MOF 90	20	NHN 250K	91	OC 527	51
L929 CTT	103	LRV 996	70	MOO 177	77	NHU 2	66	OCK 985K	29
L932 CTT	110	LST 873	115	MOR 581	62	NHY 947	66	OCK 988K	77
LAA 231	62	LSX 16P	49	MPU 52	23	NJA 568W	95	OCK 995K	84
LAE 13	67	LTA 629	74	MPX 945R	105	NJO 703	45	OCK 997K	84
LAK 309G	34	LTA 813	93	MRT 6P	31	NJW 719E	52	OCU 769R	91
LAK 313G	34	LTA 906	118	MSD 407	79	NKD 5367	87	OCU 807R	91
LAX 101E	109	LTC 774	38	MSD 408	79	NKD 5407	87	OD 5489	104
LC 3701	86	LTE 491P	83	MSF 122P	80	NKJ 849P	78	OD 5868	104
LCD 52	29	LTN 501	42	MSF 750P	49	NKR 529	65	OD 7497	118
LDJ 985	43	LTV 702	104	MSJ 385P	80	NKU 214X	84	OD 7500	104
LDS 201A	48	LTX 311	109	MSJ 499	102	NKU 245X	34	ODL 400	32
LDS 279A	77	LUC 210	26	MTC 540	92	NLE 537	86	OEM 788S	88
LED 71P	44	LUO 692	117	MTE 635	33	NLE 603	77	OFC 205	45
LED 73P	44	LUS 524E	48	MTJ 771S	88	NLE 643	116	OFC 393	45
LEN 101	75	LVK 123	72	MTJ 84	113	NLE 672	26	OFC 902H	70
LEO 734Y	64	LWB 377P	110	MTL 750	18	NLE 939	102	OFM 957K	57
LEV 917	82	LYF 104	108	MTT 640	112	NLJ 268	65	OFN 721F	76
LF 9967	89	LYF 282	108	MV 8996	90	NLJ 272	65	OFR 970M	84
LFM 302	117	LYF 377	116	MWD 908	90	NLP 389V	97	OFS 777	47
LFM 404	99	LYF 399	109	MXX 23	52	NLP 645	89	OFS 798	48
LFM 717	117	LYM 729	90	MXX 261	77	NMA 328D	50	OHK 432	35
LFM 734	117	LYR 533	33	MXX 283	26	NMS 358	79	OHY 938	66
LFM 753	67	LYR 542	54	MXX 289	114	NMS 366	48	OJ 9347	20
LFR 529F	84	LYR 672	109	MXX 332	101	NMS 576M	80	OJD 172R	26
LFR 540G	84	LYR 826	26	MXX 334	26	NMY 631E	114	OJD 192R	34
LFS 288F	48	LYR 854	114	MXX 360	114	NMY 634E	115	OJD 903R	80
LFS 294F	48	LYR 910	26	MXX 364	86	NMY 646E	115	OJF 191	85
LFS 296F	98	LYR 915	100	MXX 410	102	NMY 655E	78	OJI 4371	84
LFS 480	47	LYR 969	114	MXX 421	43	NNB 125	38	OJO 727	70
LFW 326	35	LYR 997	23	MXX 430	102	NNB 547H	95	OLD 587	114
LHA 870F	21	M627 HDV	103	MXX 434	101	NNB 589H	95	OLD 589	86
LHL 164F	75	M939 XKA	39	MXX 481	76	NNC 854P	117	OLD 714	35
LHN 784	54	MAH 744	31	MXX 489	101	NNU 123M	40	OLJ 291	89
LHN 860	63	MAL 310	44	MYA 590	26	NNU 124M	40	OLV 551M	88
LHT 911	82	MBN 177	92	N143 PTG	69	NNU 234	65	ONE 744	29
LHW 918	66	MBO 512F	69	NAC 416F	46	NOB 413M	52	ONF 865H	95
LHY 937	108	MCK 229J	75	NAE 3	66	NOC 600R	103	ONO 49	23
LHY 976	66	MCN 30K	91	NAG 120G	48	NOE 544R	52	ONO 59	35
LIL 9929	49	MCO 669	104	NAH 135P	77	NOE 602R	21	ONV 425	104
LJ 147	65	MDJ 555E	43	NAH 941	76	NOV 796G	52	OOX 825R	21
LJ 500	104	MDL 954	32	NBB 628	29	NOV 880G	103	OP 237	20
LJF 30F	97	MDT 222	54	NBD 311F	101	NPD 145L	28	OPV 47	114
LJH 665	117	MFM 39	109	NBN 436	64	NRG 154M	30	OPV 821	98
LJW 336	20	MFN 888	28	NBU 494	38	NRG 26H	80	ORB 277	52
LKG 678	69	MFN 898	76	NCK 106J	92	NRN 397P	84	ORC 545P	45

ORJ 83W	39	PNF 941J	95	RHS 400W	49	SHN 80L	40	TDL 9987	87		
ORU 230G	65	PNU 114K	40	RKC 262	88	SJ 1340	47	TDV 217J	103		
ORV 989	70	POR 428	62	RLN 230W	110	SKB 168	88	TE 5780	81		
ORV 989	70	POU 494	78	RLN 237W	105	SKB 224	88	TE 7870	112		
OSJ 620R	82	PPT 446P	91	RLS 469T	49	SKB 695G	88	TE 8318	35		
OSJ 629R	49	PRA 109R	40	RMS 400W	80	SKL 681X	76	TEC 599N	65		
OSJ 636R	115	PRN 145	92	RMS 714	48	SLT 56	86	TET 135	96		
OST 502	24	PRN 79K	93	RN 7588	92	SLT 57	86	TF 6860	33		
OT 8283	62	PRN 906	92	RN 7824	38	SLT 58	26	TF 818	35		
OT 8592	62	PRX 187B	98	RN 8622	92	SLT 59	114	TFA 987	109		
OT 8898	62	PSJ 480	43	RNA 220J	95	SMK 686F	91	TFJ 808	104		
OT 8902	62	PSL 234	104	RNA 236J	99	SMK 701F	44	TFN 980T	76		
OTA 632G	103	PSX 189Y	110	RNE 692W	110	SMK 716F	109	TGM 214J	48		
OTA 640G	93	PTC 114C	39	ROD 765	74	SMK 732F	91	THM 684M	114		
OTT 43	93	PTD 640S	95	RPU 869M	110	SMK 734F	84	THM 692M	57		
OTT 55	89	PTD 655S	83	RRM 148M	77	SMK 747F	109	THX 101S	78		
OTT 98	103	PTE 944C	39	RRM 386X	49	SMM 90F	78	THX 220S	110		
OTV 137	54	PTF 714L	93	RRN 405	84	SMS 120P	49	THX 271S	114		
OTV 161	44	PTF 718L	93	RRN 428	92	SND 455X	95	THX 402S	114		
OU 7951	83	PTF 727L	93	RRS 46R	49	SND 460X	95	THX 646S	78		
OU 9286	78	PTT 106R	105	RRU 903	102	SND 501X	95	TJ 6760	92		
OUH 177G	69	PTW 110	23	RRU 904	65	SO 3740	47	TJO 56K	70		
OV 4090	51	PUA 294W	110	RSC 194Y	80	SOA 658S	21	TKG 518J	69		
OV 4486	51	PUF 165H	98	RSD 973R	80	SOA 674S	101	TKU 467K	34		
OVF 229	76	PV 817	31	RSJ 747	101	SOE 913H	52	TME 134M	91		
OVL 465	35	PV 8270	31	RSK 615	109	SOI 3591	82	TMS 585H	48		
OVL 473	101	PV 9371	31	RTC 645L	44	SOU 456	62	TNA 496	38		
OWC 182D	101	PVH 931	55	RU 2266	65	SOU 465	62	TNA 520	38		
OWC 720M	109	PW 8605	89	RU 8678	46	SPT 65	90	TNB 759K	95		
OWE 116	96	PWL 413	45	RUF 186	112	SPT 963V	72	TOB 377	20		
OWE 271K	52	PWL 999W	70	RUF 37R	98	SPU 985	85	TOB 997H	103		
OWS 620	48	PWS 492S	82	RV 3411	41	SR 1266	27	TOE 527N	103		
PAJ 829X	91	PY 6170	108	RV 4649	41	SRB 424	27	TOJ 592S	116		
PBC 113G	85	Q124 VOE	52	RV 6360	43	SRJ 328H	39	TPD 109X	101		
PBC 734	27	Q995 CPE	104	RV 6367	70	SS 7486	47	TPJ 61S	86		
PBC 98G	85	RAG 400	79	RV 6368	41	SS 7501	47	TRJ 109	43		
PBJ 2F	77	RAG 411	48	RVB 977S	76	SSA 5X	80	TRJ 112	38		
PBN 668	109	RAG 578	48	RVO 668L	109	SSF 237H	48	TRN 481V	93		
PCD 80R	110	RAO 733	105	RWB 87	96	SSN 248S	80	TRN 731	92		
PCG 888G	97	RB 4757	81	RWC 608	67	SSX 602V	49	TRU 947J	109		
PCG 889G	97	RBC 345G	99	RWC 637K	109	STJ 847L	84	TRY 122H	85		
PCK 618	92	RBD 111M	101	SAS 859T	80	STL 725J	109	TSJ 47S	80		
PCN 762	90	RBD 319G	101	SB 8155	20	SUG 591M	102	TSK 736	113		
PCW 203J	91	RBW 87M	70	SBD 525R	101	SUK 3	52	TSO 16X	80		
PDH 808	52	RC 2721	35	SBF 233	52	SV 6107	92	TTA 400H	109		
PDJ 269L	44	RC 4615	51	SCD 731N	98	SVA 438	65	TTD 386H	39		
PDL 515	32	RC 7927	20	SCH 237	21	SVF 896G	109	TTR 167H	97		
PDL 519	32	RC 8472	54	SCN 268S	91	SVS 281	54	TUO 74J	74		
PDU 125M	27	RC 8575	54	SCS 333M	49	SVV 587W	101	TUP 859	72		
PDU 135M	52	RCH 629L	40	SCS 335M	80	SWS 671	48	TUX 906J	99		
PFE 542V	35	RCM 493	57	SCS 366M	49	SWS 715	48	TV 4484	54		
PFN 865	45	RCP 2377	87	SDA 757S	53	SWV 155J	91	TV 9333	54		
PFN 867	76	RCS 382	48	SDK 442	38	TAX 235	69	TVS 367	79		
PFR 346	84	RCU 588S	91	SDL 268	32	TBC 164	18	TWH 689T	83		
PFR 554H	84	RCU 838S	91	SDL 638J	32	TBC 50X	85	TWH 809K	64		
PFR 747	100	RD 7127	68	SDX 57	23	TBK 190K	70	TWL 928	45		
PFW 935	109	RDB 872	67	SEO 209M	63	TCD 374J	98	TWM 220V	88		
PHA 370M	52	RDB 872	73	SFC 610	45	TCD 383J	98	TWW 766F	34		
PHH 149W	105	RDH 505	52	SFV 421	92	TCD 481J	98	TWY 8	75		
PHJ 954	23	RDL 309X	32	SG 2030	29	TCD 490J	98	TXJ 507K	39		
PHN 831	90	REN 116	38	SGD 407	23	TCK 465	92	TYD 888	47		
PJX 232	33	RFE 416	35	SGD 448	79	TCK 726	92	TYJ 4S	98		
PJX 35	75	RFM 435	109	SGD 500	79	TCO 537	90	UBD 757H	101		
PKG 532H	69	RFM 453F	44	SGD 65	79	TDH 912	21	UBN 902	64		
PKG 587M	69	RFM 641	43	SGR 935V	72	TDJ 612	43	UCS 659	48		
PKH 600M	110	RFR 424P	91	SHA 431	52	TDK 322	96	UCX 275	75		
PKW 434J	109	RFU 689	69	SHA 645G	52	TDL 564K	32	UDT 455F	55		
PND 460	38	RGS 598R	77	SHN 301	90	TDL 566K	32	UF 1517	19		

UF 4813	19	UXD 129G	101	VOD 101K	72	WRA 12	96	XSL 945A	48
UF 6473	19	UZH 258	25	VOD 123K	109	WRJ 179	50	XSN 25A	48
UF 6805	19	VBD 310H	99	VOD 545K	74	WRJ 448X	95	XSU 913	73
UF 7428	19	VCO 772	110	VOD 550K	74	WRL 16	104	XTA 839	74
UFC 430K	46	VCO 802	110	VOD 88K	74	WRP 767J	101	XTF 98D	117
UFF 178	47	VD 3433	47	VOI 8415	82	WS 337	109	XU 7498	89
UFJ 292	90	VDV 123S	74	VPT 598R	72	WS 4522	47	XUA 73X	75
UFJ 296	118	VDV 137S	103	VR 5742	38	WSD 756K	80	XUF 141	98
UFM 52F	57	VDV 752	117	VRD 186	22	WT 7101	33	XUH 368	69
UFP 175S	85	VDV 753	117	VRD 193	55	WT 7108	42	XUO 721	74
UFP 233S	85	VDV 760	96	VRF 372	100	WT 9156	81	XUR 290K	99
UGB 138H	56	VDV 798	74	VSB 164M	80	WTG 360T	112	XUS 575S	80
UGB 196W	80	VDV 817	74	VSC 86	48	WTS 266T	49	XVU 341M	95
UHA 255	52	VDV 818	118	VTU 76	33	WTS 270T	80	XVU 352M	39
UHA 941H	52	VER 262L	46	VTY 543J	105	WTS 708A	90	XVU 363M	95
UHA 956H	52	VF 2788	31	VUD 30X	70	WV 1209	31	XVX 19	23
UHA 963H	109	VF 8157	31	VV 5696	69	WW 4688	54	XW 9892	22
UHA 981H	52	VFJ 995	109	VV 8934	35	WWH 43L	95	XWS 165K	48
UHG 141V	80	VG 5541	93	VVK 149G	91	WWJ 754M	55	XWV 416A	98
UHG 353Y	40	VH 2088	81	VVP 911	52	WWM 904W	88	XWX 795	55
UHY 359	67	VH 6217	65	VWM 83L	88	WWY 115G	99	XX 9591	25
UHY 360	66	VHB 678S	80	VY 957	38	WX 2658	64	XYJ 418	33
UHY 362	103	VHF 57V	88	VYO 767	101	WX 3567	29	YD 9533	73
UHY 384	66	VIB 5069	110	WAJ 112	48	WYL 137	110	YDB 453L	95
UIB 5303	99	VIL 8730	64	WBN 955L	95	WYP 203G	109	YDK 590	38
UK 9978	21	VJG 187J	76	WBR 246	33	WYV 4T	114	YDL 3157	87
UKA 23V	88	VJO 201X	70	WBR 248	90	WYW 28T	114	YEV 308S	24
UKA 562H	88	VJW 882	32	WCG 104	78	WYW 6T	26	YFR 351	84
ULS 716X	49	VK 5401	42	WDA 4T	116	XAK 355L	34	YFS 310W	49
ULS 717X	49	VKB 711	88	WDA 700T	21	XBU 17S	39	YG 7831	89
UMA 370	38	VKB 841	88	WDA 835T	53	XBU 1S	95	YHT 958	67
UMP 227	26	VKB 900	88	WDA 956T	53	XC 8059	86	YHY 80	67
UNB 524	109	VKE 566S	110	WDF 569	52	XCV 326	109	YJG 807	76
UNB 629	38	VKU 78S	105	WDK 562T	117	XCW 955R	93	YL 740	45
UO 2331	104	VL 1263	35	WEX 685M	75	XDH 516G	52	YLG 717F	34
UOA 322L	40	VLT 111	114	WFM 801K	34	XDH 519G	22	YLJ 286	29
UOU 417H	78	VLT 143	115	WG 1620	47	XDH 56G	52	YMA 99W	44
UOU 419H	78	VLT 163	115	WG 2373	79	XDH 72	20	YNA 321M	95
UP 551	42	VLT 216	116	WG 3260	47	XDL 122L	32	YNU 351G	109
UPB 312S	101	VLT 235	115	WG 4445	79	XFM 42G	48	YNW 33X	105
UPE 203M	101	VLT 237	115	WG 8107	47	XG 9304	47	YPT 796	72
UPT 681V	91	VLT 242	115	WG 8790	47	XGA 15J	80	YR 3844	86
URE 281	109	VLT 25	77	WG 9180	47	XGM 450L	80	YRT 898H	29
USV 324	98	VLT 250	109	WH 1553	35	XHA 482	52	YSD 350L	49
UTC 672	113	VLT 268	114	WHA 237H	91	XHA 496	52	YSG 101	48
UTC 768D	43	VLT 281	115	WHL 970	75	XHO 370	62	YSL 334	115
UTF 732M	93	VLT 298	114	WHN 411G	91	XJA 534L	95	YT 3738	22
UTG 313G	69	VLT 44	23	WJY 758	33	XLG 477	33	YTE 826	29
UTN 501Y	72	VLT 85	114	WKG 284	109	XLV 140W	44	YTG 304	98
UTU 596J	52	VLW 444G	101	WKJ 787	93	XLV 156W	88	YTS 916A	79
UU 6646	25	VM 4439	38	WKO 137S	28	XM 7399	86	YWL 134K	70
UUA 212	90	VMO 234H	101	WKO 138S	110	XMD 47A	19	YYB 118	100
UUA 214	33	VMP 10G	80	WLT 371	115	XMS 252R	49	YYJ 914	48
UUF 110J	112	VMP 8G	48	WLT 506	20	XNG 770S	31	YYS 174	79
UUF 116J	98	VNB 101L	39	WLT 529	55	XNX 136H	21	ZJ 5904	24
UUF 335J	98	VNB 132L	95	WLT 646	114	XNY 416	69	ZO 6960	24
UVK 290T	91	VNB 173L	95	WLT 893	114	XO 1048	25	ZS 8621	25
UVL 873M	35	VNB 177L	95	WLT 900	114	XON 41J	21	ZU 5000	24
UVX 7S	110	VNB 203L	95	WLT 902	114	XPK 51T	101	ZV 1510	91
UWH 185	64	VO 6806	89	WNO 478	23	XRD 23K	109	ZY 1715	24
UWW 7X	73	VO 8846	44	WP 6114	64	XRU 277K	65		

Index of Museums, Collections and Heritage Bus Services

New in 1981 to Western National's Devon General fleet, Bristol VRT/ECW 1215 (LFJ 862W) shows off the new Devon General company's post-privatisation livery while participating in the Llandudno Festival of Transport in May 2008. *Philip Lamb*